Understanding Digital Color

by
Phil Green

Graphic Arts Technical Foundation
4615 Forbes Avenue
Pittsburgh, Pennsylvania 15213-3796
United States of America
Telephone: 412/621-6941
Fax: 412/621-3049

Library of Congress Catalog Card Number: 94-73205
International Standard Book Number: 0-88362-174-6

Printed in the United States of America

Order No. 1433

A catalog of GATF text and reference books, Learning Modules, audiovisuals, and videotapes may obtained on request from the Graphic Arts Technical Foundation at the address given at the bottom of the title page.

Printed on
S.D. Warren 70-lb. Patina Paper

Printed using
3M Viking G1 Plates

Contents

Preface

This book was written from a desire to meet the need for a guide to those who have embarked on the route to desktop color reproduction and want to get the best that the graphic arts industry has to offer—those for whom "good enough" doesn't even come close.

I would like to thank the many organizations that have contributed to this project, by supplying information and illustrations, or by providing material for the CD. In particular, Jim King, director of Advanced Technology at Adobe Systems, gave comprehensive feedback on the coverage of the PostScript language; Tony Hodgson, technical development manager of Kall Kwik (UK), reviewed the entire text; and Deborah Kamofsky of Anderson Fraser provided extremely helpful comments on the diagrams. I would also like to acknowledge the assistance provided by fellow lecturers at the London College of Printing and Distributive Trades. All remaining errors and omissions are entirely my own responsibility.

Pam Groff edited the text and Tom Destree prepared illustrations from rough sketches, and without their care and attention to detail the book would not have been possible. Finally, I would like to express my profound gratitude to my partner Ruth who suffered patiently while I was absorbed in the writing.

Phil Green
London, England
November 1994

To Rosalie and Anna

1 The Desktop Opportunity

The graphic arts industry has witnessed fundamental changes in the way that color is reproduced. Every single aspect of color reproduction is undergoing a complete transformation as the industry moves towards digitally based methods of production. The work involved in preparing color pages for printing has moved away from dedicated high-end equipment at specialist trade shops to standard desktop computers, often at the designer or publisher. The consequence is that color originals are now being created and reproduced in ways that are almost unrecognizable to anyone involved in color reproduction a decade ago. The products of the graphic arts industry themselves are also undergoing a radical change, with a growth in new short-run products at the expense of some of the traditional mainstays of the industry.

The Future of Color Reproduction

The changes in color reproduction are by no means over. Technology is continually opening up new opportunities, and creating new threats for those businesses that fail to adapt. No one can predict the future for color reproduction with any certainty, but some drivers for change and key trends for future developments stand out:

- The move from proprietary systems to open platforms is overwhelming. Users want standard desktop computers that will run a wide range of off-the-shelf software, and to which they can connect peripheral devices that work together transparently. Nearly all the high-end vendors have accepted that the future lies in using their expertise to add value at specific points in the workflow, rather than to continue to push a complete proprietary system.
- Central to the move toward open systems is the role of the PostScript page description language, which enables the different platforms to communicate without the need for

endless translations between formats. PostScript has come to dominate the world of desktop systems, and its key role has been further enhanced as virtually all of the proprietary high-end systems have accepted the need to communicate with the PostScript environment. PostScript is also an enabler of new methods of information distribution, through language dialects such as Adobe Acrobat and PostScript Fax.

- The market for short-run color printing is exploding. As it becomes economically feasible to produce color in quantities of five copies instead of 5,000, businesses are developing all kinds of novel products that exploit this new capability. The pressruns for traditional products are also falling as publishers use just-in-time production strategies to reduce their inventories.
- Expertise in production processes is increasingly being embedded in software. For the human operator, the emphasis is subtly shifting from knowing how print works to knowing how to make applications work. New skills are in demand, especially in integrating systems and configuring them for optimum results.
- The performance of desktop systems will continue to increase as new processing and storage technologies are developed, and present limitations (such as the time it takes to process high-resolution files) will sooner or later disappear. In doing so, desktop systems will become more like today's high-end workstations, while, at the same time, new needs will arise that will push forward the demand for performance.
- Color prepress work, traditionally carried out by specialist trade shops due to the capital-intensive nature of the equipment and the specialist skills required, is increasingly being performed by designers and publishers. For many printers, the new methods of production are also an opportunity to bring prepress work in-house and improve the range of services they can offer to their customers.
- The new players in desktop prepress have different requirements. For trade shops and printers, volume has always been a high priority, but for designers and publishers, issues of control and portability are of equal or greater importance.
- As prepress work is handled by people who are not color reproduction specialists, there is pressure on software developers to make applications as simple and as intuitive

to use as possible. Increasingly, the new users will be shielded from the intricacies of color processing by utilities that transparently manage color-space conversions, file compression, and so on.

- The importance of information as a key business resource is increasingly being recognized. Timely access to the relevant information—information about the product, the technology, the market, the client, and the competition—is of critical importance in achieving business goals. Information management, including interactive tools to search and process data, will be increasingly central to the function of organizations.
- For publishers, decisions about how information should be marketed, packaged, and distributed are becoming as important as those relating to the intellectual content itself. The media available for information distribution are multiplying and, increasingly, print is just one channel among many, and not automatically the most cost-effective one.

Changes in technology make changes in the product inevitable. With short-run color an economically viable proposition, a vast array of new products becomes possible. For example, the falling costs of prototyping and test-marketing new products can reduce the risks of innovation.

New ways of doing business are also bringing about fundamental changes in transactions and communications between and within organizations. The business document is increasingly being distributed electronically as well as in hard copy form, using technologies including modem, fax, and ISDN. There is a growing expectation that business documents will include color where it will enhance the content and that products such as Adobe Acrobat are being developed to assist in maintaining the appearance of color documents when communicating them across different platforms.

Inevitably, the changing prepress market is forcing a redefinition of the roles of the organizations within it. Traditional trade shops are finding the market for scanning and page planning is being drastically reduced as printers, publishers, and designers increasingly take on these roles themselves. Some trade shops may evolve into digital color resource centers, offering a wide range of creative services including image manipulation, access to digital picture libraries, and digital camera studios, as well as powerful processing and communication facilities.

While many printers will continue to offer a complete range of services, others will reposition themselves further downstream as their clients supply work to them in completely digital form, ready to be imaged on to the printing plate (or directly to the press) with all prepress functions such as imposition, trapping, and color separation already completed or the necessary instructions embedded in the files as tags.

The publisher has a choice about how far downstream they wish to take their work. The further downstream they wish to go, however, the more responsibility they will acquire for getting things right, and the more they will need the skilled personnel to achieve this.

The designer will play an increasingly central role in both creative and production activities, as the downstream functions between design and final output disappear. The network manager or systems integrator is also a key figure as publishers depend more on their management of digital information.

When color prepress was first attempted on the desktop, the necessary tools were not available and the results were disappointing. The algorithms used in desktop applications to convert color values into CMYK for output, using PostScript Level 1 for example, failed to achieve the quality of color reproduction that publishers had become accustomed to from printers and trade shops. Moreover, key issues like the difference between the appearance of a color displayed on screen and printed on paper were poorly understood. The results often lacked definition and seemed dull and gray, lacking the sparkle and brilliance of professional color separations.

Since then, the quality of color reproduction that can be achieved on the desktop has risen to a level that is adequate for the needs of a large proportion of commercial printing. Successive versions of the major page layout and image editing applications have refined the capabilities on the desktop to a point where, with the support of color processing facilities such as those in PostScript Level 2, consistently good quality can be achieved.

Despite the advances in digital color reproduction, top-quality color is still often the domain of highly skilled operators using expensive high-end scanning and page-composition equipment. Nevertheless, technology has now reached a point where the quality that can be achieved within the PostScript environment using standard hardware platforms is equal to and often better than that produced on traditional high-end systems. The real barrier to improving the quality of output is often the user's understanding of the process rather than the inherent capability of the technology.

Business Strategies

Competition in color reproduction is intensifying, and maintaining a competitive advantage is becoming increasingly difficult. Thanks to digital communications, publishers are able to buy print anywhere in the world, and the increased competition is continuing to drive down prices. Traditional graphic arts suppliers have held a clear lead over desktop alternatives when it comes to quality, but this advantage is disappearing fast. Instead, they are moving toward differentiation through the range of value-added services that they can offer.

Good use of color graphics and photographs has become a vital element in any publication. Color is used to convey meaning, identify brands, and enhance content, making it more likely that the products advertised will be sold. The quality of the reproduction is of the utmost importance; poor color reproduction causes real, tangible losses.

The current pace of technological change makes it very difficult to plan an investment. In fact, the obsolescence cycle has become so short that choosing the right direction to take is to steer a course between the Scylla of technological promise that ultimately turns out to be a dead end, and the Charybdis of old and uncompetitive equipment.

Being the first to adopt new ways of doing things is very risky, and only for those few visionaries capable of clearly seeing and grasping new opportunities. Hanging on to old ways can also be very risky in the long term, and there are countless businesses that have sadly failed after being unable to adapt to change. It must also be admitted, however, that there are many organizations that have a base of old but still productive equipment and are doing well thanks to their low fixed costs. In times of recession, the most vulnerable organizations are often those with the highest fixed costs.

So how are businesses to make the right prepress investments at the right time? There is no simple answer to this question, but there are some basic guidelines that can be suggested:

- Buy into proven technology that has been around for long enough for its problems to have been fixed, unless you

understand the technology sufficiently to have confidence in its future success.
- Consider all the implications of new technology, including space requirements, training, productivity, and how the new system will mesh with other elements of the business.
- Consider whether you can be reasonably confident of an acceptable payback period.
- Look for market trends that represent "an idea whose time has come" and therefore should be around for awhile.
- Aim to have your most costly piece of hardware as your main production bottleneck—queue other production areas to it rather than the other way around.

A key question that faces all businesses in the field of graphic communications is to what degree should they aim for vertical integration. There are no longer any technological barriers to carrying out the prepress work on the desktop, even for a large and complex publication. Many of the functions that have hitherto been the province of highly skilled craft specialists, such as image capture, trapping, imposition, and film output, can now be completed with commercially available software. It is even possible for a publisher to bring production in-house from start to finish, although a commercial printer can still put ink on paper better, cheaper, and faster unless the run lengths are very short.

The real barriers to extending vertical integration are the capital costs of the necessary equipment, together with the skills needed to operate this equipment successfully. Most businesses find it a better use of their financial resources to focus their investments on their core activities, and would need to be convinced of the economic case for diverting funds to in-house prepress. Moreover, interfacing with the complex and technical world of digital prepress involves an entirely new set of production skills and almost continual troubleshooting. Taking on the responsibility for production also means taking on the responsibility for getting it right.

However, despite the drawbacks there are undoubted benefits to be realized. In-house production allows the publisher to maintain control over costs, content, and schedules right up to final output. It eliminates the purchasing activity associated with external suppliers (a particular benefit with small orders), and it reduces the direct cost component of a product.

The final decision on how far to take vertical integration must be based on the costs and benefits in each case. A logical approach is to begin with front-end activities, such as text and image capture, and gradually extend the range of activities downstream into the production workflow. This minimizes the amount of separate subcontracting that becomes necessary and allows an orderly extension of both technology and skills.

Publication costs have two basic components. The first, fixed, component corresponds to the prepress work that occurs before the job starts printing. The second, variable, component is incurred when the presses begin to roll and depends entirely on the unit costs of production. On long-run work, the fixed prepress costs are a smaller proportion of the total costs, and efficient production is achieved with fast, highly specialized printing equipment. Prepress costs become a much larger proportion on short-run work, and it becomes even more important to contain them. By using desktop color prepress together with digital color printing, publishers can achieve significant savings on production costs.

The opportunities for greater control over the end product, combined with major cost reductions, mean that no business can afford to ignore the digital revolution in color reproduction.

2 Fundamentals of Color

To get the most out of your investment in desktop color publishing, you need to understand the fundamental properties of color and the way in which it is perceived. These issues are the subject of this chapter.

Designers are concerned not only with the physical reproduction of color, but also with the meanings attached to color through the influences of association and symbolism. These meanings are often cultural rather than innate; they are learned rather than intrinsic to our physical makeup. The domain of color meaning and psychology has been written about elsewhere, and our intention here is to focus on the domain of color reproduction. There are, however, many cognitive aspects of color vision that play an important role in the way we see color, and some of these are considered later in this chapter when we look at the subject of color perception.

Color has three fundamental components: light, human color vision, and the properties of the colored surface.

Light

Light is produced when electrons move from a higher energy level to a lower one, and, in the process, energy is emitted. If some of this radiated energy has a wavelength that falls within the visible part of the electromagnetic spectrum, then it will be detected by the human eye as visible light.

The light that we see is but a tiny part of the **electromagnetic spectrum,** which also includes microwave, ultraviolet (UV), and infrared (IR) radiation, and radar and radio waves. The wavelengths of the visible spectrum lie between approximately 400 and 700 nanometers (one nanometer equals one millionth of a millimeter) with blue light at one end and red light at the other. Microwaves, x-rays, and ultraviolet light (with shorter wavelengths) and infrared and radio waves (with longer wavelengths) lie beyond the visible

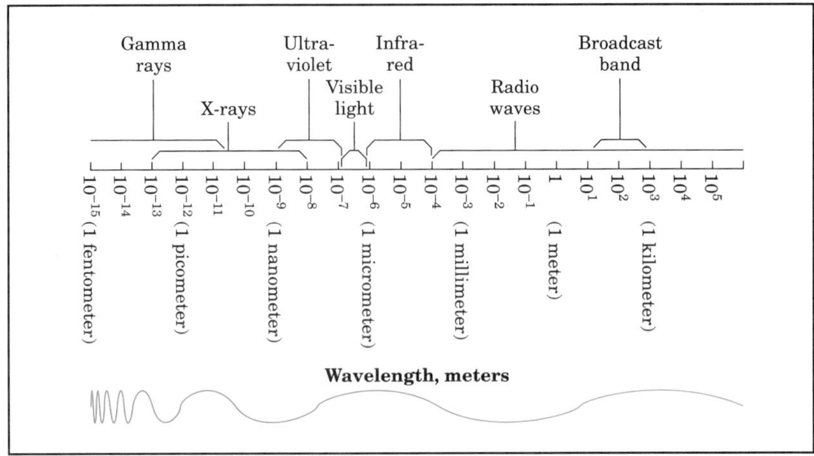

Figure 2-1.
The electromagnetic spectrum.

spectrum. The term "visible spectrum" is slightly arbitrary, since, for many mammals, the visible portion extends into the UV or IR regions.

Light can be understood both as a wave and as an energy-carrying particle called a **photon.** Its wavelength governs the perception of hue, while its particle behavior determines the way it causes light-sensitive media, such as photographic emulsions, to undergo chemical or physical changes.

Figure 2-2.
Light can be split by a prism into its component wavelengths. ©*David Parker, Science Source: Photo Researchers.*

The color spectrum that we see in a rainbow or in a light beam split by a prism does not have clear boundaries between the different colors. The main bands of pure color that we see in the spectrum—blue, green, yellow, and red—blend into each other, producing intermediate colors such as turquoise and orange. Blue, green, yellow, and red (and shades of these colors) make up the palette of colors that we observe most often in the world.

Light is usually more or less colorless, or "white," but when some of the wavelengths are removed, the color we see is made up of the remaining wavelengths. For example, if a red filter is placed over a light source, the green and blue components are masked and the eye is only able to see red.

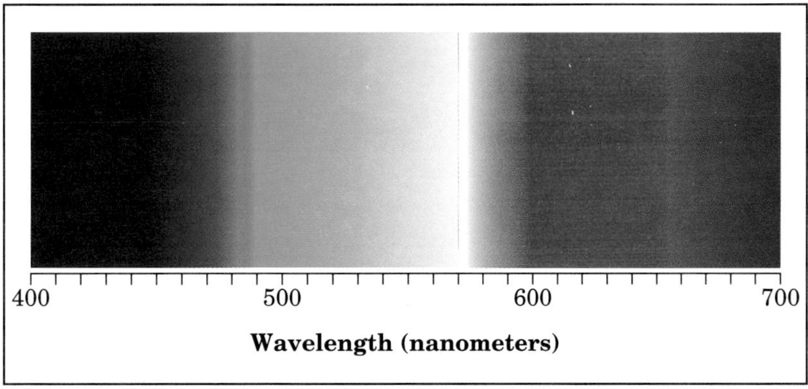

Figure 2-3.
The visible spectrum.

White light comprises all wavelengths, so if red, green, and blue lights are combined, the result is white light. However, if red, green, and blue light in different proportions are combined the result is not white but a color. For example, by combining red and green light with little or no blue, we see a yellow. Similarly, green and blue lights together make cyan, and blue and red combine to produce magenta.

Computer monitors and television screens follow this principle of emitting light from individual red, green, and blue phosphors in different proportions to synthesize millions of different colors.

Spectral Reflectance Curves

For any color, measuring the amount of light reflected at each wavelength allows us to plot a spectral reflectance curve that is a unique "fingerprint" for that color. Each wavelength corresponds to a different hue, and white light is composed of more or less equal amounts of all the wavelengths in the visible spectrum. When different wavelengths are combined, they create a new color. This makes additive color mixing quite unlike mixing inks or paints, which produce their secondary colors by absorbing and subtracting wavelengths. Thus, on a computer monitor, yellow is displayed by firing electrons at red and green phosphors, causing them to emit light that the eye perceives as yellow. On paper, yellow is made by printing an ink film containing

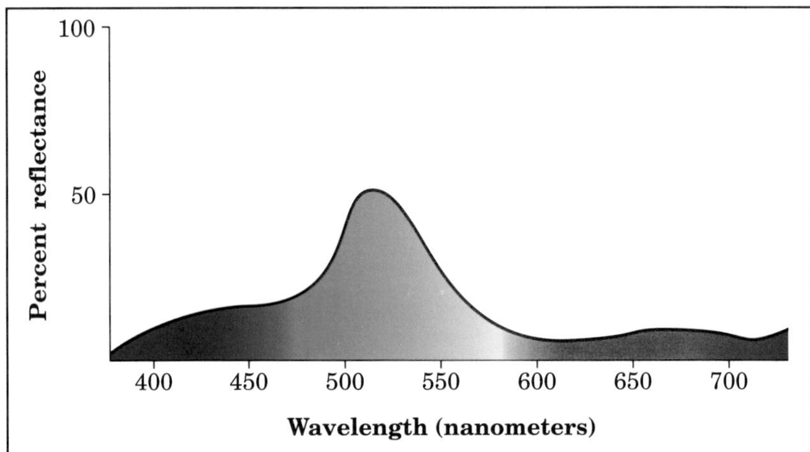

Figure 2-4.
A spectral curve.

a pigment that absorbs the blue component and reflects the green and red components of the light that strikes it.

Some colors are missing from the spectrum: the cool reds, magenta, the purples, violets, and mauves. If we turn the spectrum into a circle, these colors lie between red and blue. The "color wheel" formed in this way is extremely useful in choosing colors and in looking at the relationships between them. All possible hues lie within the circle, and opposite colors form complementary pairs.

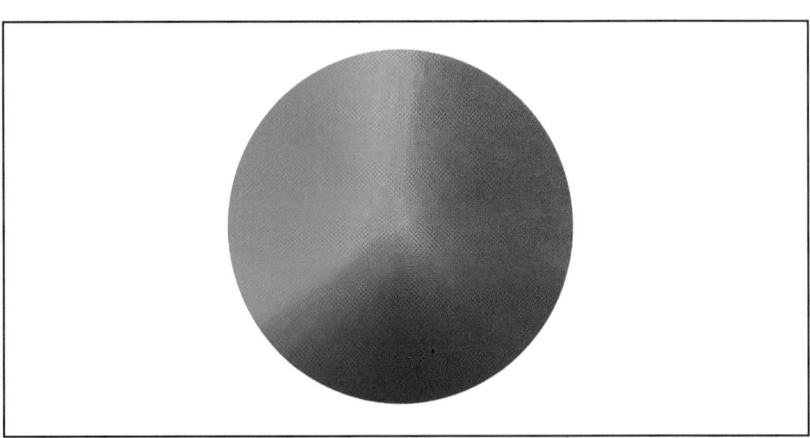

Figure 2-5.
The color wheel.

Human Color Vision

The way in which we perceive color is still not fully understood, but what we do know reveals an extraordinary apparatus with some surprising features. It has evolved over millions of years from very simple light-sensitive cells, and it is astoundingly good at things like distinguishing between different colors and recognizing people and objects on the basis of subtle variations in color. Although we do not all see exactly the same colors, most people see color in a very similar way, with minor differences caused by factors such as age, fatigue, and a small amount of natural variation between individuals.

The elements of the human visual apparatus are shown in Figure 2-6. Light enters the eye through the lens and is focused on to the retina, where an array of tiny cells, known as **photoreceptors,** respond to the light by stimulating specialized nerve cells, which pass on signals to the brain. The

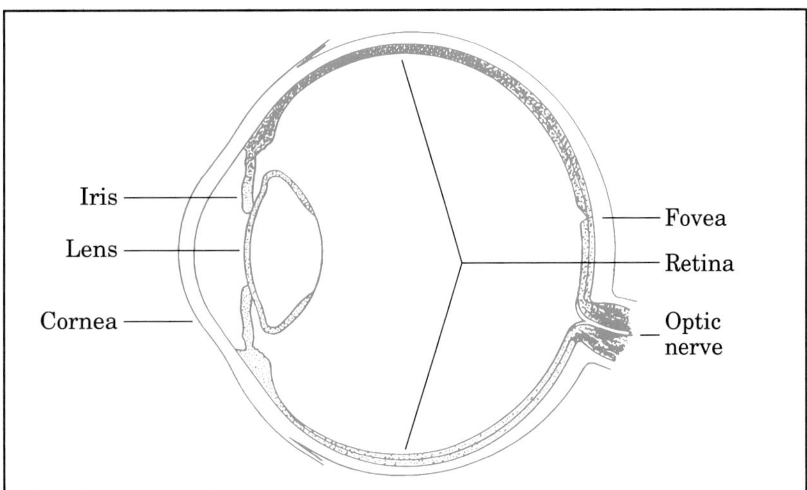

Figure 2-6.
The human eye.

light receptors in the retina of the eye are called **rods** and **cones.** Rods, which are not sensitive to color and work best at low levels of illumination, capture only lightness information. In other words, they can only tell how much light they receive, not what color it is. Because they are distributed throughout the retina, rods can respond to images throughout the visual field.

The cone photoreceptors are used to perceive color. Cones, which need higher levels of illumination than rods, are concentrated in the central region of the retina, corresponding to a central region of focus within the visual field. They contain a pigment called **rhodopsin,** which acts as a color filter, and in humans there are three versions of it. One allows only the shorter wavelengths to pass through, another allows only the longer wavelengths, and a third the middle region of the visible spectrum. These three bands of sensitivity correspond to peaks in the red, green, and blue regions of the spectrum. (In other creatures, these peaks may be different. Many animals can "see" in the ultraviolet region, and sensitivity peaks in the yellow region are also known.) The greater the amount of light that falls on the retina, the greater the response produced by the rod and cone cells.

The six million or so cones are stimulated when light passes through the lens and strikes the retina. The impulse is

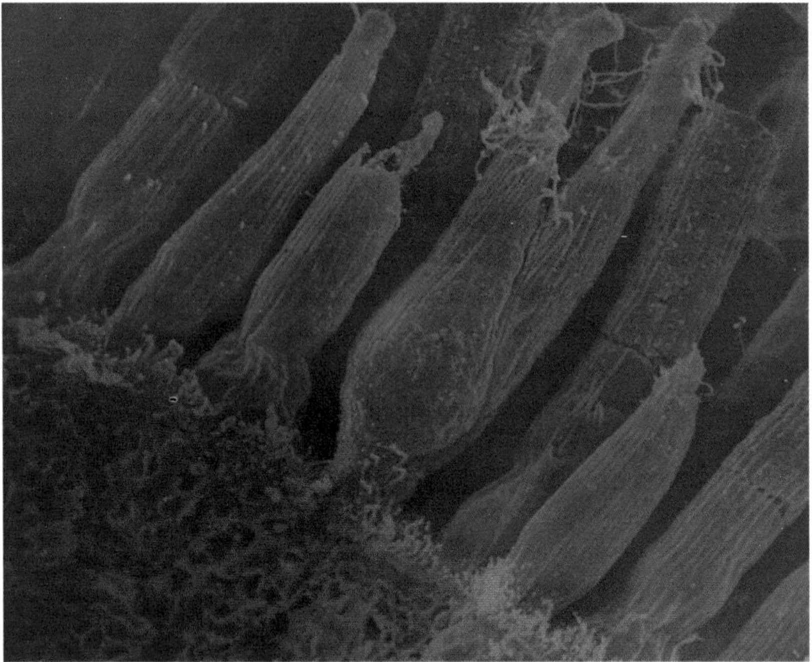

Figure 2-7. Scanning electron microphotograph of rod and cone cells in the eye. As in all mammals, these cells are inverted, facing away from the light. *©Omikon, Science Source: Photo Researchers.*

first processed in the ganglion cells immediately behind the retina, then it is sent through the optic nerve to the region of the brain known as the **visual cortex** where further image processing takes place.

For every photoreceptor cell in the retina, there are around 100 neurons in the visual cortex grouped together in information-processing regions that specialize in different attributes of the perceptual image. These regions extract information about edges, movement, color, faces, and so on, and synthesize it into the image we recognize. The perception of edges is given a great deal of weight, and this makes sharpness (or definition) a vital criterion for judging image reproduction.

It is tempting to draw an analogy between the human visual system and an optical image sampling system such as the charge-coupled devices (CCDs) used in video recorders and scanners. They both respond to light of different wavelengths and intensities by sending out signals; they both require an optical system to focus the image onto an image-capture plane; and they both use filters to analyze the red, blue, and green components of the image. However, the analogy cannot be taken any further since the perceptual image in the human visual system is more than a photographic

Figure 2-8.
A comparison of the human eye to a color scanner.

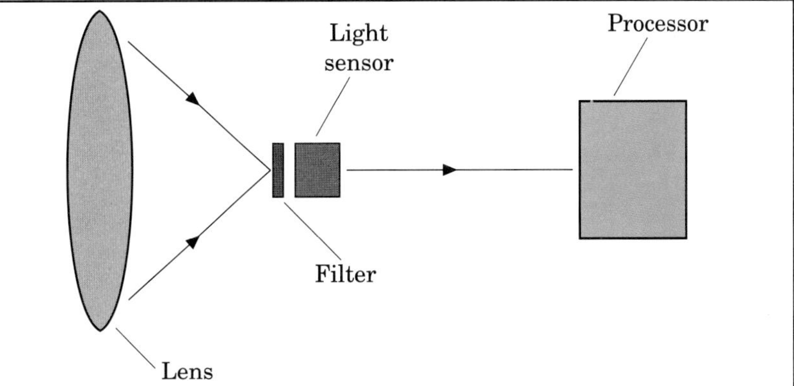

The human eye shares some of the features of color scanners: light is focused by a lens, through a color filter, on to a light-sensitive cell, stimulating it to respond and send a signal to a processing mechanism. The most important difference between the two is that the human visual mechanism carries out far more complex processing of the response.

record of the real world; it is also an active image made up of elements from the different regions of the brain that have processed signals from the eye. Unlike a color scanner, the human visual system does not sample the visual field as a static array of point intensities, but as a dynamic, moving image. The brain discards much of the available information from the visual field in its search for patterns and objects that it can relate to images recalled from memory. A slightly better analogy might be the compression of moving pictures by encoding only the differences in a scene in each of the successive frames.

The responses produced by rod and cone cells when light falls on them are not uniform; the higher the level of intensity, the greater the response, which means that the output from the photoreceptor cells is logarithmic rather than linear. The three types of cones in the eye each respond to a different band of wavelengths, which peak in the long (red), medium (green), and short (blue) regions of the visible spectrum. As can be seen in Figure 2-9, there is considerable overlap among the three cone responses, and this causes some complications in color reproduction. In addition, the cones are not equally distributed among the red, green, and blue receptors, but are present in a ratio of 40:20:1. The green cones are most sensitive and blue the least, and as a result we are more able to discriminate between colors in the red-yellow-green-cyan regions of the spectrum than in the blue region. Thus designers should avoid the use of blue for text and other graphic elements where recognition is very important.

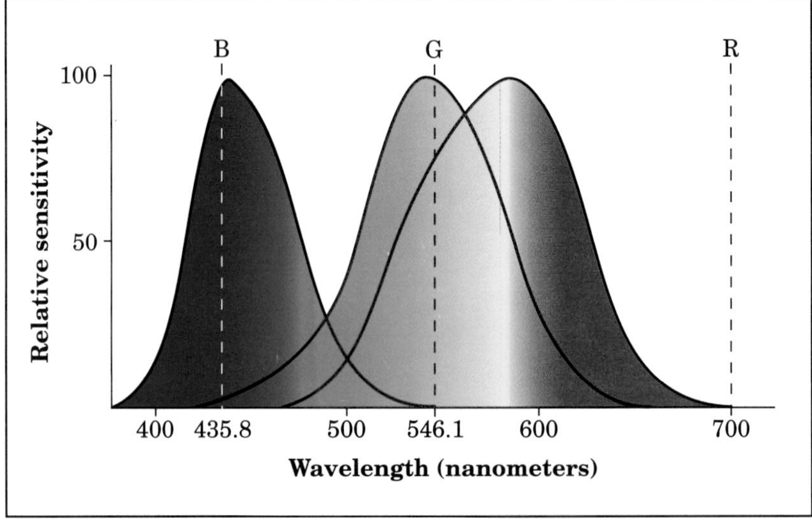

Figure 2-9. Curves showing the sensitivity of the three types of cones in the retina. Also shown are the R, G, and B wavelengths used to define the CIE Standard Observer (see Chapter 3). From *Measuring Color* by R. W. G. Hunt.

There is a delay of around 0.4 seconds between the time the image falls on the retina and the brain becomes conscious of it, although intense flashes of light are processed more quickly. Once perceived, the sensation may take up to two minutes to fade, sometimes leading to after-image effects. This phenomenon is exploited by film, television, video, and computer monitors, which display a rapid succession of still images that are refreshed before the perceptual image has decayed.

Unusual Color Perception

A small percentage of the population does not see color in quite the same way as everyone else. An individual whose color vision differs from the majority of the population often has some type of inherited malfunction of one of the cones, but some cases of visual divergence are caused by damage to one of the brain's "image-processing" centers, often due to an accident or a stroke. There have, for example, been cases of people who have normal visual systems but a complete inability to recognize faces. Other instances of unusual color perception include the phenomenon of **synaesthesia,** the very rare ability to produce a color sensation from a different sense, such as sound, smell, or taste. (The artist Vasily Kandinsky was a synaesthetic, and many of the images he produced were influenced by music that he heard or composed.) Divergences in color perception may be inconvenient for the individual, but give us powerful insights into the ways in which the brain is organized and the mechanism of color perception operates.

Divergent color vision can lead to errors in color matching, and it is recommended that those people involved in making critical judgments in color selection or color reproduction take color vision tests, if only to become more aware of any limitations they may have. About one in ten men and one in a hundred women experience some form of divergent color vision, the most common being confusion between red and green. Typically, yellows are found to appear to be more red or more green to these people than to people with normal color vision. In extreme cases, the individual is likely to be conscious of the problem, but, in more borderline cases, he or she may not be.

Discriminating between Colors

The ability to discriminate between different colors is very important in color reproduction, as it makes us very sensitive to colors that are similar but not identical. We are especially sensitive to differences between neutral colors (i.e., white, grays, and near-grays). This makes it necessary to take special care in their reproduction, as we are more likely to notice slight differences between neutrals than between intense, saturated colors.

Paradoxically, we are more sensitive to changes in lightness (owing to the larger numbers of cells in the human eye that are dedicated to lightness detection and analysis), but we find changes in color more objectionable.

The implications of this are:

- The lightness information in an image should ideally be given greater precision in sampling and encoding than the color information.
- If both lightness and color are sampled with equal precision, some color data can be discarded without affecting the appearance of the image.
- Once a proof has been approved by a client, deviations in color balance are more likely to cause dissatisfaction than a reproduction that is slightly lighter or darker than the proof is.

How many colors should a digital color system be able to support? Conventionally, 256 intensity levels are allocated to each of the three additive primaries (red, green, and blue). For the purposes of binary storage, 256 is 2^8 and thus requires eight bits (a single byte) of storage. The possible permutations of the three primaries can then be represented by $(2^8)^3$ or 2^{24}, which naturally requires twenty-four bits of storage. Hence twenty-four-bit color has become the standard for systems that attempt to replicate the range of colors available to human perception. However, this does not mean that twenty-four-bit color is the same as human perception. Firstly, our responses to different parts of the color gamut are not uniform. We have greater sensitivity to neutral colors than to saturated colors, to lighter colors than to darker colors, and to certain hues over others. Our perception is said to be nonuniform: identical changes in color do not produce identical responses.

Secondly, the adaptive nature of perception makes us respond to relative differences in color rather than absolute ones. The adjustment of the iris and the ganglion cells for different light intensities allows us to recognize objects despite enormous differences in the actual color intensity received by the retina. To replicate the full range of intensities we would need a system with many millions of gray levels, although at any given level of illumination we can discriminate among only a restricted number of gray levels.

Research suggests that the number of hues that we can discern is around 200, and the number of gray levels is between 60 and 150, depending on such factors as the level of background illumination. It is difficult to explore the degrees of saturation that can be identified, as the available pigments do not reach the limits of saturation. Within the gamut that can be produced by the process colors cyan, magenta, and yellow, it is likely to be less than 100.

This may suggest that the gamut of colors available to human perception can be represented adequately within a twenty-four-bit system, but because perception is non-uniform with greater discrimination in certain parts of the gamut this is not quite true. What we can say is that the twenty-four-bit system approximates the range of colors that we can see, but, in most cases, either too much or too little information is obtained.

Human color vision is subject to a number of factors that influence our color perception, some of which are discussed here.

Color Constancy

Human vision can recognize objects under enormous variations in lighting conditions. Daylight varies in intensity from one lux at dawn to 100,000 and more in bright sunshine, and in color from the pink of dawn to the orange of sunset, through the yellow of direct sunshine to the bluer light of an overcast sky. Indoors, artificial lighting is normally lacking in blue wavelengths, making objects appear more yellow. Yet an object is always recognizable—we perceive a cornflower, for example, as the same flower outdoors or indoors, despite its blue color changing to violet. Equally, we can recognize the brightness of a color at widely different levels of illumination.

The evolution of the visual mechanism, through successive adaptations from early sightless creatures to birds and mammals with high visual acuity, is linked to the success of each organism in terms of its survival and reproduction, through its ability to recognize objects and features under widely different lighting conditions. Two of the ways in which it does this are:

- Holding the perceived image constant regardless of the color or intensity of the surrounding lighting.
- Maximizing the differences in color and intensity within an image.

The factors that influence perception can be understood as a result of the light capture mechanism of the eye and image-processing carried out by the neural cells in the eye and the brain. The iris controls the amount of light entering the eye by adjusting its opening over a range of 1.5 to 8 mm, rather like a camera aperture. The ganglion cells also contribute to the “normalizing” of the perception of light intensity. In the brain, the perception of an object is not just a “scan” of the visual field but a result of comparing it with its surroundings and a memory of what the object looks like. By looking at the difference between the object and its surroundings, the brain perceives relative color rather than absolute color. Changing the immediate surroundings must then lead the brain to adjust its perception of the color of the object.

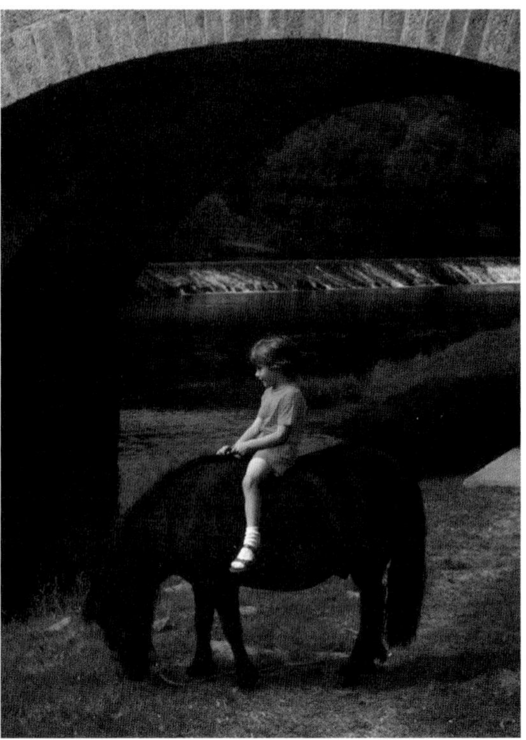

Figure 2-10. Hue induction. The hue of the girl’s shirt is an illusion caused by adaptation to the surrounding black/cyan duotone.

Many people are familiar with these effects on a computer screen. The appearance of the color display varies considerably according to whether the room is lit by daylight or artificial light, and the brightness of the screen colors appears to increase as the day draws to a close and the eye adjusts to lower light intensities.

Some consequences of the phenomenon of color constancy for color viewing and assessment are:

- The tendency to perceive any near-white as neutral and not identify color casts unless by comparison with other neutrals.
- The tendency for color perception to be influenced by any surrounding colors.

Figure 2-11. Chromatic induction targets. The color targets appear different due to the influence of the surrounding colors.

Color Temperature

The exact color of white light is important, since, if it tends towards one part of the spectrum, anything viewed by its illumination will have a color cast. The color of light is not measured or specified in the same way as the color of an ink or a display monitor. Instead the concept of **color temperature** is used. This principle states that when a body heats up it emits light, glowing first red, then yellow, and continuing through a colorless white to a blue.

Color temperature is measured on the Kelvin scale (0 K is equal to –273° Celsius), and a completely neutral white light source is considered to have a color temperature of 5,000 Kelvin. Lower color temperatures are more yellow, and higher color temperatures are more blue.

Two other concepts that are relevant to viewing color are the **color rendering index** and **spectral power distribution.** The color rendering index is a measure of how well a light source conforms to the color rendering of natural daylight, on a scale of 0 to 100. The spectral power distribution of a light source is a measure of how much light is present at each wavelength, and is usually shown on a spectral radiation curve (similar to a spectral reflectance curve). A light source with a color temperature of 5,000 K and a spectral power distribution similar to natural daylight is known as a

D_{50} illuminant. The spectral power distribution of a light source in effect combines both its color temperature and color rendering index.

Figure 2-12.
Correlated color temperature of typical light sources

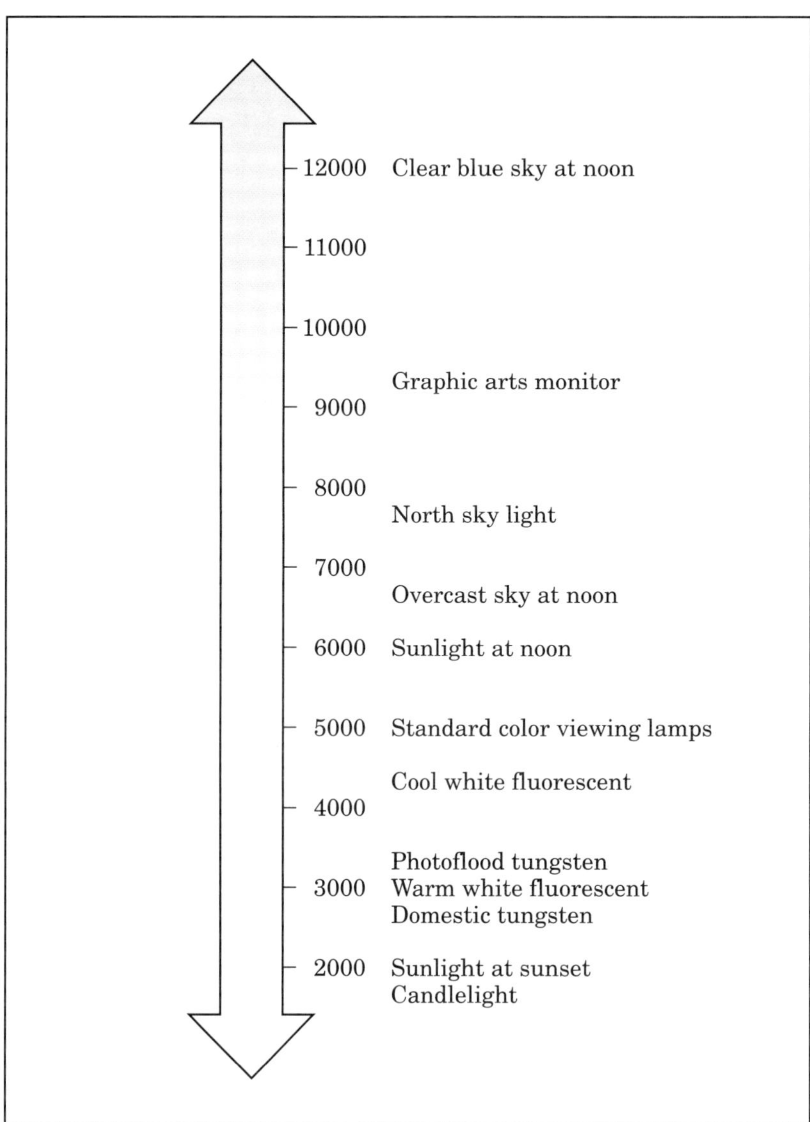

Viewing Conditions

The eye will always adapt to the ambient light source and see it as neutral white, adjusting the perception of any colors viewed under it. Moreover, if the spectral power distribution of the light source is uneven and weak in some wavelengths, it will be impossible to judge colors accurately. For example, the blue cornflower viewed under a tungsten light source appears violet because of the relative absence of blue wavelengths. The manner in which the eye adapts to changing ambient light causes the colors viewed on a computer monitor to appear to alter in both hue and intensity.

The various visual phenomena described above make it extremely important to have some standardization of viewing conditions in the graphic arts. The American National Standards Institute (ANSI) has specified viewing conditions for the graphic arts in ANSI PH2.30-1989, *Color Prints, Transparencies, and Photomechanical Reproductions—Viewing Conditions; Part 1.* Many other national and international standards, such as BS 950 in the UK and the international standard ISO 3664, are now functionally identical to the ANSI standard.

The standard specifies characteristics of the light source to be used, as summarized in Table 2-1. In addition, the chromaticity coordinates of the light source and the tolerances allowed are defined.

Table 2-1.
Viewing conditions.

	Chromaticity coordinates	Color temperature	Spectral power distribution	Color rendering index	Intensity
Transparencies	x=0.3457 y=0.3586	5000 K	D_{50}	> 90	1400 cd/m^3 +300 cd/m^3
Photographic prints	x=0.3457 y=0.3586	5000 K	D_{50}	> 90	2200 lux +470 lux
Reproductions	x=0.3457 y=0.3586	5000 K	D_{50}	> 90	2200 lux +470 lux

The standard is mainly directed at manufacturers of color viewing equipment. Points that users need to be aware of are listed here.

In general:

- Lamps should warm up for 15–45 minutes before use to reach a stable temperature.
- You should allow time for your eyes to adjust to the D_{50} illuminant.
- Any ambient lighting that is not standardized should be reduced or eliminated—room lights should be dimmed or turned off and blinds or drapes closed.
- Bright colors on furniture or clothing should be avoided as they will cause a color cast.

- All surfaces surrounding the viewing area should be a neutral gray in color with a reflectance of 60% (Munsell N8/).
- Manufacturers recommend that lamps should be changed after 2,500–5,000 hours of use because the color temperature changes as the lamps age.

For transparencies:
- Inspect on a transparency viewer equipped with D_{50} lamps.
- Have a 2-in. (51-mm) white border around the transparency, with a gray surround beyond it.
- Place the transparency viewer in a viewing cabinet with D_{50} overhead lamps, or under D_{50} room lamps.

For prints:
- Use a viewing cabinet equipped with D_{50} lamps and an interior painted neutral gray.

For monitors:
- Calibrate the monitor to a 5,000 K color temperature.
- Ensure that ambient lighting is minimized unless it conforms to the standard.
- Keep the intensity of ambient lighting consistent throughout the day.
- Remove any light sources that shine directly on the color monitor.

Figure 2-13. Transparency viewer with standard 5000 K lamps. *Courtesy Leslie Hubble Ltd.*

There is some variation even within standardized lighting conditions, due to factors including lamp characteristics, ambient temperatures, and the amount of electrical power available. Once color viewing equipment has been installed, it is difficult to test how well it conforms with the standard, unless expensive equipment, such as a spectroradiometer, is used. The GATF/RHEM Light Indicator is a useful visual guide to identify nonstandard light sources. It is a small printed target that is attached to color proofs and prints. When examined under 5,000 K light, it appears to printed in a single ink color, while stripes of two different colors are apparent when it is examined under many other illuminants.

Standard viewing conditions are not required in all design and production areas, only where color matching or appraisal takes place. It is perfectly acceptable for colors to be selected in the lighting conditions in which they will be viewed by the end user, such as store or office lighting, but standard viewing conditions should be used when comparisons between originals, proofs, and prints are made to ensure accuracy. If colors selected from a computer screen will ultimately be printed, it is preferable to carry out selection under standard viewing conditions with reference to printed samples.

Implementation of standard viewing conditions is costly, but it is the only way you can have assurance of accurate color appraisal. The minimum installation is a D_{50} viewer for color transparencies and a D_{50} cabinet for color proofs and prints; it is possible to install D_{50} lamps into a home-made cabinet if attention is paid to the detailed points of the standard on viewing geometry and so on.

Surface Properties

A surface does not itself have a precise color but rather an ability to absorb certain wavelengths of visible light. A leaf appears green, for example, because it contains a pigment that absorbs red and blue wavelengths, reflecting only green to the observer. As long as the light remains constant, the green appears the same, but as the light source changes (such as when the sun is obscured) so does the color seen by the observer.

The reflection of light from a colored surface has two components. First, some light is reflected unchanged from the first layer of the surface. The remainder enters the substrate and undergoes scattering and multiple reflections inside the material. Eventually, unless the light energy decays within the material, it emerges from the surface as a diffuse reflection. Where the light meets a pigment particle within the surface, some wavelengths will be absorbed while others will be reflected and allowed to continue on their path through the material. Any light that emerges will be perceived by an observer as having a color corresponding to the unabsorbed wavelengths.

The light that is reflected from the first layer of the surface (the "first-surface reflection") makes the surface appear lighter, since light has been reflected without any part of it being absorbed. In the case of a computer monitor, incident light that strikes the surface and is reflected to the user causes the screen display to lose contrast, since all of the dark areas appear much lighter. This effect is known as **flare.**

Figure 2-14.
Light reflectance.

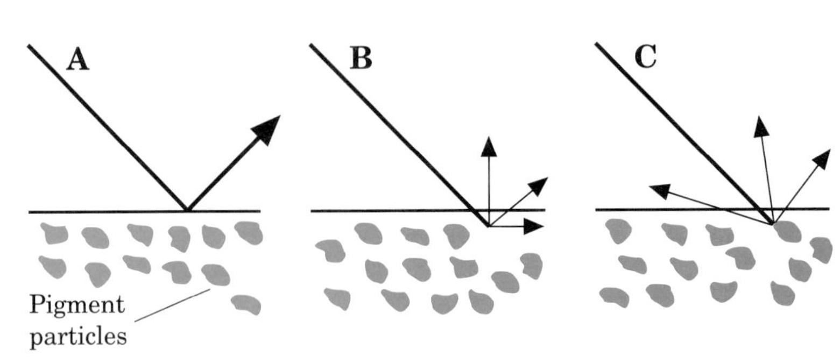

Light arriving at the surface either (A) reflects from the first layer of the surface or (B) enters the material and is scattered internally, some being absorbed but some re-emerging as diffusely reflected light. If pigment particles are present, (C) only certain wavelengths will re-emerge.

Subtractive color systems, such as the inks used in commercial printing processes and the dyes in photographic prints and transparencies, produce their range of colors by absorption, subtracting wavelengths of light rather than adding them together. The subtractive primaries (cyan, magenta, and yellow) are the opposites, or complementaries, of the additive primaries of light. Each of the subtractive primaries absorbs one of the additive primaries (thus cyan absorbs red, magenta absorbs green, and yellow absorbs blue), giving the widest gamut possible with just three colors. Just as combining different proportions of the additive primaries (red, green, and blue) allows millions of different

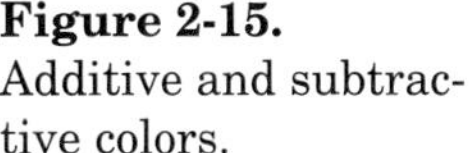

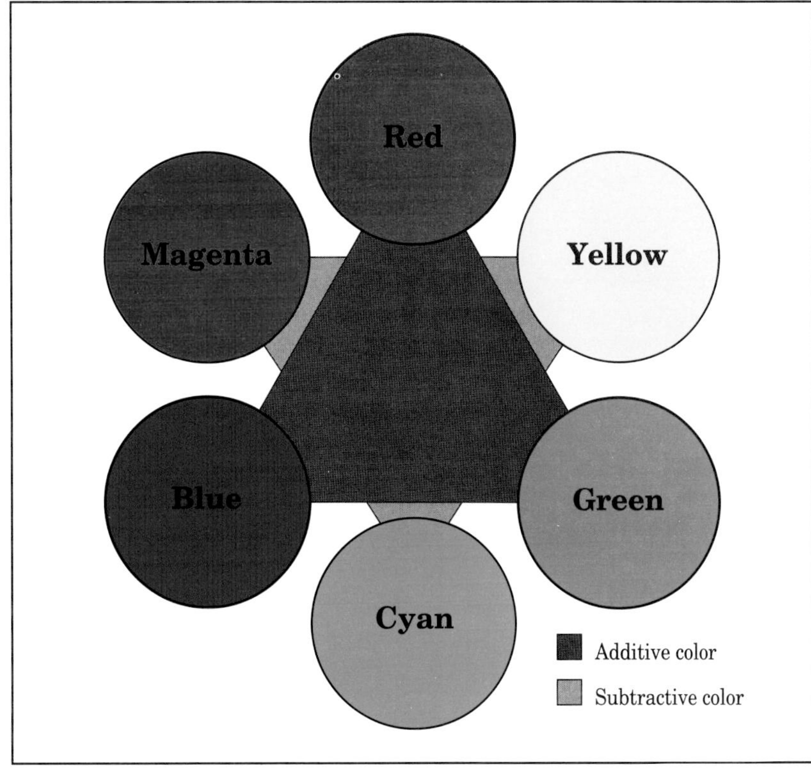

Figure 2-15.
Additive and subtractive colors.

colors to be produced, the overprinting of different amounts of cyan, magenta, and yellow also creates a large gamut of different colors.

For the process color illusion to work, the inks must be transparent, so that wherever they overprint the color seen is made up of all the colors present. Special colors, such as PANTONE colors, are normally opaque because they are not intended to overprint with other colors. (Inks are described as either opaque or transparent, although in practice they are never fully opaque or fully transparent.)

The process colors used in printing are formulated to have levels of absorbance close to the spectral response of the three types of cones in the retina of the eye. Overlaps in the cone responses and slight deficiencies in the pigments available to formulate the inks make the situation a little more complex, and corrections have to be made if the color balance of an original is to be reproduced accurately.

A midtone neutral gray is made up of approximately 50% cyan, 40% magenta, and 40% yellow, although this varies slightly with different scanners and separation software. Equal values of the three colors, such as 50% cyan, 50%

magenta, and 50% yellow, would create a decidedly reddish color cast. Neutral gray is somewhat more subjective: outside of Europe and North America, people sometimes prefer a different color balance, and nominate different proportions of cyan, yellow, and magenta to create a neutral gray.

If the absorbance of the three process colors were correctly matched to the spectral response of the eye, printing cyan, magenta, and yellow on top of each other would absorb all of the additive primaries (red, green, and blue) to produce black. In practice, overprinting these three colors creates a dark brown, so to enable a wider range of densities to be printed a black ink must also be used. The black also

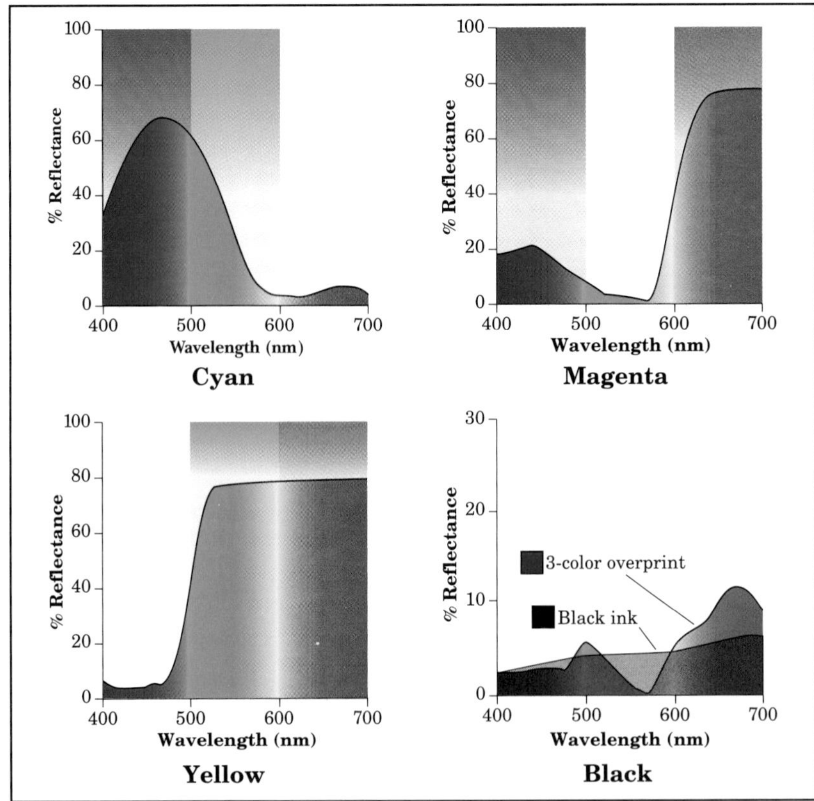

Figure 2-16. The spectral reflectance curves of the three process colors and black.

enhances the edges of an image and reduces the amount of expensive colored inks that need to be used. The four colors cyan, magenta, yellow, and black are often abbreviated as CMYK, with the last letter of the word black used instead of the first to avoid confusion with blue. Many people in the graphic arts industry refer to cyan and magenta as "process blue" and "process red" (or, confusingly, as just blue and red).

As well as any pigment that may be present, substrates have other properties that affect color appearance. The precise way in which a surface reflects the light that falls on it will be crucial to the appearance of color; hence properties such as gloss, texture, absorbency, and fluorescence must be considered when choosing or comparing colors. These properties cannot be reproduced on a computer monitor.

The gloss of a surface is determined by the way in which light is reflected from it. The greater the proportion of incident light that is reflected at the same angle as it strikes the surface, the glossier the surface appears. A surface that scatters light randomly has a diffuse appearance. Paper

Figure 2-17. Reflection from (A) a matte surface and (B) a glossy surface.

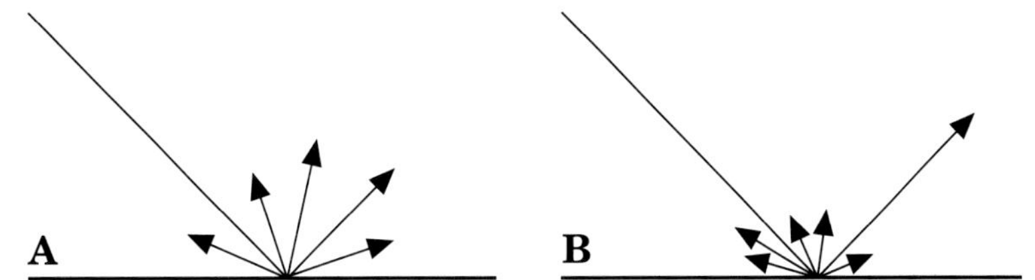

On a matte surface (A), light is reflected randomly in all directions. On a glossy surface (B), a larger proportion is reflected in the "specular" angle, and when viewed from this angle the surface appears to glare.

Because gloss affects the first-surface reflection rather than reflection from inside the substrate, its effect on a printed surface is to reduce the amount of colorless light reflected and intensify the appearance of the color, except when viewed in the specular angle.

gloss depends mainly on smoothness and the type of surface coating applied. It can also be altered by finishes, such as varnishing and laminating.

Textured surfaces and pearlescent and metallic inks affect appearance by changing the way in which light is scattered and reflected. Absorbent papers make colors look duller and darker and can also make hues seem slightly redder.

Fluorescence occurs when ultraviolet radiation from just outside the visible spectrum is absorbed and re-emitted as visible light, thus increasing the total amount of light reflected from a surface. Fluorescent brightening agents are commonly added to paper and boards to make them brighter and whiter and to increase the possible density range that can be achieved when printing on them.

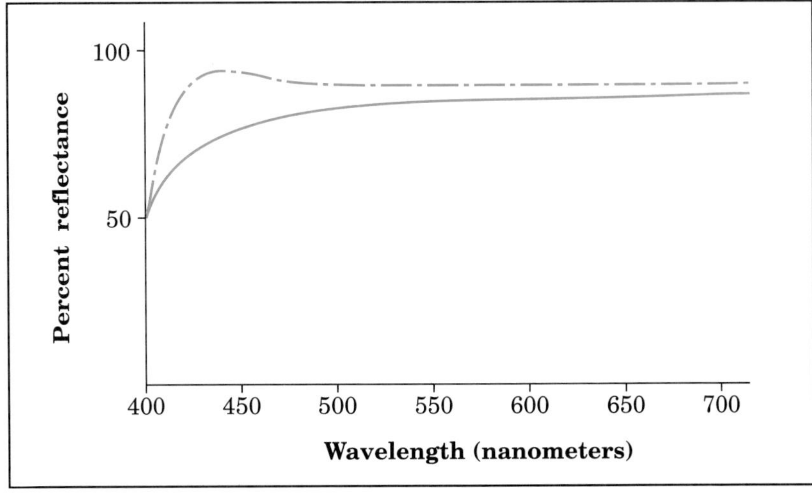

Figure 2-18. Spectral reflectance curves produced by two paper samples. One has a peak reflectance at 440 nm caused by the presence of fluorescing pigments. It has absorbed radiation in the ultraviolet region and re-emitted it as visible light. From *Color and Its Reproduction* by Gary Field.

Image Capture and Color Separation

The red-green-blue (RGB) system, which forms the basis of video, television, and color monitors, corresponds closely to the way in which the human eye perceives color. Image capture devices, such as video recorders and color scanners, analyze the amount of red, green, and blue present in a color image, and the result can be stored as an electronic file that describes the intensity of each of the three colors present in terms of values for each pixel.

The subtractive CMYK color system is used whenever color is to be printed on a surface that will be viewed by reflective light. Converting the RGB values into CMYK is called **color separation,** a complex process that adjusts for the differences between the two systems. Some of the problems in electronic color reproduction arise from the different color gamuts that are available in these two different systems and from the complications involved in converting additive to subtractive colors. Color separation is discussed further in Chapter 7.

3 Color Specification and Assessment

The printing processes can reproduce a vast range of different colors. This chapter will help you to specify the colors you want more effectively and to judge whether or not they have been accurately reproduced.

When we want to communicate information about a color to someone else, we have the same problem that we have in describing other sensations such as taste or smell; we have relatively few words in our language with which to describe the millions of possible colors that exist in our world. For this reason, colors are specified by reference to color models, color sample systems, and, where necessary, color measurement.

Color Models

A **color model** is a systematic method of arranging individual colors. Using a color model is like referring to a map of the colors available—and just as it is possible to have different kinds of maps for different purposes, so, too, are there different color models. For designers and printers, color models are extremely valuable tools for visualizing, specifying, quantifying, and controlling colors. Shifts between two colors can be quantified precisely, since the axes of the color model provide coordinates for the location of the colors.

Electronic images are displayed using the red, green, and blue (RGB) phosphors of the computer screen, and are thus specified in the RGB model. RGB is an unsuitable color model for interchange or output because its steps are based on the characteristics of the display device, rather than any visual appearance criteria. These steps do not produce uniform changes in perceived intensity, and the three color signals cannot be combined in ways that are analogous to the human visual mechanism. The process colors—cyan, magenta, and yellow—that are combined with black during four-color printing can also be considered a color model known as

CMYK. However, just as the RGB system is not directly related to human color vision, changing CMYK values produces similarly nonuniform results.

The appearance of a color specified in the RGB and CMYK color models depends on the characteristics of the system used to output it. On a monitor, the precise nature of the phosphors and the shadow masks and the exact potentials used by the electron gun determine the actual color displayed from a given RGB specification. In printed output, the color is specified in terms of the dot percentages of cyan, magenta, yellow, and black, but other factors, such as the characteristics of inks and presses and the type of paper used will contribute to the final appearance.

Thus both RGB and CMYK are device-dependent color models that are inevitably of limited use in communicating

Table 3-1.
Uses of color models.

Type	Purpose	Examples
Perceptual	Visualization of color attributes and relationships	HSL
Input	Device-dependent sampling of color values in original image	RGB
Encoding	Storing color image in terms of its lightness and color attributes	YCC
Interchange	Device-independent color space for absolute color values and interchange between other color spaces	CIE, CIELab, CIELuv
Output	Device-dependent specification of color output	RGB, CMYK
Selection	Library of color samples	PMS, Munsell
Colorimetric	Objective measurement of color values	CIE, CIELab
Color difference	Uniform color space for specification of color tolerances and color differences	CIELab

and converting information about colors among different color devices. They also have different **color gamuts,** or ranges of reproducible colors. For example, monitors can display many colors that cannot be printed, especially in the saturated red, green, and blue regions. Other color models are based on the idea of a device-independent color space, where colors are specified in terms of an objective color measurement system closely related to human color perception.

Perceptual Color Models

When our eyes perceive a color we observe three things about it:

- Its **hue.** (What are the proportions of red, green, blue and yellow? In other words, what wavelengths are present?)
- Its **colorfulness.** (Is the hue clearly visible or is it contaminated by other colors?)
- Its **brightness.** (How much light is it reflecting?)

These three subjective attributes of human color perception form the basis of a number of broadly similar color models. Examples include hue, saturation, and lightness (HSL); hue, saturation, and brightness (HSB); hue, saturation, and value (HSV); and luminance, chroma, and hue (LCH). These perceptual models all give hue more or less the same meaning, but differ in their definition of the other components. Saturation or chroma corresponds to the colorfulness attribute, and luminance, lightness, or value to the brightness attribute.

All the perceptual models are organized around a brightness axis and two axes that contain the hue and colorfulness

Figure 3-1. A color image and its HSL components: hue *(upper right);* saturation *(lower left);* and lightness *(lower right).* The picture was split into HSL channels in Aldus Photostyler, with gray-scale values for each pixel determined from the hue angle and saturation percentage.

information. These last two axes can be thought as forming a two-dimensional **chromatic plane** where the color information is defined independently of luminance. As you can see in Figure 3-1, the luminance information is the most important for the recognition of the subject.

As noted earlier, the term hue is used to define a color in terms of the balance of red, green, blue, and yellow that is

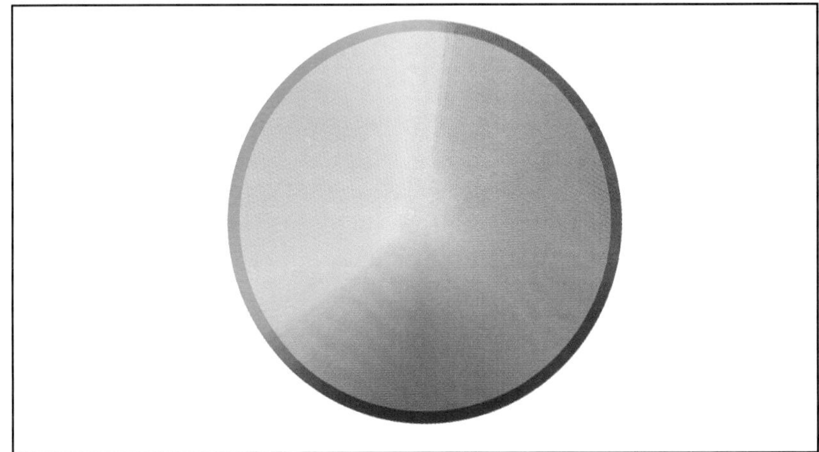

Figure 3-2.
Hue axis *(top)*, and spectral reflectance curve *(bottom)*.
The hue axis in the HSL color model is circular, hues being defined by the angle they make (red is 0°).

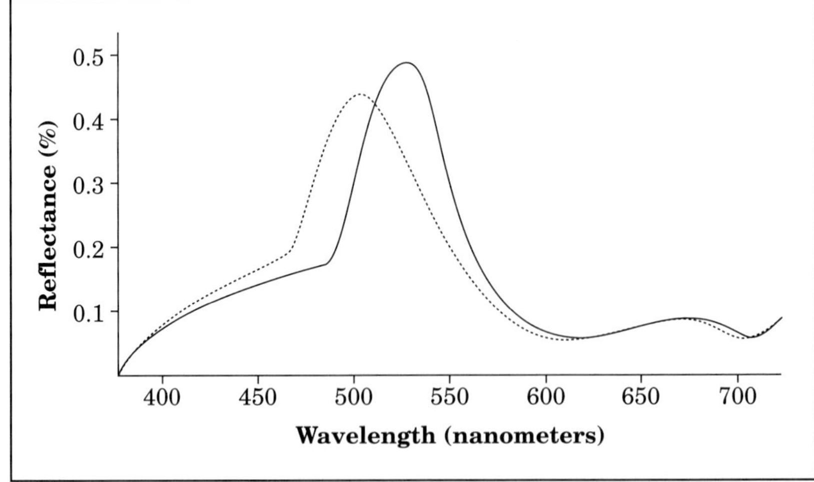

Hues are also differentiated by their peak wavelengths on a spectral reflectance curve. Two greens are shown here, one of which is slightly closer to the blue end of the spectrum.

present. The hue of a color can be communicated by its position around the circumference of a color wheel, or its position in the visible spectrum (shown as the peak wavelength on a spectral reflectance curve). Thus a color with a "hue angle" of 120° would be a green and would have a peak wavelength of 520 nm.

HSL Color Model

The absolute colorfulness and brightness of a color vary according to the intensity of the surrounding lighting conditions. Because the human visual mechanism actually responds to the relative difference between colorfulness and brightness and not to their absolute values, it is more useful to use the attributes saturation and lightness for the actual color model.

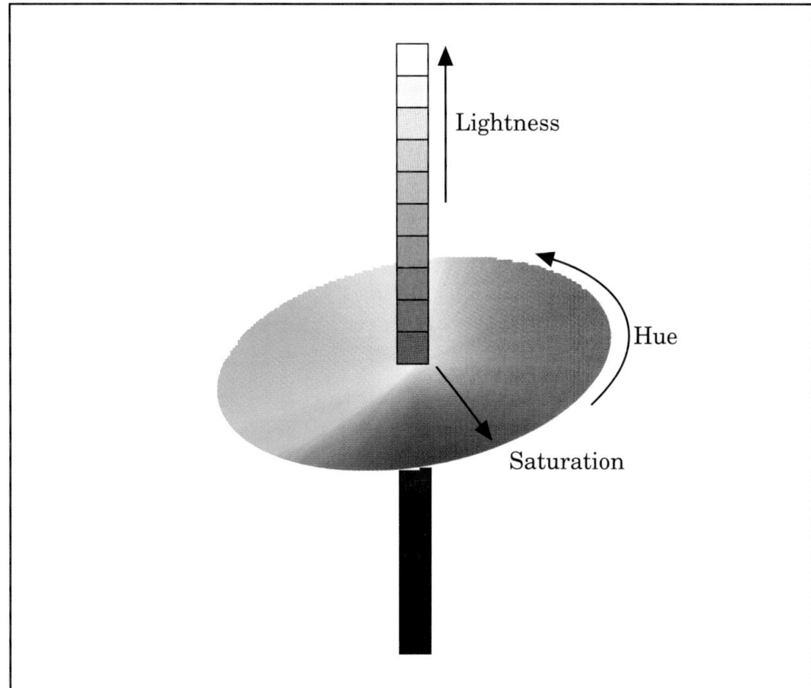

Figure 3-3.
The HSL color model.

Saturation indicates the intensity or purity of a color: highly saturated colors are said to be vivid, while desaturated colors are referred to as dull or dirty. Saturation can be considered as being colorfulness relative to a neutral gray that has the same brightness. On a color wheel, it is represented by the distance from the center of the wheel—the nearer to the periphery, the higher its saturation is.

The lightness of a color is simply a description of the amount of light reflected from it. It can be defined as the color's brightness relative to a white. Lightness itself is an **achromatic** attribute in that it contains no information at all about the color of an object, only about how light or dark it is.

Perhaps the most important property of the HSL model is that each attribute is independent of the others. If, for

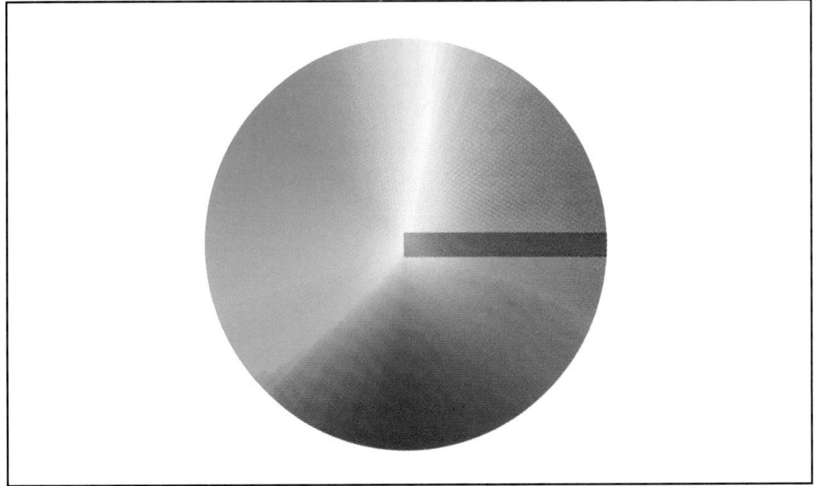

Figure 3-4.
Saturation axis.
The saturation axis in the HSL color model extends from neutral gray at the center to the saturated colors at the periphery. Colors can have a saturation value from 0 at the center to 100 at the periphery.

example, the hue of a color is changed, the lightness and saturation will retain the same values unless they, too, are changed. In this respect, the HSL model provides an intuitive way for humans to visualize the physical properties of colors and their relationships with each other.

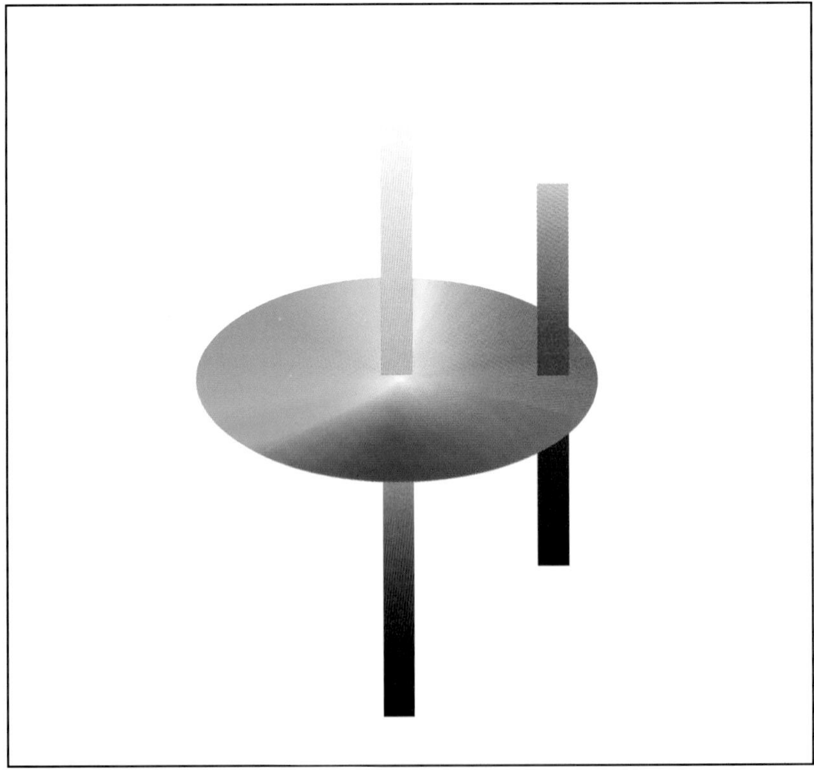

Figure 3-5.
Lightness axis.
The lightness axis in the HSL color model is at right angles to the chromatic plane. Colors have a lightness value from 0 (black) to 100 (white).

HSB Color Model

In the HSB model, the hue, saturation, and brightness components are similar to the HSL model described above, but with an important difference. As used in the graphic arts, HSB is actually based on the RGB intensities of the computer color display monitor. What this means in practice is:

- The hue of a color is adjusted by altering the balance of RGB intensities, keeping the total intensity the same.
- The saturation of a color is adjusted by increasing or decreasing the intensities of the complementary RGB color, keeping the dominant color the same.
- The brightness of a color is adjusted by scaling the RGB intensities up or down equally, keeping the balance of intensities the same.

Many computer applications support the specification of colors in HSB, for example through controls with separate "sliders" for hue, saturation, and brightness. The Color Picker on the Macintosh, which interfaces with the QuickDraw graphics controller, allows colors to be selected in both the RGB and HSB models.

If you experiment with the Color Picker, you will see that maximum saturation can only be achieved at maximum brightness. At 50% brightness, the saturation range is greatly reduced. This means that saturation and brightness are not independent of each other in the "display" HSB model.

In comparison, the HSL model exhibits a different relationship between saturation and lightness. Maximum saturation

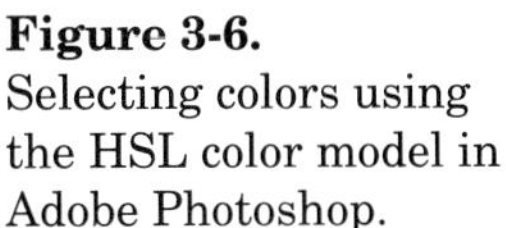

Figure 3-6.
Selecting colors using the HSL color model in Adobe Photoshop.

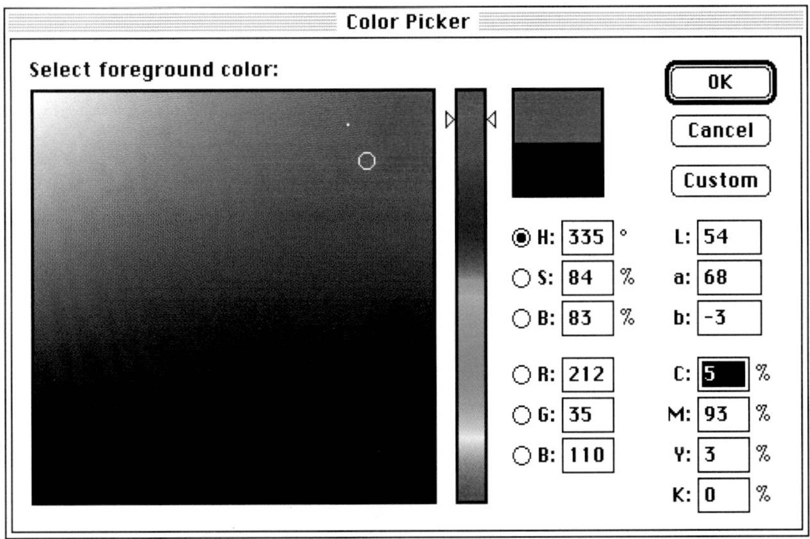

can only be achieved at the midpoint on the lightness axis. Where lightness is at a maximum, the color is white and the saturation is zero.

CIE Color System

A truly independent and objective method of defining colors must be ultimately based on human visual perception and also be independent of both input and output device. The CIE system, developed by the Commission Internationale de l'Eclairage (CIE) of France in 1931, is universally accepted as the standard basis of color specification and measurement.

The 1931 CIE system is based on the appearance of color to an average person, defined as a theoretical **standard observer.** The CIE definition followed experiments with a sample of seventeen human observers, and although the sample size was very small the results have since been confirmed in many other experiments. CIE measurements can be expressed in two different ways, as **tristimulus values** or as **chromaticity coordinates.** Although the precise derivation of these is outside the scope of this text (readers interested in the subject should refer to the books listed in the bibliography), a brief and highly simplified summary is presented here.

The CIE definition of the standard observer is based on three wavelengths of light, red (R), green (G), and blue (B), shown in Figure 2.9. (Note that in the CIE system, RGB values relate to objective color measurements and should be distinguished from the device-dependent RGB system used in color monitors.)

Tristimulus (X,Y,Z) values are derived from the relative amounts of RGB present in a color. Tristimulus values can be determined by colorimeter measurements using red, green, and blue filters that are similar to the response of the eye's retinal cones, or they can be computed from spectral data (reflectance measurements made at a series of wavelengths across the visible spectrum).

The chromaticity (x,y) coordinates are derived mathematically from the X,Y,Z values. The resulting x and y values can be plotted on a two-dimensional chromaticity diagram, the horseshoe-shaped space shown in Figure 3-7. Each point on the diagram indicates a hue and its saturation level. Wavelengths from the blue end of the spectrum through to the red are labeled around the curved rim of the horseshoe. Colors closer to the rim are more saturated (just as in the color wheel discussed earlier).

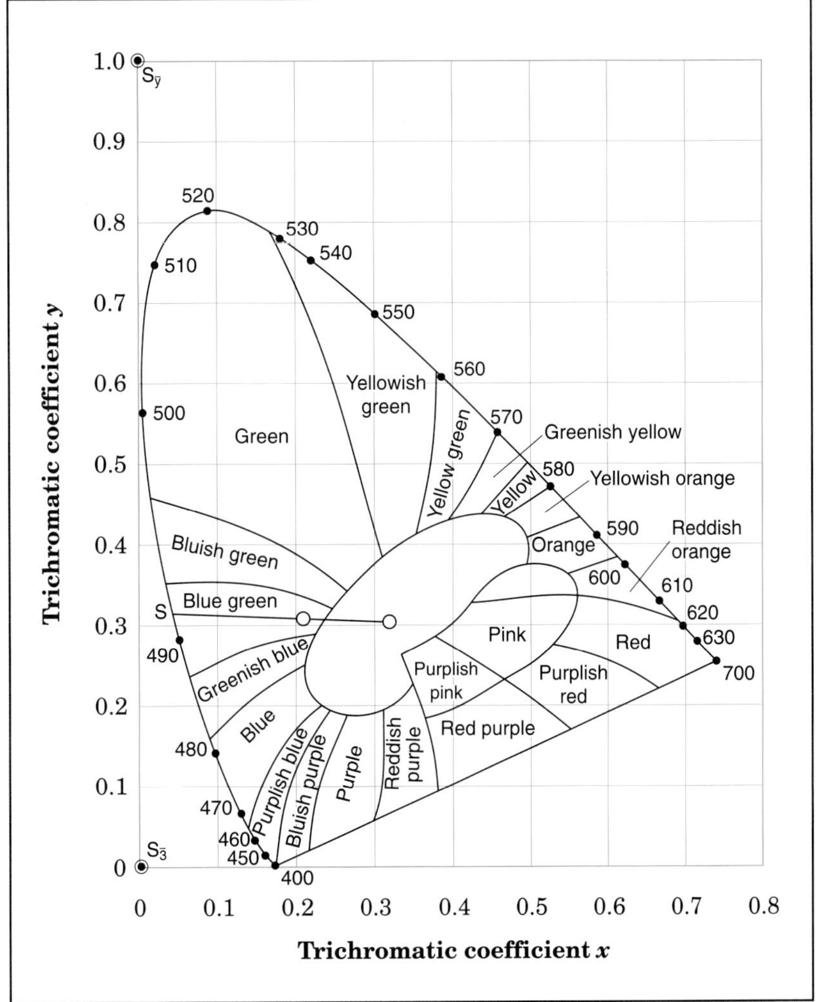

Figure 3-7.
The CIE chromaticity diagram showing the wavelengths of light and the x–y coordinates. Values for Y (lightness) are at right angles to the x–y plane.

The luminance, or Y, value is expressed on a 0–100 scale that is at right angles to the chromaticity plane. Higher numbers indicate lighter colors. Any color can then be specified by giving its x and y chromaticity coordinates and its Y luminance value.

The 1931 CIE system underlies all color measuring and encoding systems. Yet using it as a conceptual model does have some drawbacks:

- The x,y values can be difficult to interpret as they do not relate directly to any of the perceptual attributes of color.
- The chromaticity diagram is not perceptually uniform (equal distances in it do not represent equal shifts in color appearance).

There have been a number of modifications to the 1931 CIE system that have made the color appearance of the model more uniform by transforming the x,y values. Adaptations of 1931 CIE system are widely used in the specification and measurement of color. The 1976 CIELAB system is used mainly for reflective color samples, including paints and textiles as well as prints on paper, and the CIELUV system is used for self-luminous color displays (TV, video, and computer monitors). CIELAB and CIELUV have a vertical lightness dimension and two-dimensional chromatic coordinates (like the HSL model).

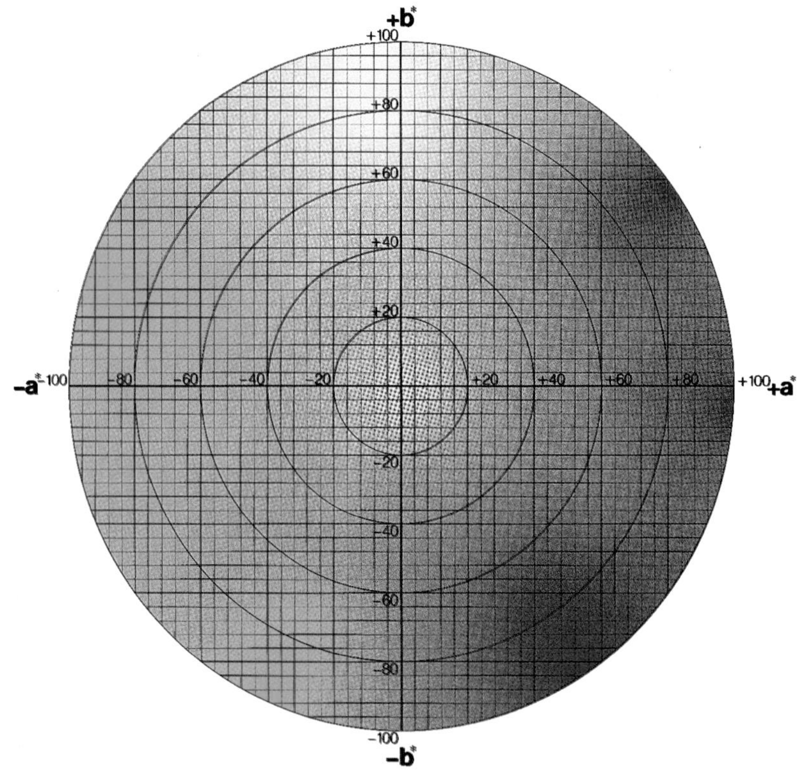

Figure 3-8.
The 1976 CIE L*a*b* transformation of the CIE color space. The a* and b* coordinates form a chromatic plane, with lightness (L*) at right angles to it. There is no absolute limit to the values for a* and b*, although, in this illustration, they are shown bounded by a circle.

In the CIELAB system, the lightness (L*) value of a color ranges from 0 (black) to 100 (white), while the chromatic axes are called a* (red-green) and b* (blue-yellow). A neutral gray has a zero value for both a* and b* components. Unlike CIE x,y and CIELUV, there is no chromaticity diagram for CIELAB, although it is common to depict the a* and b* axes in diagrammatic form for illustration purposes.

At this writing, a new version of CIELAB is being prepared, and it is expected that it will be adopted in 1995 or 1996.

All CIE-based color spaces rely on the same underlying system of defining colors, and, as a result, conversion from one CIE space to any other CIE space is a relatively simple mathematical task.

YCC Color Model

The YCC color model is becoming increasingly important in the graphic arts as it is the basis of the Kodak Photo CD system. It was originally developed by Eastman Kodak as a method of encoding color images destined for display on TV screens or computer monitors. Like the perceptual color models, it encodes lightness information separately from chromatic information, and a smaller file is created than when the image is stored as RGB or CMYK values.

Images are encoded in YCC by converting the red, green, and blue components recorded by the scanner to one luminance component (Y) and two chromatic components (C_1 and C_2). The three channels are then quantized (given digital values within a specified range) to eight bits per component.

A feature of the YCC model is that it is designed to be able to encode the full range of luminance values in the original scene captured by the photographer, values which are often greater than the display capabilities of a color monitor. When Photo CD images are translated back to RGB, the YCC data must be scaled to the levels available or highlight information may be lost.

When the YCC data is written as a Photo CD file, the chromatic data is subsampled, so that only one bit of color information is stored for every four luminance bits (making use of the characteristic of human visual perception that gives greater prominence to lightness than to color). When the file is converted back to RGB, the color data is restored by interpolation.

PostScript-Supported Color Models

The PostScript page description language supports RGB, CMYK, HSB, and CIE-based color spaces, as well as a single-component gray device spaces. It also defines the special color spaces Separation, Indexed, and Pattern, which are always transformed into one of the other color spaces before output.

The Separation color space is used to define the individual colors of an object, and is not limited to the four process colors. It allows applications to support the creation of plates for five or more colors.

The Index space is used to define an image with fewer colors than the full twenty-four-bit palette. It allows for up to 4,096 colors. Indexing is useful for graphic elements, for which twenty-four-bit color is unnecessary, and for creating eight-bit versions of twenty-four-bit color images for display purposes. Adaptive indexing selects the optimum color palette for any image and can provide a better display on an eight-bit system than a twenty-four-bit image that has to rely on the system to select which colors to display. The index or palette can be saved separately and applied to a series of images.

The Pattern color space stores small images that can be tiled and used as a fill for graphic elements, such as boxes and backgrounds.

In Adobe Photoshop the native color model is the device-independent CIELAB, and color values for display or output are derived from the CIELAB values.

The PostScript language incorporates the ability to convert information among different color spaces. Level 1 uses simple conversions from one device to another, while Level 2 uses CIE X,Y,Z as a basis for converting between device color values. PostScript color processing is discussed further in Chapters 9 and 14.

Color Specification

There are two basic methods of specifying color in printing: process color and special color.

Process (or CMYK) colors are specified as combinations of cyan, magenta, and yellow, plus black. They can be printed solid, or in tints of specified percentages. The advantage of specifying process colors for graphic elements is that a large palette of colors is made available to the designer without the need for additional printing plates.

Special colors (also referred to as accent, spot, highlight, and PANTONE colors) require an additional plate for each color that is used. They have the advantages of a larger color gamut than process colors and easier matches for identity colors.

Often both process and special colors are specified for one printed piece. Both systems are based on selection from visual samples in the form of printed tint books or swatch books. To achieve consistent color reproduction, it is essential to choose from printed samples rather than a computer display, as the screen representation cannot accurately simulate the printed color.

When specifying colors in digital prepress, it is important to distinguish between process colors and special colors. Where a special color is selected in an image-editing, page-makeup, or illustration program, it will be converted into a process color unless it is defined as a separation and output as a separate film. Special colors that have been converted to process colors (process-color simulations) seldom match the color originally chosen.

Although color specification systems are based on printed color samples, the increasingly divergent types of output media used for color reproduction, with different colorants and substrates, have led some vendors to adopt device-independent color measurements as the basic reference point for their color specifications. Different output devices can then be calibrated to give the closest match possible with the colorants available. The PANTONE and Focoltone specification systems have both followed this approach.

Specifying CMYK

Most color jobs are printed on multicolor presses that have at least four printing units to carry the black, cyan, magenta, and yellow inks. Specifying tints of these process primaries allows the designer to incorporate a huge range of colors in the graphic elements of a job at no additional cost for extra plates or passes through the press. However, the designer must still take the constraints of the printing process into consideration.

For the printer, precise control of tints is especially difficult when printing them alongside pictures and solids. It is therefore important to avoid tint combinations using three or more colors whenever a color match is important. You can match any three-color tint by using two colors and a black, and this combination is easier to control on press. (See gray component replacement in Chapter 7.)

The hues produced by most printing presses are fairly similar, but the amount of dot gain can vary tremendously. In CMYK tints, any variations in the amount of dot gain can affect the color that is reproduced. The paper used will also affect the appearance of the printed color. Prints on coated papers exhibit low dot gain and appear cleaner and brighter, while on uncoated papers dot gain is higher and colors appear duller.

The traditional photomechanical method of creating a tint for a color job involves exposing a piece of film with the appropriate dot size. These mechanical tints are available only in 5% or 10% steps and in a limited range of screen rulings. Digital tint generation methods allow tint selection in 1% increments and full control over dot sizes and shapes as well as screen angles and rulings. This permits the use of such effects as graduated (or gradient) tints and blends and pastel colors, together with more accurate matches of special colors. Due to the cost of original tints, many trade shops use second-generation copies that distort the tonal values and may be slightly uneven when printed. The use of digital tints ensures that clean, first-generation tints appear on the final films for platemaking.

Tints can be selected from printed samples, known as tint charts, tint books, or color atlases. One of the potential problems with standard tint selectors is that they may not be printed on the same paper that will be used for a given job or with the same densities and dot gain values as the printing press where the final reproduction will be created. If the job is being printed on a device that conforms to one of the industry standards for density and dot gain, including SWOP and

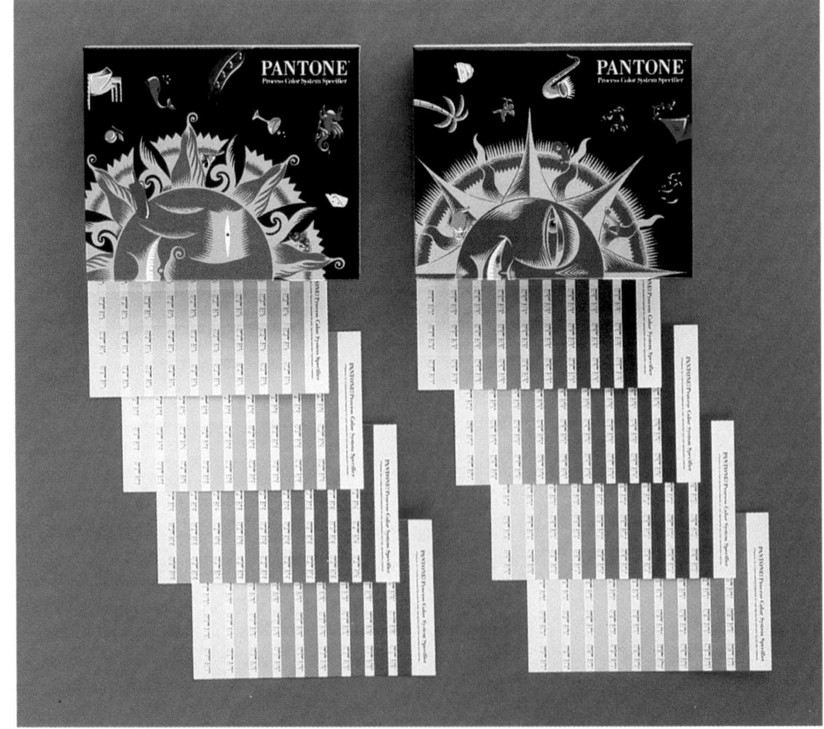

Figure 3-9.
Printed tint selectors, such as the PANTONE Process Color Tint Selector, are available commercially. Many printers also produce their own versions to show the effect of specifying CMYK colors on their own presses.
Courtesy PANTONE Inc. and Anderson Fraser Ltd.

Figure 3-10. PANTONE Process Color System Specifier. *Courtesy PANTONE Inc. and Anderson Fraser Ltd.*

Eurostandard on litho presses, it is possible to use tint selectors printed to the same standards, such as the PANTONE Process Color Selector. Alternatively, you can use a tint selector produced by your printer to reflect the actual characteristics of the printing press and inks available.

Several tint selectors are described here:

PANTONE. The PANTONE Process Color Tint Selector shows all the possible combinations of the process colors in 10% steps. Available in both SWOP or Eurostandard versions, it allows the accurate selection of CMYK colors, including black.

Focoltone. Focoltone's library of CMYK colors is arranged as a series of color palettes that group contrasting colors together. This method is preferred by many designers over the traditional tint chart system, which displays colors according to their CMYK values. The Focoltone color samples, selected

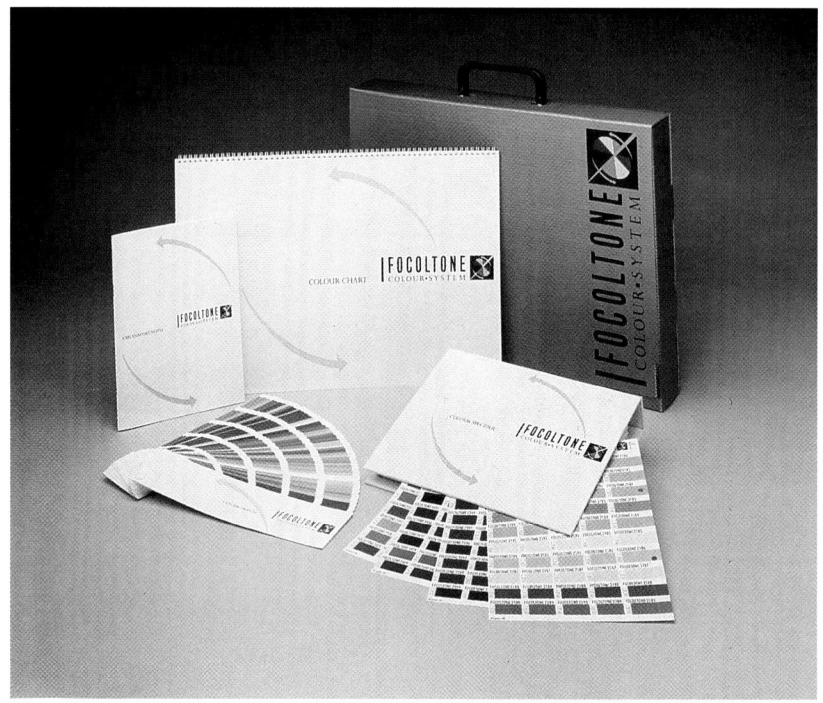

Figure 3-11.
Color swatches for the Focoltone specification system.
Courtesy Focoltone Ltd.

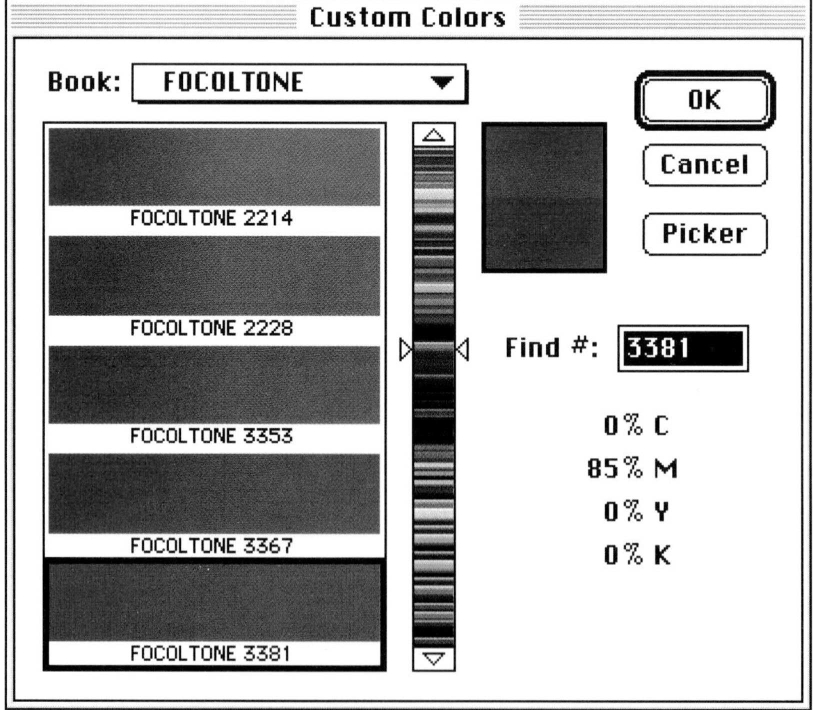

Figure 3-12.
Selecting Focoltone colors in Adobe Photoshop.

to minimize moiré, are available in the form of color charts, swatches, and tear-off chips. To ensure consistent reproduction across different printing processes and papers, the dot percentages are adjusted accordingly. Swatches are available in coated, uncoated, and newsprint versions. Focoltone color selectors are available in many electronic page-makeup and image-editing applications.

TRUMATCH. TRUMATCH offers another method of ordering colors, this time according to their perceptual attributes. The TRUMATCH system contains a series of colors ordered by hue, with saturation and brightness steps for each. The ratio of cyan, magenta, and yellow (and thus the color balance) for each hue remains constant, and the steps for saturation and brightness are created by altering the overall amount of color and the amount of black.

TRUMATCH is available as a swatch book printed in editions for coated and uncoated papers, and as a CMYK color selector in applications such as Photoshop, Illustrator, QuarkXPress, PageMaker, and Cachet. TRUMATCH also markets a printer utility that outputs a tint chart to any PostScript color printer, giving the designer an instant means of comparing screen and output colors.

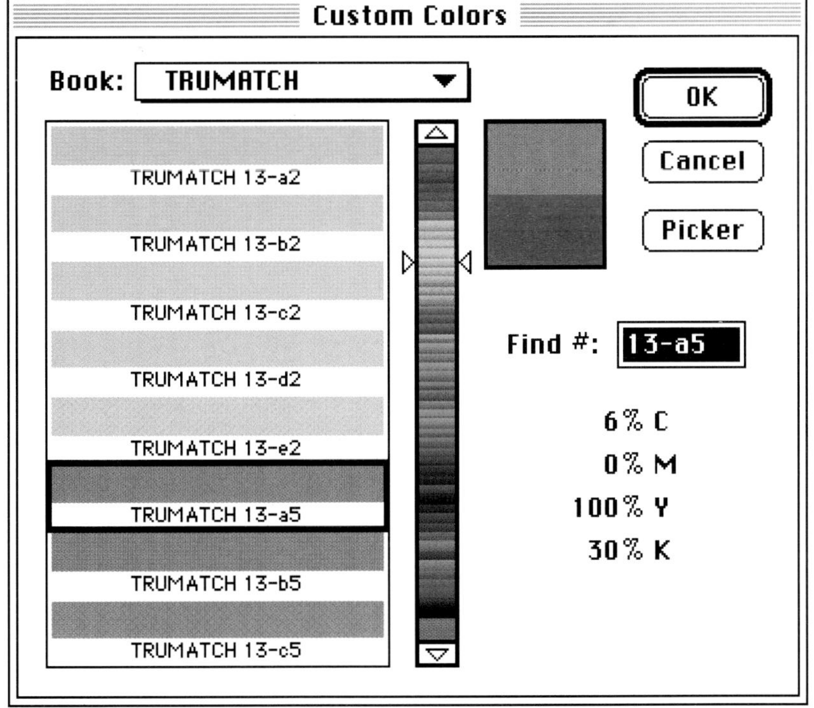

Figure 3-13. Selecting TRUMATCH colors in Adobe Photoshop.

Specifying CMYK Colors in Electronic Applications

In image-editing and page-makeup applications, CMYK tints can be specified either by entering the values directly or by using one of the proprietary extensions mentioned above. To enter the dot percentage values directly, the file must be in the CMYK rather than the RGB mode, and the desired CMYK values are entered as the current foreground color in the Color Picker.

If the CMYK tints you specify are to reproduce consistently and match the original sample in a printed tint book, it is essential that no global edits (such as RGB/CMYK conversion, color correction, etc.) are carried out on the file after the tints have been specified. Similarly, CMYK colors selected from color libraries, such as the PANTONE Process Color Tint Selector or the Focoltone system, already incorporate the effect of dot gain during printing, and further compensation should not be applied through transfer curves.

Specifying Special Colors

Special colors are mixed from a set of intense, saturated base colors. By combining different amounts of a base color and adding black and transparent white, a palette of a thousand or more colors can be created. These colors are used extensively in advertising and product packaging where brand identification and logo recognition are of utmost importance. Many printers (especially those who print packaging) have multicolor presses with five or more printing units. These presses can be used to add special colors to a four-color print. Each special color used requires a separate printing plate, and although it is possible to print a tint of a special ink color, it is not a good idea to overprint combinations of them because (unlike the process colors) special inks are opaque and the resulting colors are difficult to predict.

Special colors are typically used:

- *On jobs that are not printed in CMYK.* Some jobs that do not contain color pictures are printed in only two or three colors.
- *In cases where accurate color matching is essential.* Using a special color to print a corporate logo or a product package eliminates the risk that the hue will change as the ink weights or dot values of process colors fluctuate during printing.
- *For improved matching of design elements.* When backgrounds, rules, or borders appear on several pages, there is a risk that their appearance will not be consistent, espe-

cially if the tint is two or more colors. Special colors improve the consistency of design elements from page to page.

- *For non-gamut colors.* If the design calls for a color that is outside the range that can be reproduced in CMYK, such as highly saturated colors and pastels, special colors can be used to extend the printable gamut.
- *For printing inks with special optical characteristics.* Metallic, fluorescent, and pearlescent finishes cannot be rendered with normal printing inks. Greeting-card and gift-wrap printing are among the jobs that require these specially formulated inks.
- *To print large areas of solid color.* Printing large solids can lead to problems, such as setoff, tracking, ghost patterns, or an excess of ink in other images on the printed sheet. Using special inks can assist in avoiding these difficulties.
- *To avoid a visible screen pattern.* Special colors produce smooth flat colors with no visible dot pattern.
- *To replace a CMYK color.* It is common in some types of work, such as packaging, to substitute a special color for a CMYK color where the special color allows better color matching of the subject of the reproduction. For example, printing a dark brown in place of a black on a pack of chocolates gives a better and more consistent match to the chocolate colors. Color substitution avoids the cost of additional colors, but the color separations must be adjusted to allow for the hue of the new color.
- *To extend the colors available in CMYK.* One or more additional colors can be incorporated into a CMYK separation to extend the range of colors that can be printed throughout an image; to add a **bump color** to intensify color in selected parts of an image or in certain tonal values; or to incorporate a metallic color into the separation.

The set of primary colors can be extended beyond the basic four-color CMYK system to seven or more colors. The use of these additional, or extra-trinary, colors is discussed further in Chapter 7.

If the cost can be justified, the intensity of special colors can be extended by printing the same image twice, or **double-hitting** the color, to give a much denser and more saturated result. This technique is particularly effective with fluorescent colors. On CMYK jobs, a fifth color may also be used to heighten the color intensity in selected parts of an image or in certain tonal values.

The color specification sent to the printer should always incorporate a physical sample of the color to be matched as well as the reference number, if it is part of a sample system. Providing an actual sample of the color allows the ink manufacturer and printer to check that the original specification, the ink mix, and the pressrun are all in agreement, thus eliminating the problem of color shifts caused by differences between samples when the designer relies on reference numbers alone.

The most widely used specification system for special colors is the PANTONE Matching System. It was the first standardized system for color communication among designers, clients, and printers, and has since been adopted in most countries throughout the world. Before the PANTONE Matching System was developed, ink manufacturers produced their own ink sets using their own unique pigment blends.

The PANTONE system has nine base colors, plus black, transparent white, and a selection of fluorescent and metallic colors. A second series of four colors, which are used to substitute for some of the base colors on jobs where lightfastness is essential, provide an additional selection of saturated

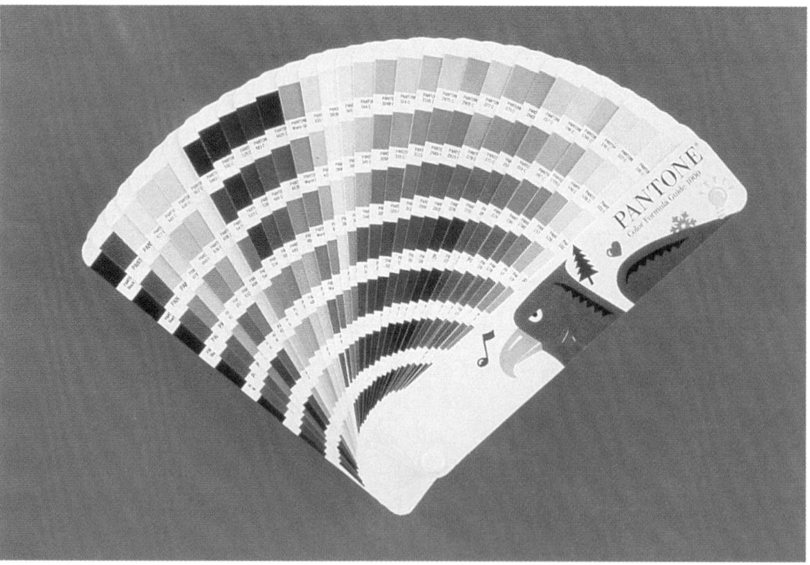

Figure 3-14. PANTONE Matching System swatch. *Courtesy PANTONE Inc.*

colors. The Color Formula Guide shows the 1,012 colors in the system and the mixing formula for each one. PANTONE also produces books of tear-off color tabs that designers can attach to jobs to ensure that their printers can match the visual samples that they have shown to their clients.

PANTONE reference samples are available on coated and uncoated stock, with the suffixes U or C used to distinguish between the two. However, it is not necessary to actually write U or C on the specification as this refers to the paper chosen and not the ink. Further, it is not possible to print a C color on uncoated paper or vice versa.

Alternative Specification Systems for Special Colors

Proprietary color specification systems produced by ink manufacturers continue to be marketed and used because they often offer a range of highly saturated pigments and an improved color gamut in comparison with other systems. Yet unless these proprietary systems are adopted by both specifiers and printers, incompatibilities can result. It is therefore important that the use of a proprietary color specification system is agreed to by the printer.

Toyo. Foremost among the proprietary color specification systems is the Toyo Color Finder, produced by the Toyo Ink Company of Japan. Based on the HSL color model, it arranges colors in hue order and provides for degrees of saturation and lightness for each hue. The Toyo system is widely used in Japan and southeast Asia, and is supported in many imaging applications such as Adobe Photoshop.

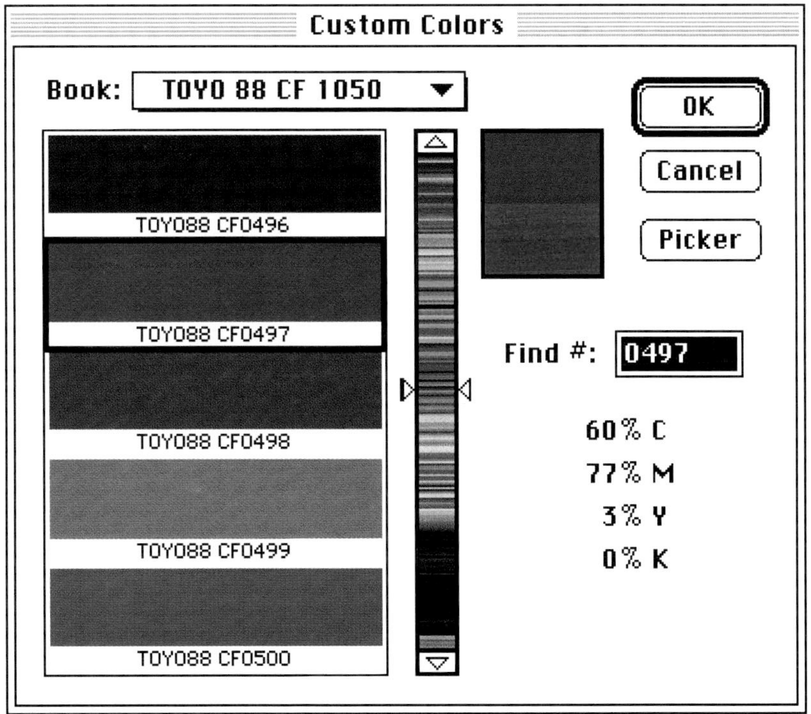

Figure 3-15. Selecting Toyo 88 colors in Adobe Photoshop.

Munsell. The Munsell system is also based on the three-dimensional HSL color model and provides a method of classifying colors that is used by designers in many different fields. It is not universally known in the graphic arts industry, and printers may have difficulties in matching colors specified in the Munsell notation. The Munsell system continues to be developed by the Macbeth Corporation, which has produced extensions for applications such as Aldus PageMaker.

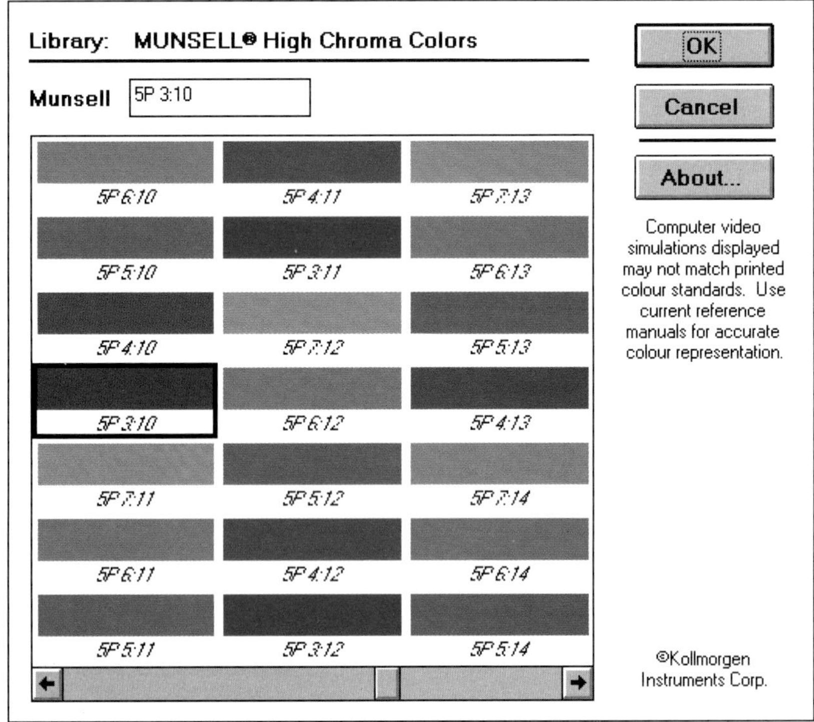

Figure 3-16. Selecting Munsell colors in Aldus PageMaker.

Specifying Special Colors in Electronic Applications

Special color specification systems are available as custom color selectors in page-makeup and image-editing applications. The color models available in these applications (RGB, CMYK, CIE) do not support the inclusion of special colors as separately defined colors, so colors selected with these systems have to be:

- Defined as a separation and output directly to film.
- Defined as a separation and saved as part of a DCS-2 file (see Chapter 5) for import into another application or for output.
- Converted to CMYK as a process color simulation.

Since special color systems have larger color gamuts, many special colors cannot be matched accurately in CMYK. If the chosen color is eventually to be printed in CMYK, there is little advantage in using a special color selector; it is better to make the initial selection from a printed CMYK tint book rather than to choose an unprintable color on the basis of its screen appearance.

Custom libraries of special colors usually incorporate pre-calculated CMYK conversion values, so that when a color is selected it is immediately converted into CMYK. If the file

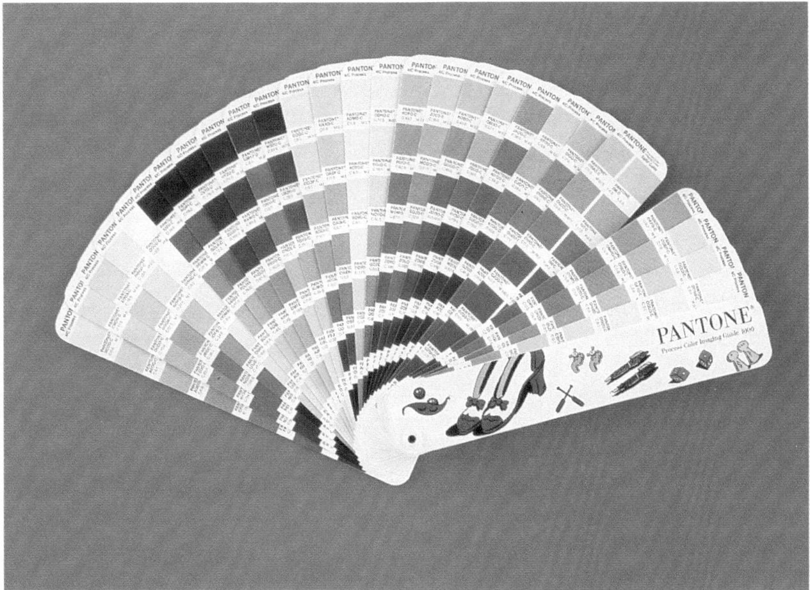

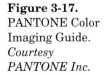

Figure 3-17. PANTONE Color Imaging Guide. *Courtesy PANTONE Inc.*

is not in the CMYK mode (or if the mode is subsequently changed), the values will be changed during separation to CMYK before output. In addition, different applications will handle the color separation process differently, and the actual dot values generated by different applications (and thus the output color) can vary slightly.

The most widely used process color simulation system is the PANTONE ProSim system. PANTONE ProSim selectors are available in many page-makeup and image-editing applications, and PANTONE provides the CMYK values from its PANTONE Color Imaging Guide. The letters CV (for computer video) are prefixed to the PANTONE number to remind the designer that the color selected on screen will not exactly match the printed output, and the color should always be checked against a printed color sample. Other special color specification systems that support CMYK simulations include Munsell, Toyo, and the DIC (Dainippon Ink and Chemicals) Color Guide.

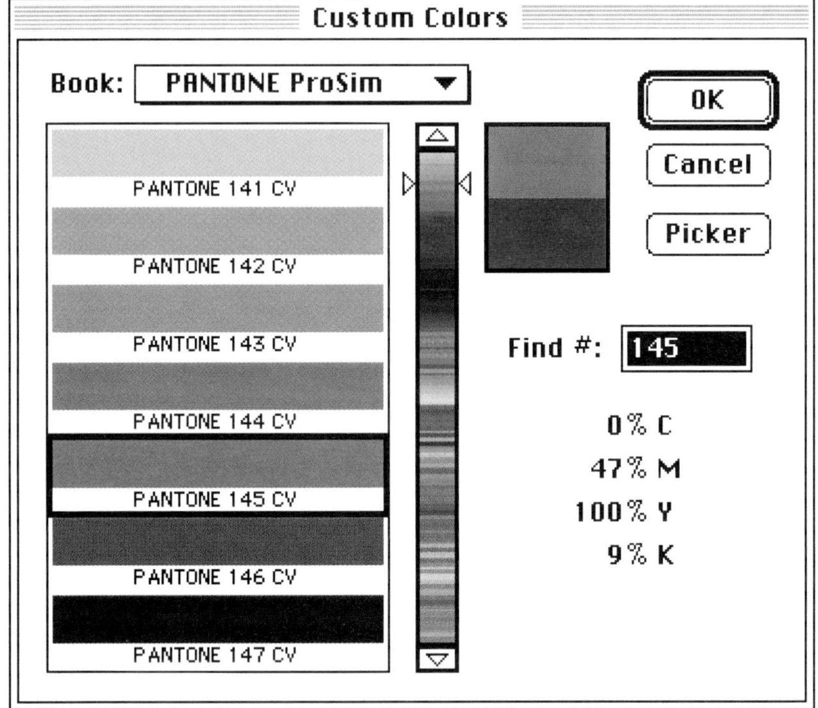

Figure 3-18. Using the PANTONE Process Simulator (ProSim) to choose approximate CMYK equivalents of special colors in the PANTONE Matching System. *Courtesy PANTONE Inc.*

PANTONE produces device profiles for RGB and CMYK color output devices (such as monitors and printers), characterizing the color that is printed or displayed by the device and providing a means of calibrating it to output PANTONE colors as closely as possible within the available gamut. This is especially important for digital color output devices that are restricted to printing in CMYK.

User-Oriented Specification Systems

Color specification systems tend to be arranged either according to the characteristics of the system producing them or to some perceptual color model. The CMYK tint selectors are arranged by increasing dot values (PANTONE) or by the HSL color model (TRUMATCH). The original PANTONE Matching System was based on a combination of both: the mixing formulae were arranged to allow the printer to make a one-pound ink mix using multiples of one ounce, and the swatch book was arranged so that most pages contained a single hue with a number of lightness variations.

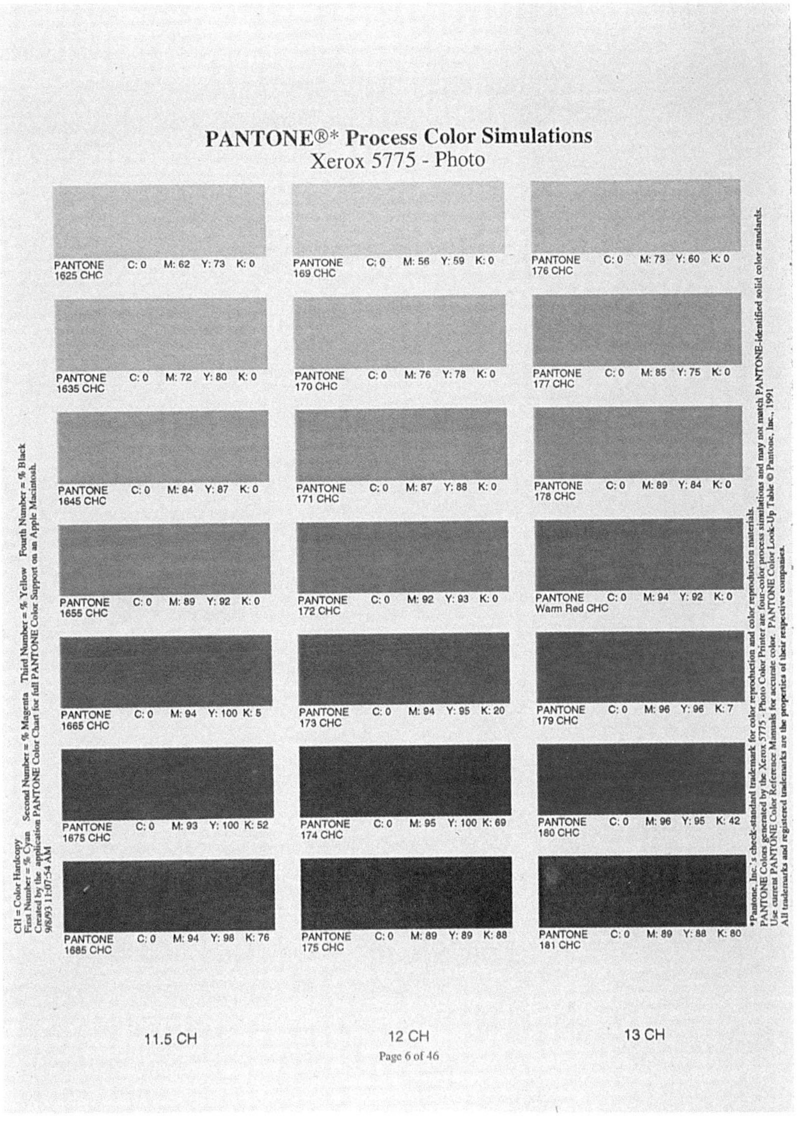

Figure 3-19. Output from PANTONE Color Chart software, showing how PANTONE Matching System colors are simulated on a Xerox 5775 digital color printer using CMYK process colors.

The drawback with both of these methods of ordering the colors available is that similar colors appear together and the effects of contrasting colors that might be used in a graphic design are not readily seen. This problem is addressed by alternative arrangements such as the one provided in the Focoltone system, where colors that share the same CMYK values appear together. The advantage of using common colors is that knock-outs do not require careful trapping of adjacent colors but simply the removal of one of the component colors.

PANTONE's ColorUp software also gives the designer a more user-oriented method of selecting color. Based on design principles and research into perceptual factors such as the legibility and conspicuity of different colors, it offers recommendations on background and foreground color combinations.

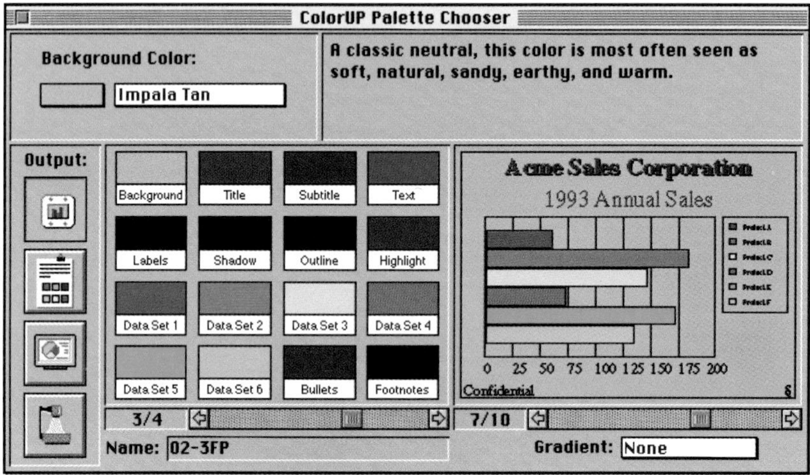

Figure 3-20. Using PANTONE ColorUp. *Courtesy PANTONE Inc.*

Color Matching

When a color is required that does not appear in one of the standard sample systems, the best way of specifying it is to select the PANTONE or CMYK color closest to it. It is possible to supply a physical sample of an item to be matched, such as a piece of fabric, although differences in texture and pigment will inevitably lead to differences in color appearance.

If a precise color match is required, ink can be mixed specially. The mix can be created by the printer or by the ink manufacturer, who can prepare quite small quantities quickly and economically. They will often make use of a computer-based matching system. The sample to be matched is measured by spectrophotometer, compared with the nearest shade in the system's sample library, and the mix is predicted by the program. A test mix is prepared and remeasured, and any deviation from the original sample is noted. Correction routines are then used to recalculate the proportions of ink needed to achieve a more accurate match, and the process is repeated if necessary.

Evaluating Color

When a color has been output, the printed color can be compared with the color of the original, or the specified color, to determine how well it has been reproduced. Differences between two colors may need to be communicated: for example, it may be necessary to mark up originals and proofs to show desired color changes, or to evaluate the difference between two colors that should match. Depending on the degree of precision required, color can be evaluated by eye or with the aid of color measuring instruments.

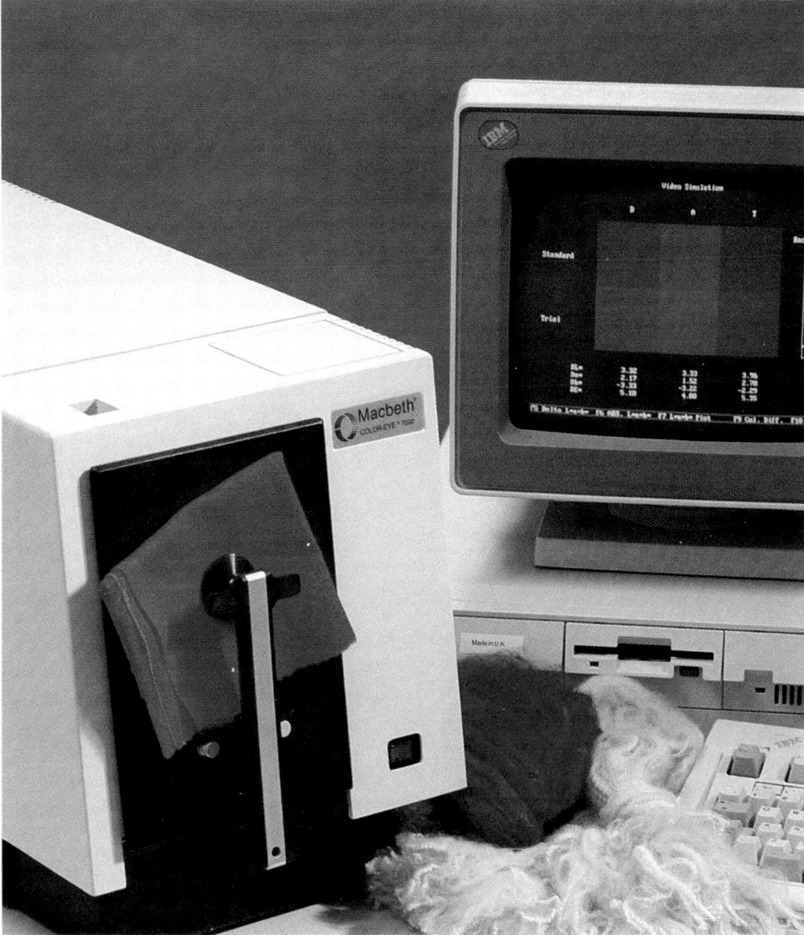

Figure 3-21. Spectrophotometer and color matching computer. *Courtesy Macbeth Division of Kollmorgen (UK) Ltd.*

The human eye is a very good judge of color, as long as it is not deceived by variations in lighting conditions or surrounding colors. Always make a comparison between two colors on identical backgrounds (one method is to punch a hole in a piece of gray card) and under standard lighting conditions. Very small differences, at the limits of perception, should be discounted since it is not possible to match colors with absolute precision.

The differences between colors can be described by referring to the HSL model described earlier. Differences in hue are often described as simply warmer or colder, as shown in Figure 3-22. However, the perception of warmness and coldness is a little subjective, and it is often preferable to base hue changes on the "psychological primaries" or "real-world" colors—red, green, blue, and yellow. Hue changes are described as more green, more red, and so on.

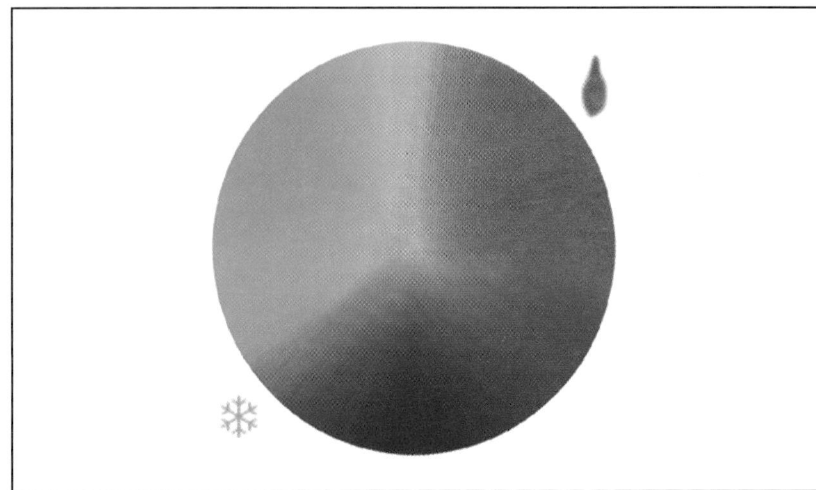

Figure 3-22.
Colors are described as warmer or colder according to their proximity to red and cyan.

Differences in saturation and lightness are often described together, as changes made to one often affect the other. The twelve terms for saturation and lightness in the ISCC-NBS Color Name Chart are an effective way of describing differences in these color attributes. Alternatively, changing saturation can be described as making a color cleaner or dirtier, and changing lightness as making it lighter or darker.

These terms can be used to achieve a reasonable degree of precision and reduce ambiguity in evaluating color samples and in marking up proofs for correction. Gary Field in *Color and Its Reproduction* recommends using the modifiers slight, moderate, and significant to specify the amount of change required.

Changing the hues of special colors can only be done by remixing the base inks, while changing the hues of CMYK tints or color images requires altering the color balance in the color separations or adjusting the ink weights on press. It is not possible to alter ink weights without unanticipated and possibly unwanted effects on other elements in the page, so it is usually necessary to correct the color separations.

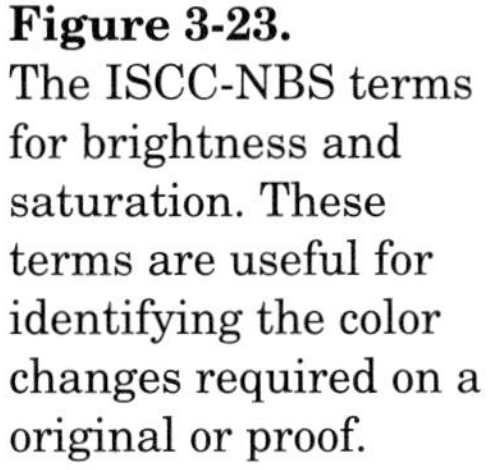

Figure 3-23.
The ISCC-NBS terms for brightness and saturation. These terms are useful for identifying the color changes required on a original or proof.

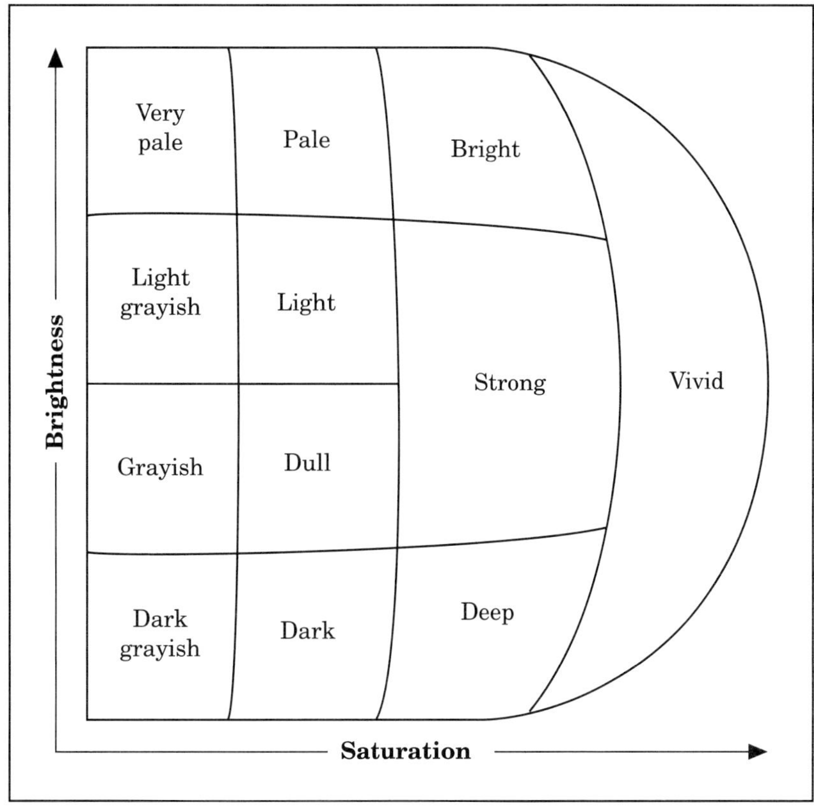

Color Measuring

On some occasions it is essential to provide an exact specification for a color, or to quantify the precise range of acceptable color variation. In practice, the number of times this is necessary is relatively small, except in certain product areas like packaging. Nonetheless, some knowledge of the principles of color measurement is useful to anyone involved in color reproduction.

Some color measurement is completed with densitometers, which take a reading of the amount of light reflected from a surface. This reflectance reading, expressed as a density value, provides a way of measuring the thickness of a layer of ink since density has a direct relationship to ink-film thickness. The measurement is only useful if the colors of the inks are already standardized. In other words, a densitometer cannot tell you if your PANTONE color is the wrong hue because it was incorrectly mixed. Densitometers are also useful in measuring tint percentages on film or on prints, and thus can be used to monitor dot gain.

Most printers and trade shops make extensive use of densitometers, as do some designers and print purchasers. For more accurate color measuring, and for information about the other color attributes hue and saturation, there are two approaches: colorimetry and spectrophotometry.

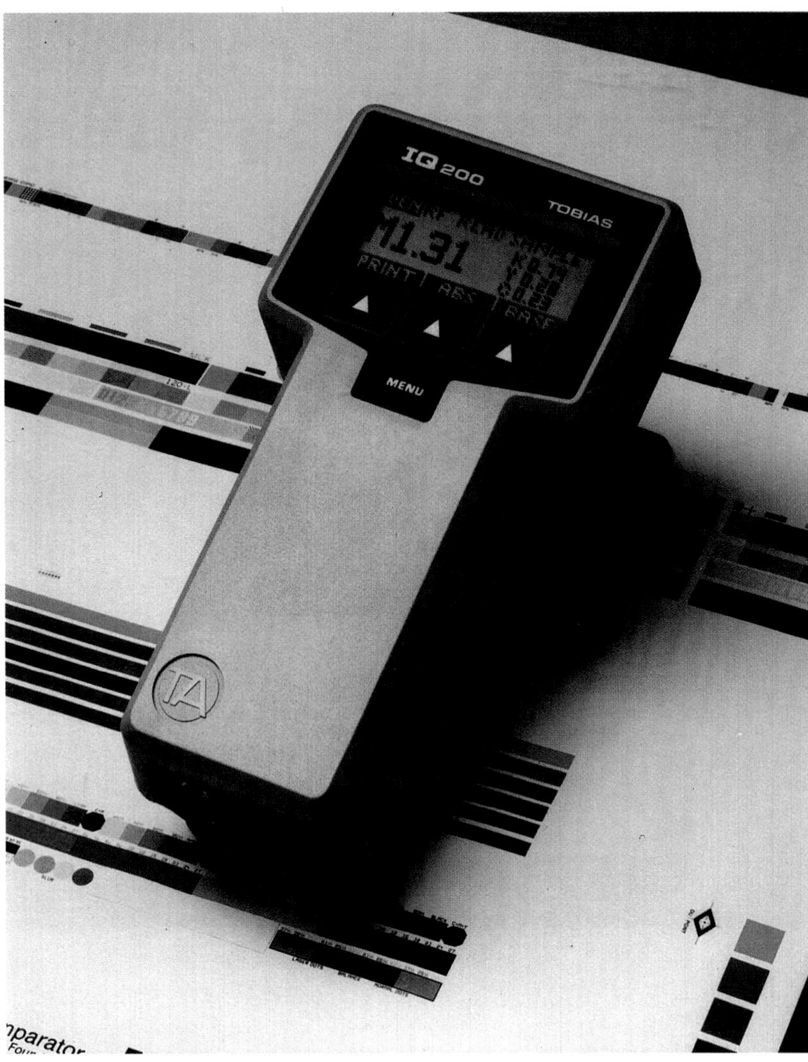

Figure 3-24. Tobias IQ 200 reflection densitometer. Measurements taken through color filters to give density values for the process colors CMYK.
Courtesy Tobias, Inc.

Colorimetry is based on the RGB cone responses of the eye. A colorimeter takes measurements through red, green, and blue filters that respond to light in a manner similar to that of the human eye. Measurements are usually expressed as CIE x,y values, although they can be transformed into other color models as well. Scanners and video recorders are effectively colorimetric devices, as they record RGB values for each pixel, even though they produce device-dependent color measurements.

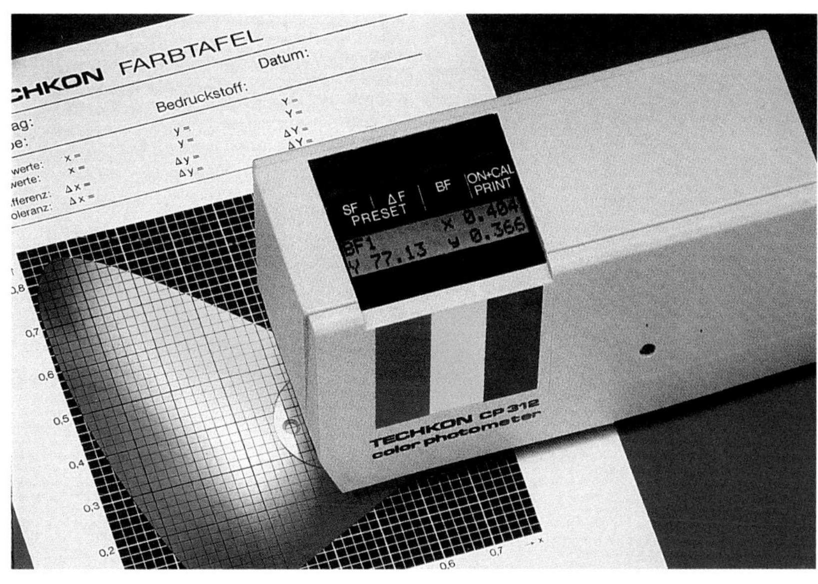

Figure 3-25.
A Techkon colorimeter. Reflectance measurements are made with red, green, and blue filters. The results can be shown as X,Y,Z tristimulus or x–y chromaticity values.
Courtesy Techkon

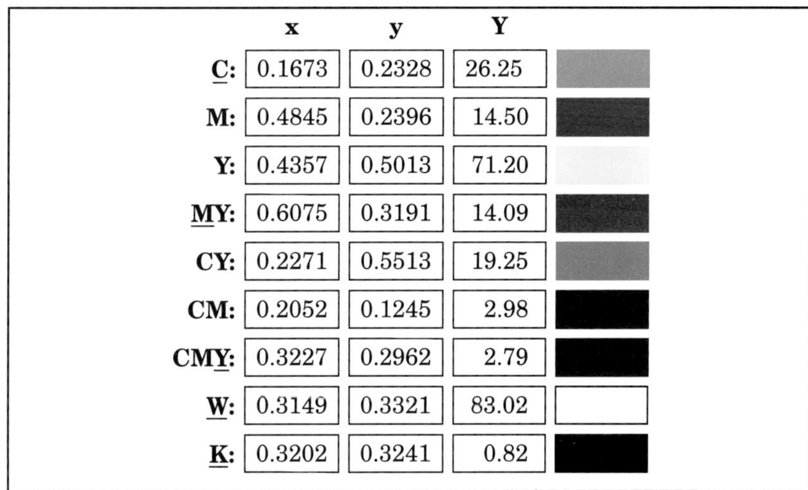

	x	y	Y
C:	0.1673	0.2328	26.25
M:	0.4845	0.2396	14.50
Y:	0.4357	0.5013	71.20
MY:	0.6075	0.3191	14.09
CY:	0.2271	0.5513	19.25
CM:	0.2052	0.1245	2.98
CMY:	0.3227	0.2962	2.79
W:	0.3149	0.3321	83.02
K:	0.3202	0.3241	0.82

Figure 3-26.
Chromaticity values for solid and overprint CMYK colors for SWOP inks.

Spectrophotometric measurements are made by analyzing the reflectance from a color sample at a series of wavelengths across the spectrum. Spectrophotometers use either a set of filters or a diffraction grating to sample reflectance at different wavelengths. The data yielded by the measurements can be used to output a spectral reflectance curve or to calculate CIE x,y or CIELAB values. Packaging and pharmaceutical printers and ink manufacturers are currently the primary users of spectrophotometers, but they are increasingly being used to characterize and calibrate digital color systems.

Spectrophotometers are often linked to match prediction software that will analyze a color sample and calculate the

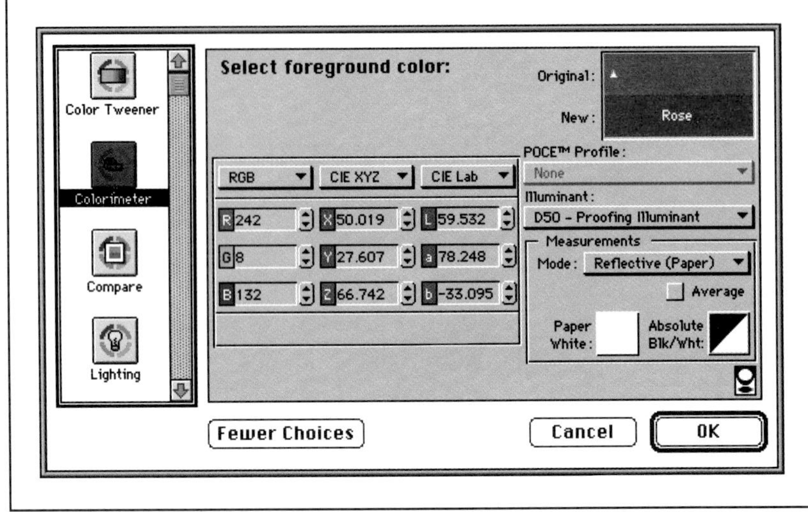

Figure 3-27. Software for the COLORTRON spectrphotometer incorporates a powerful set of tools for color specification and measurement. Third-party developers can also produce their own tools. *Courtesy Light Source, Inc.*

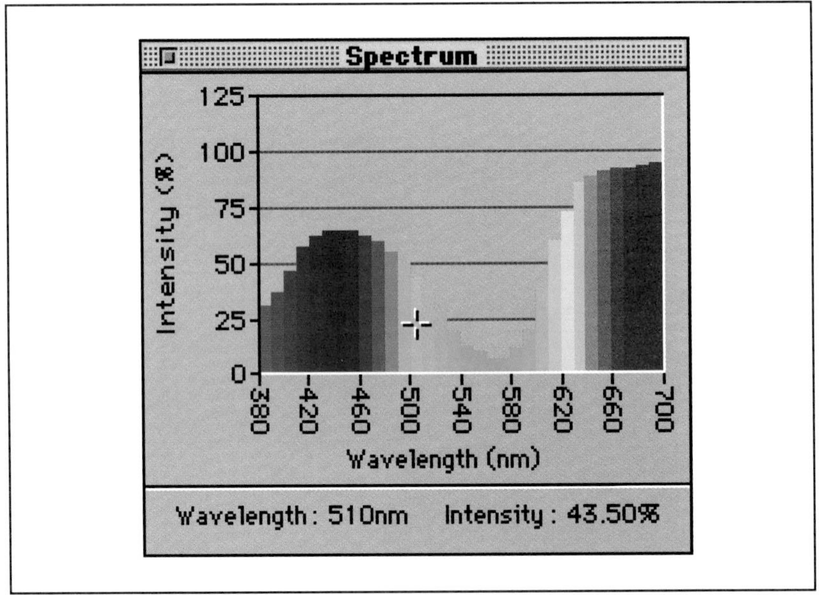

Figure 3-28. The COLORTRON Spectrum tool displays a spectral curve. *Courtesy Light Source, Inc.*

proportions of base colors that should be mixed to give an accurate match. Some multicolor printing presses are equipped with on-line spectrophotometers for monitoring of colors during printing.

Color Difference

The difference between two colors can only be defined precisely by reference to measured color values. Quantifying color difference values is a useful means of meeting tolerance limits for color reproduction or determining whether a color has been reproduced acceptably.

For printed colors, differences are defined as the distinction between the values of L*, a*, and b* for the target and the sample. The difference between target L* and sample L* is written ΔL*; similarly, differences in a* and b* are written Δa* and Δb*. The three difference values can be combined in the value ΔE.

The ΔL*, Δa*, and Δb* values are 1976 CIELAB measurements, unless the CMC weightings are used to make them more perceptually uniform. The limit of human visual ability to discriminate between colors is considered to be around two ΔE units, and tolerance limits are normally set at around eight ΔE units.

4 Tone Reproduction

The real world is unquestionably analog. Look closely at a photograph, for example, and you will see shades that vary in a smooth and continuous way between the lightest and darkest tones in the picture. These tones convey all of the image information in the picture, including light, shade, color, and detail, and allow us to recognize the different objects that are present.

There has been a move toward digital methods of recording and reproduction in many fields, such as audio, video, photography, and graphic reproduction. The benefits include freedom from the distortions that accompany analog reproductions, the ability to manipulate the digital signal in more powerful ways, and a potentially more accurate reproduction of the original.

Analog systems suffer from degradation during the transfer from one medium to another, often due to **noise** (random fluctuations in the signal that convey no information), and sophisticated methods have to be employed to prevent or reverse this degradation. Digital systems can also suffer from noise, but because the digital signal is encoded in binary forms, the reproduction is usually unaffected.

It may appear that a digital system can never match the fine modulations of an analog signal. However, if the analog signal is sampled at a higher frequency than the limits of human perception, the reproduction will be perceived as identical to the original. The problem is to achieve a high enough sampling rate when the amount of data that are generated may be beyond the ability of current computer power to store and process at acceptable speeds and the human mechanisms of perception tend to respond in an uneven way to stimulus, rather than in the discrete steps of equal size that are the basis of digital systems.

Figure 4-1.
Analog and digital transmission.

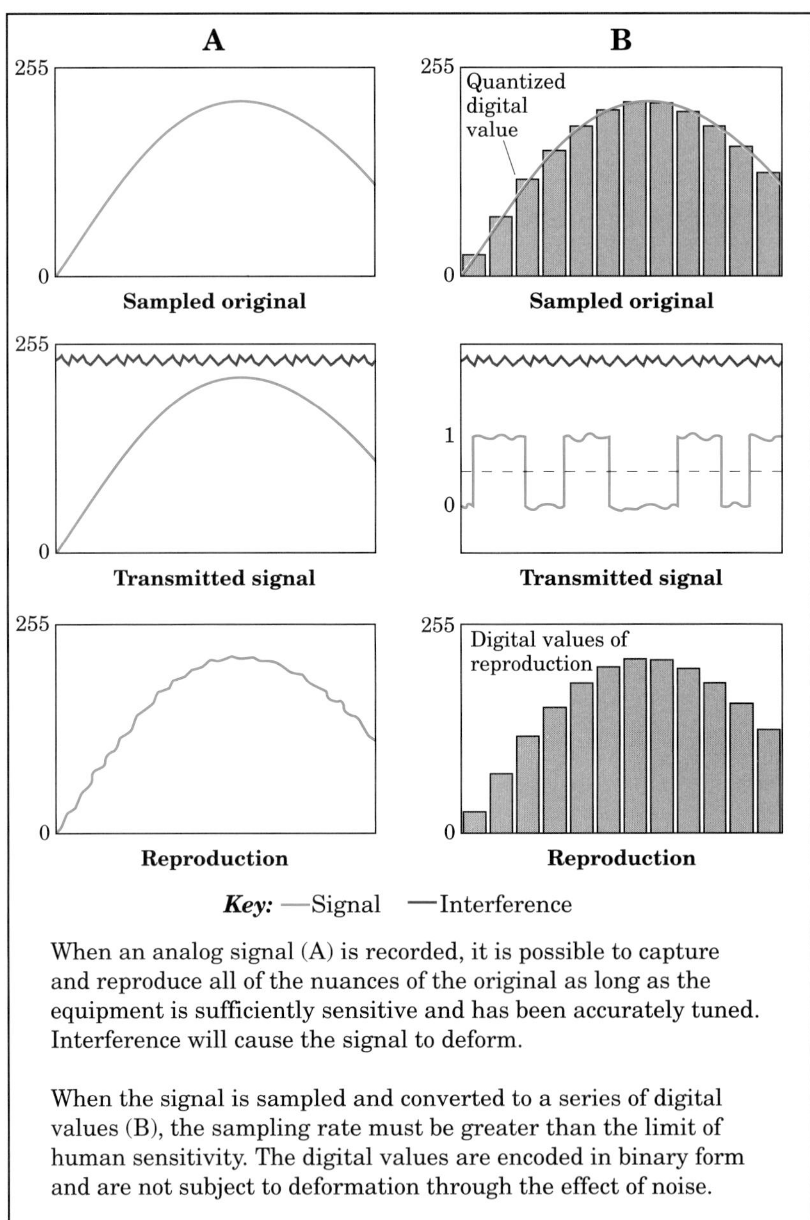

When an analog signal (A) is recorded, it is possible to capture and reproduce all of the nuances of the original as long as the equipment is sufficiently sensitive and has been accurately tuned. Interference will cause the signal to deform.

When the signal is sampled and converted to a series of digital values (B), the sampling rate must be greater than the limit of human sensitivity. The digital values are encoded in binary form and are not subject to deformation through the effect of noise.

Fundamentals of Tone

The challenge of tone reproduction is to convey the full range of tones accurately, and, at the same time, preserve picture aspects like color and detail.

A photographic original has a vast range of tones or gray levels between its lightest and darkest values. Because the tonal gradation is continuous, rather than a series of discrete steps, a photographic original is called continuous tone (often abbreviated to contone or CT). Reproducing the photograph by conventional printing involves recording the tonal values of the original and then transferring them on to an image carrier that will be inked during printing. In photographic reproduction using a process camera, the recording and transferring are completed as a single stage, while in digital reproduction the two stages are treated separately. Correct mapping of the tonal values to the image carrier then depends on a processing stage.

Whether the reproduction is intended to look as much like the original photograph as possible, without any effects caused by the mechanics of the printing process, or whether the original is to be enhanced to create a more acceptable or more striking image, precise control over tonal reproduction is essential.

The process used should ideally be capable of achieving:

- *High contrast.* (It should be possible to match the highlight and shadow densities of the original image.)
- *Good tonal rendering.* (It should be possible to reproduce all the tones in the original accurately.)
- *Good tonal gradation.* (It should be possible to emphasize the areas of interest and maintain good separation between the tones of the original.)
- *High resolution.* (It should be possible to retain or enhance the sharpness and definition of the original.)

It is also important to optimize contrast, resolution, and tonal gradation for the particular image and for the printing process.

There are three basic ways of defining the tones of an image: as gray scale values (or gray levels), as optical density values, or as halftone tonal values.

The Gray Scale

On a photographic print or transparency, there is a smooth transition from the lightest to the darkest regions of the image. The darkness of any one area will depend on the number of atoms of metallic silver present, and imperceptibly minute differences in tonal gradation are possible. Many other originals, such as artist's illustrations, are also continuous tone, with the darkness of any area depending on the thickness and strength of the coloring media.

Digital processes require the conversion of this analog scale into a digital one, turning a smooth transition into a series of separate steps between the lightest and darkest points on

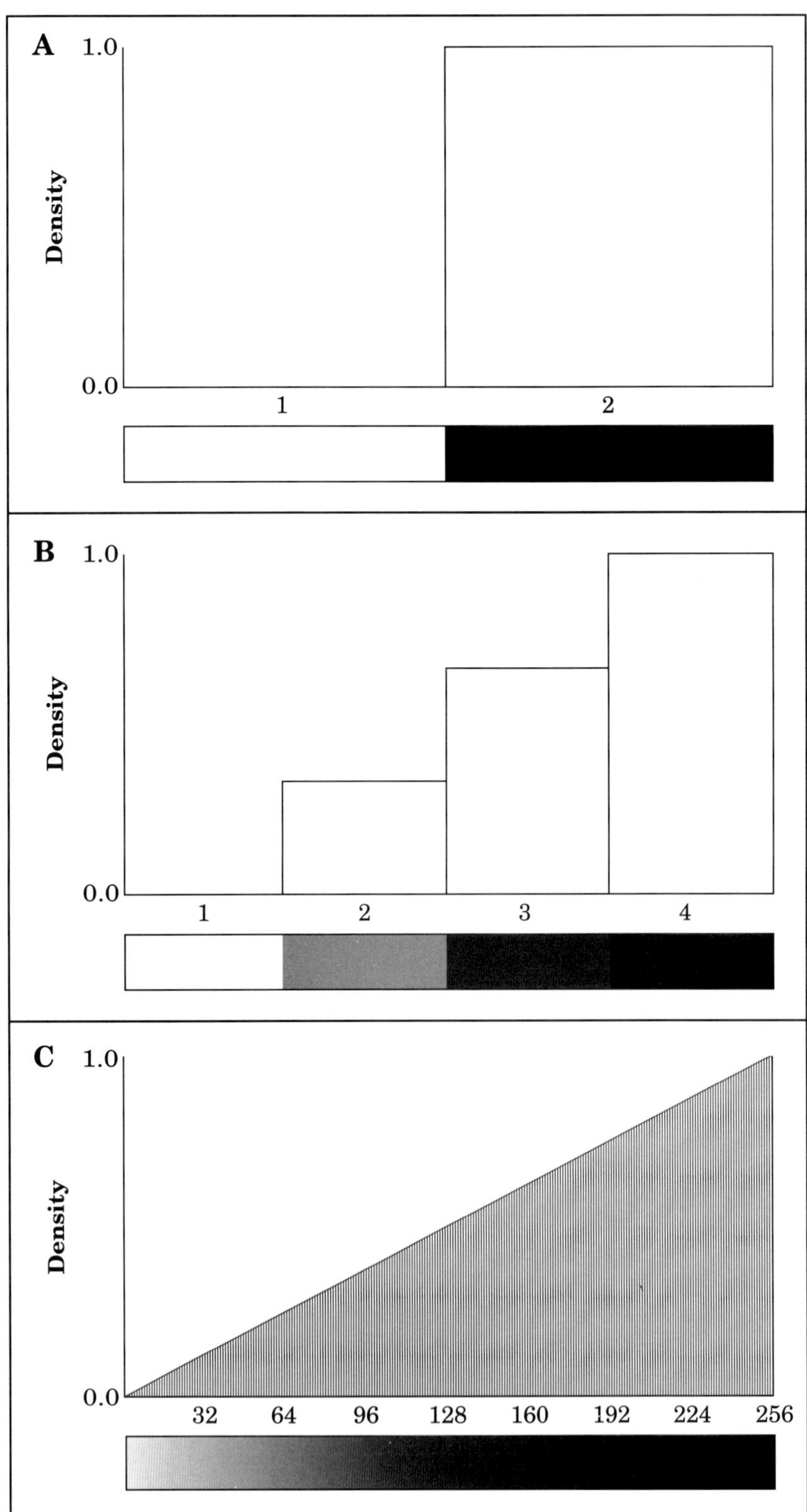

Figure 4-2.
Digital gray scales: (A) A binary gray scale has only two possible values, black or white. Only one bit of data is necessary to define such a color. ($2 = 2^1$). (B) A four-level gray scale, requiring 2 bits of data ($4 = 2^2$). (C) A 256-level gray scale, requiring 8 bits of data ($256 = 2^8$).

the scale. The separate steps are called gray levels, and a gray scale represents the number of separate steps that are possible within a particular system.

An important property of a gray scale is the number of steps that it can accommodate. Naturally, the more steps that are available, the closer the reproduction will simulate the continuous gradation of the original, but the more steps there are, the more processing and storage will then become necessary. Research suggests that the eye can distinguish up to 150 separate gray levels at any one time, but the range of light intensities that the eye can function under makes the total number of perceptible gray levels far greater. Digital reproduction systems usually aim to accommodate 256 gray levels, since 256 (2^8) is the next 2^n number after 150. This is referred to as an eight-bit gray scale, and it allows the value of each pixel to be encoded as a single byte.

Because the eye is not equally sensitive to gray levels in all parts of the gray scale (see Figure 4-3), there is some loss of information when a continuous-tone image is quantized with equal luminance levels. These quantization losses can be reduced or eliminated in two ways: by increasing the sampling precision (increasing the total number of gray levels

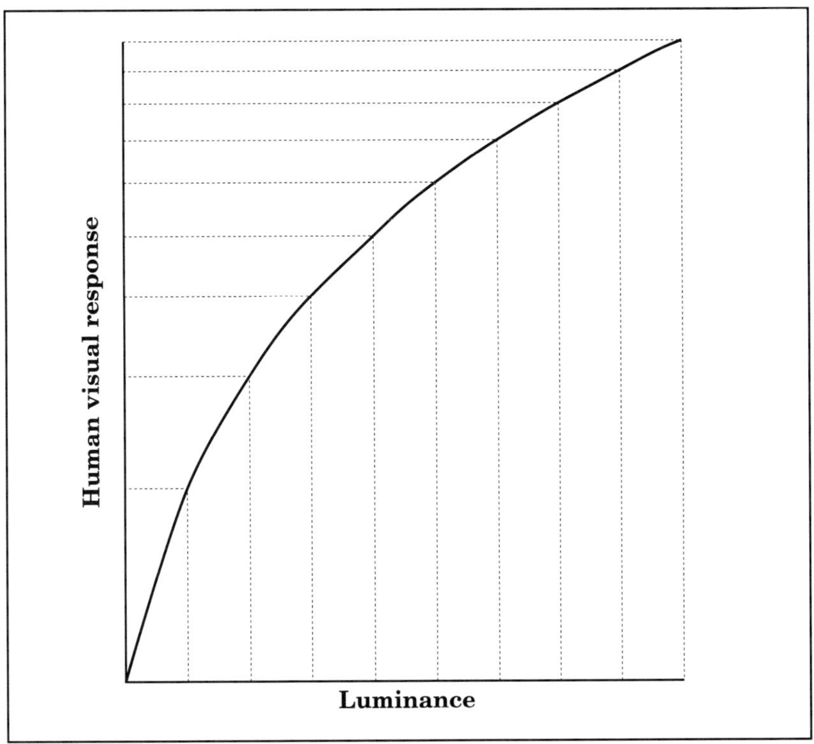

Figure 4-3.
The response produced by the visual mechanism at varying light intensities.

available until the size of the step between one level and the next reaches the limit of sensitivity of human perception), or by increasing or by using different degrees of precision in different parts of the tone scale. The latter option, while technically feasible, would create overwhelming difficulties for applications attempting to process the resulting data. Increasing the sampling precision (from eight to ten or twelve bits per pixel, for example) would simply increase the amount of data captured and the consequent file size. Sampling with twelve bits per component would give 4,096 gray levels per component, and the resulting files would have thirty-six bits per pixel instead of twenty-four bits.

A further option is to sample the luminance component with greater precision than the chrominance components. Naturally, this can only be done if the color space used has separate components for luminance and chrominance.

The PostScript language supports the use of up to twelve bits per component, although no applications or output devices currently support more than eight bits per component. Sampling with ten or twelve bits per color would increase the tonal quality of certain types of color images, but the very large files produced would be difficult to handle on current platforms.

An alternative method of dealing with images that would benefit from greater sampling precision (those with a large amount of tonal interest over a small range of tones, such as a predominantly flesh-tone image) is to introduce a very small amount of noise. This eliminates tonal artifacts without making a perceptible difference to image quality.

The number of steps in the gray scale is also important to graduated tints and blends. Graduated tints can be produced in many graphics applications and are also known as ramped tints, gradient fills, and, when two or more colors are involved, blends. If insufficient gray levels are available, the separate steps will be visible—a phenomenon called **banding.**

When an image is rendered on a monitor, the brightness of each picture element, or pixel, is controlled by the voltage of the electron beam that strikes it. The image is stored as a gray scale value for each pixel; if eight bits are available for each pixel on the video board, then a full 256 grays can be reproduced. An RGB image requires an eight-bit gray scale value for each of the three colors. The minimum intensity has a value of 0 and is rendered as zero intensity, i.e., no light from the pixel. In an eight-bit gray scale, the maximum intensity has a value of 255. A white pixel on the screen thus has RGB values of 255, 255, 255, and a black pixel has values of 0, 0, 0.

Density

It is necessary to have a practical way of evaluating the depth of tone in different parts of the image, one that is not influenced by the subjective factors of human vision, such as fatigue, surrounding illumination, and so on. The measurement of optical density is used for this purpose since it correlates both with the way that the eye sees tonal depth and with the thickness of image-forming films, such as photographic emulsions and printing inks.

Lith film and other high-contrast films are used in imagesetters and elsewhere to obtain a very high density so that when the film contacts or plates are exposed there is no danger of light penetrating the film's opaque areas.

Density is effectively a measurement of the darkness or opacity of a surface—in other words, the amount of light it absorbs. It has no direct relationship to the hue of the surface (although most hues become slightly warmer as ink weights increase), but it does affect the perceived saturation of a color. It can be evaluated by visual comparison with printed density scales, or it can be measured with a densitometer.

Table 4-1. Reflectance and density.

Percent Reflectance	Density
100	0.0
50	0.3
10	1.0
1	2.0
0.1	3.0
0.01	4.0

When a density reading is made, a filter complementary to the color being measured is selected so that the color appears to the densitometer to be a gray. A beam of light is emitted from the densitometer's light source, strikes the surface being measured, and is reflected back to a photocell that calculates the amount of light that has been reflected. The reflectance is then converted to a logarithmic density scale, using the formula $D = -logR$, where D is the density and R is the reflectance.

The reasons for using a log scale are:

- It compresses the scale and avoids the use of long numbers in the darkest regions.
- It has a linear relationship with the thickness of photographic emulsions and printed inks, so it is a useful way of measuring the weight of printed color.
- It also makes the measurement correlate closely with the way that the human visual mechanism perceives lightness, since the response of the rods and cones of the eye to the light that falls on the retina is itself logarithmic.

The hue-independence of the density measurement makes it a useful printing control tool. The ink hues for process colors are standardized, and thus the only thing that can vary on press is the ink weight, which is easily monitored by measuring the density of solid printed areas. Most people can detect a change in density of 0.1 units, and this is often used as a tolerance limit for evaluating and controlling the printing.

Typically, graphic arts materials have the maximum densities shown in Table 4-2.

Table 4-2. Maximum densities of materials and processes.

Process or material	Maximum density
Single-color lithography	1.8
Four-color lithography	2.4
Black-and-white photographic print	2.0–2.2
Color transparency	3.5–4.0
Lith film	4.5

Because many originals have a higher density range than can be reproduced in a print on paper, the density range of the original must be compressed to avoid the loss of shadow detail. Shadows are compressed more than highlights, as shown in Figure 4-4.

Contrast

The contrast of an original is the difference in tone between the lightest and darkest areas. In a photograph, the lightest tone is the unprinted white of the paper, while the darkest occurs where the photographic emulsion or printing ink is heaviest. The amount of contrast will depend both on the brightness of the paper surface and on the maximum density of the ink or emulsion.

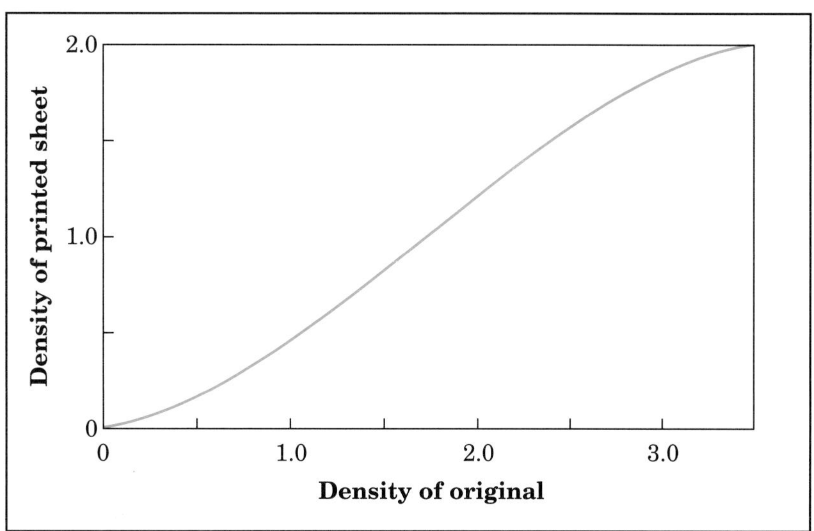

Figure 4-4.
The density range of an original must be compressed into the range that can be printed in an even way to avoid losing detail at the shadow end.

Contrast is also used to describe the distribution of tones within an image. An image with little midtone detail, heavy shadows, and bright highlights is said to be **high-contrast,** and, conversely, a picture with lots of midtone detail and little in the highlights and shadows is **low-contrast.**

In screen (RGB) and print (CMYK) color, contrast depends on the range of intensities available. Screen contrast can be increased by making the black of the unilluminated screen darker and the intensities produced by the electron guns stronger. Similarly, the contrast of a print on paper is increased by making the paper brighter and by increasing the range of ink densities.

In the HSL color model, the contrast of the luminance and chrominance components can be described separately. **Luminance contrast** is the difference between the lightest and darkest tones of an image, while **color contrast** is the difference between the most saturated colors.

An image made up mostly of grays and neutrals, relatively close together on the hue/saturation wheel, has little color contrast, while images with high color contrast are vivid and colorful.

Luminance and color contrast can only be changed independently of each other if controls for adjusting HSL components are provided.

Tonal Gradation

The tonal gradation of an image describes the way in which tones of the original are mapped to the reproduction.

The key elements of tonal gradation are:

- Controlling the placement of the **end points,** or lightest and darkest tones, to achieve the optimum contrast.
- Adjusting the distribution of intermediate tones to meet the needs of the reproduction.

The tonal range that can be printed depends on the printing process and the type of substrate. At the highlight end, the very smallest dots are either lost during transfer to the plate or they are worn away during printing. At the shadow end, the largest dots merge together during printing so that they look like a solid ink film. The printable tonal range can be as much as 1–98% in sheetfed offset litho on coated paper, or as little as 25–50% in flexo on newsprint.

The highlight dot placement is the most important setting, both in scanning the original and in adjusting the gradation before output. To make sure that highlight detail is not lost, the lightest point of the original should be mapped to the smallest dot that the printing process can hold. Reproducing the lightest areas of the original (the diffuse highlights) with the smallest dot available still allows for specular highlights, or **catchlights** (those points in the image that transmit or reflect light directly to the observer, such as street lights or light bouncing off metallic surfaces) to be reproduced as white with no printed dot at all.

Table 4-3. Smallest highlight dots.

Process	Smallest dot size on film that can be held during printing	Equivalent to percentage dot size at 150 lpi
Lithography	8 microns	4
Screen printing	20 microns	10
Flexography	40 microns	20

Note: Gravure does not use halftoning but instead uses a cell of constant size and variable depth. Films are usually prepared as for offset lithography.

Similarly, the darkest point on the original in which detail occurs should be mapped to the largest printable dot. Dot values above this will fill in when on press, and appear solid with no detail.

The intermediate tones can be distributed to control the placement of the midtones or to emphasize the interest areas of the original. The gradation can be adjusted using the gradation curves in image-editing software applications. These allow complete flexibility over the tonal gradation, so that the user can adjust each region of tone independently.

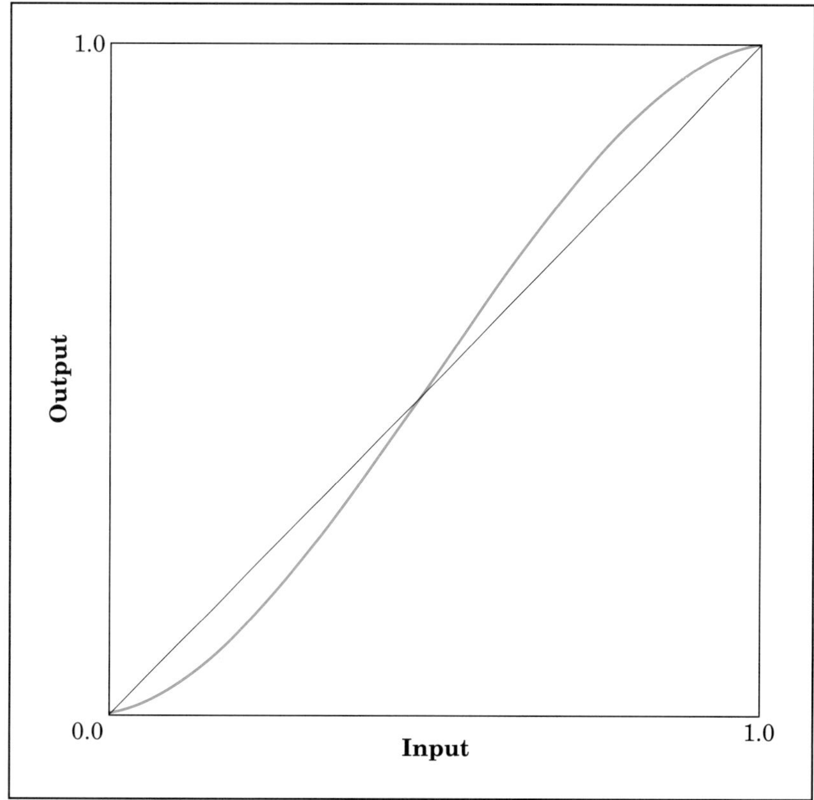

Figure 4-5. Tonal gradation can be adjusted to control the way that the tonal range of the original is reproduced, in order to emphasize areas of interest in the original.

Resolution

The resolution of a reproduction is determined initially by the number of picture elements (pixels) captured in the scan. The more pixels in a given area, the higher the resolution and the greater the information about the detail in the image that can be captured. This resolution is measured in pixels per inch (ppi). The maximum resolution of scanners ranges from 300 ppi on a low-end system to 3,000 ppi on a high-end system.

High resolution is necessary to preserve the definition and sharpness in an original image. Photographic systems can resolve detail of around 0.01 mm (0.0004 in.), and the eye can register most of this information without magnification. In good lighting, the eye may even resolve detail close to the one-micron (0.001 mm) level, such as the tracks on a CD. At these high spatial frequencies, the eye is not able to resolve color information, and, in fact, there is a trade-off between the spatial frequency of a pixel and the number of bits needed to describe its color. In other words, the smaller the pixel, the harder it becomes to see its color. Thus a 300-dpi pixel needs twenty-four bits to describe it, since the eye can identify its color, while just two bits are needed for a 3,000-dpi pixel, as the eye will, at best, just recognize its presence, without being able to see what color it is.

When an image is stored in a file, the resolution is recorded in a tag or header. This resolution can later be changed by resampling. For a lower resolution, some data is discarded, and for a higher resolution, intermediate pixels are calculated by interpolating from the values of the surrounding sampled pixels. Resampling does not create detail that was not present in the original scan, and it is preferable to make sure that the original is scanned at a resolution appropriate to its characteristics.

Resolution is also important in the different systems used for output. A PostScript imagesetter or printer records an image as a matrix of spots (or device pixels), each spot being either exposed or unexposed. The resolution in this case is dependent on the size of the spot produced by the output device.

Typically, an image might be scanned at 300 ppi and output on an imagesetter with a resolution of approximately 3,000 dpi, for a printed screen ruling of 150 lpi.

As there is no universal agreement on which terms to use to describe resolution, it is best to emphasize **scan resolution** (usually in ppi), **halftone screen frequency** (usually in lpi), and **output device resolution** (in dots per inch, elements per inch, or spots per inch).

Halftoning

A printed picture is made up of binary image elements, in the sense that the ink is either present or absent with no intermediate tones (unless it has been printed by one of the processes that can reproduce a variable density, such as gravure and dye sublimation). Since the first printing presses were built, printers have been concerned with techniques for reproducing the tonal values of an image. The basic principle is to print small areas of color that cannot be individually resolved by the eye, and which mingle with the white of the paper surface to create an illusion of tone. All kinds of techniques have been used in the past to create this illusion of tone, including woodcuts and engravings on metal. The halftone screen became the most popular through its suitability to photographic methods of image reproduction, although other methods, such as frequency modulation, are made possible by digital processing and are now being explored.

Figure 4-6.
Detail of a nineteenth-century woodcut showing William Caxton. Before the halftone process came into use, tone was reproduced by cutting lines into wood.

When an image is screened, its tonal values are reproduced by a pattern of regularly spaced dots all of which have the same density but vary in size. The tonal value of a pixel defines the amount of the substrate that is covered by the halftone dots. The larger the tonal value, the larger the area covered and the darker the tone appears to the eye. In a midtone, for example, the dots cover around 50% of the paper.

In the traditional photographic halftone process, the dots can vary from zero to completely solid. The size of the dot is controlled by the amount of light that is reflected from the original, passes through the halftone screen during exposure, and falls on the light-sensitive film. The transition between dot sizes is completely smooth, except at around 50% where the corners overlap. With conventional round or square dots, an **artifact** (a jump in tonal values), is visible at this point.

When a digital halftone is created, the tonal values are first input (by a scanner or other image capture device), then, after processing, sent to an imagesetter or laser printer for output.

The three parameters that are specified when a PostScript halftone is produced are the **screen frequency,** or **ruling, screen angle,** and **dot shape.**

Figure 4-7.
Halftone gray scales. The greater the halftone screen frequency, the less apparent the halftone screen becomes.

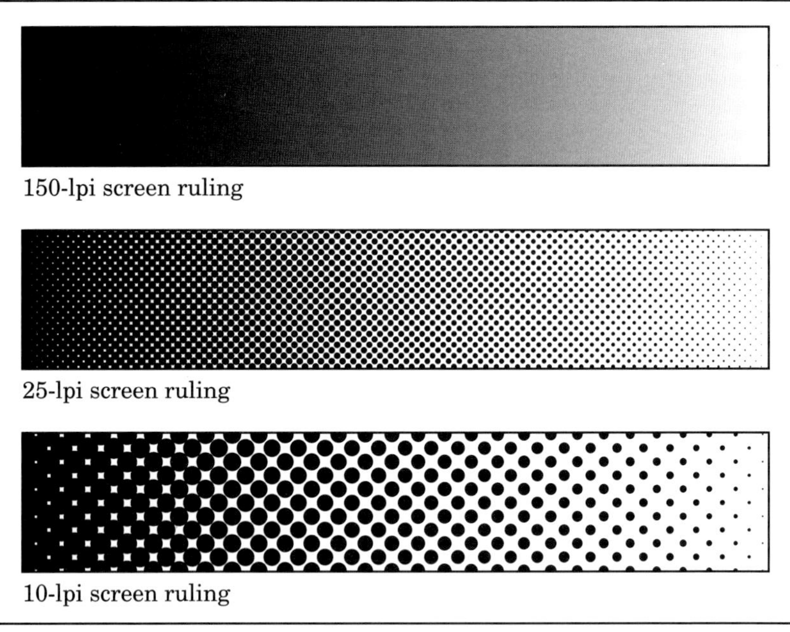

Figure 4-8.
An individual halftone dot is built from the array of device pixels defined by the output device address grid.

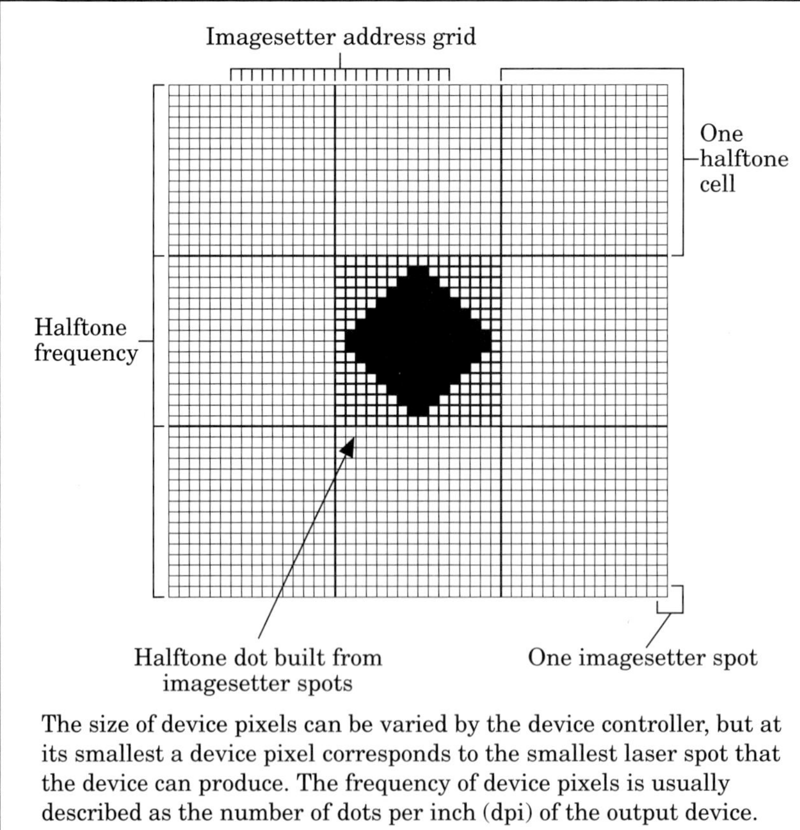

The size of device pixels can be varied by the device controller, but at its smallest a device pixel corresponds to the smallest laser spot that the device can produce. The frequency of device pixels is usually described as the number of dots per inch (dpi) of the output device.

Screen Frequency

The screen ruling chosen must be fine enough to convey the sharpness and detail of the original. At screen rulings from 150 lpi upward, the halftone dot becomes less and less visible until, at 200 lpi, it is no longer apparent at normal viewing distances.

Figure 4-9. The image on the left has a screen ruling of 100 lpi, while the same image on the right has been reproduced at 200 lpi.

Screen rulings over 200 lpi are used:

- To give extra sharpness and crispness to an image.
- To bring out the grain in an original, such as when the photographer has deliberately used a fast film.
- To retain the sharpness of scanned images that include fine detail such as type.

Screen rulings of 600 lines per inch or more have been achieved, and at these resolutions it is impossible to detect the screen pattern. However, most people agree that increasing the screen ruling beyond 250–300 lpi has little or no effect visually.

Table 4-4. Highest commercially available screen rulings.

Process	Screen ruling
Lithography	200 lpi
Screen printing	133 lpi
Flexography	150 lpi

Note: Higher screen rulings are available, especially for sheetfed offset lithographic printing on good-quality coated stock, but there is usually a premium to pay.

The screen frequency that should be used is dependent on the requirements of the product and the printing process. It may be as little as 80–100 lpi in newspapers, or it may be 200 lpi or more for a prestige brochure printed by sheetfed litho on a smooth coated paper. High screen rulings can make the printing of a job more challenging, since halftones will be more prone to dot gain and filling-in. Whenever specifying a higher screen ruling than normal, it is important to ask the printer if the process and the paper can support it.

Screen Angles

A halftone screen consists of dots arranged in a regular pattern of rows and columns. If more than one color is being printed, the screens must be rotated to prevent objectionable moiré patterns. The ideal angle between two colors, which reduces moiré patterns to a minimum, is 30°. In four-color printing, it is not possible to angle all four colors at 30°, as the fourth color would end up at the same angle as the first color. Many high-end systems use the angles originally developed by Linotype Hell:

Cyan	15°
Magenta	75°
Yellow	0°
Black	45°

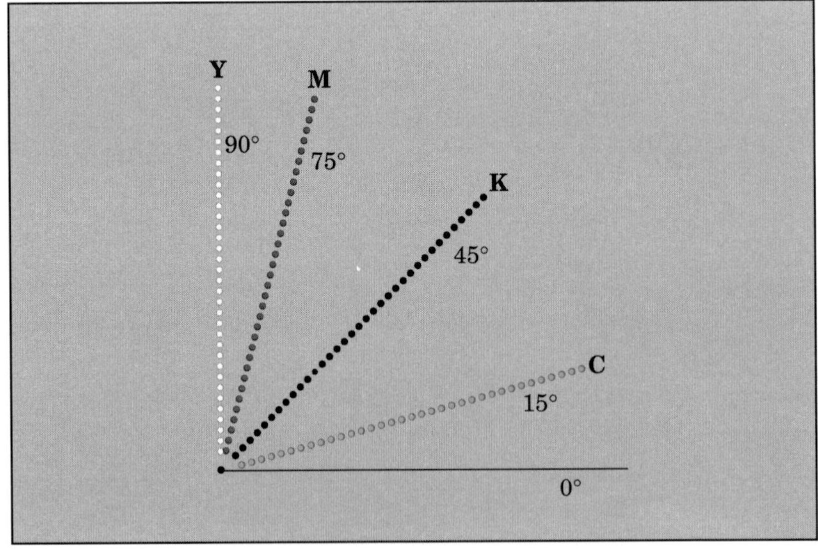

Figure 4-10. The most commonly used screen angles for four-color process work, keeping a 30° separation between colors likely to cause moiré.

The thinking behind this choice of angles is that the black screen will tend to be most visible to the eye and so is set at

45°, the angle that is least noticeable. Because the yellow screen is the least visible color it occupies the angle that would be most obvious. The cyan and magenta pair, which are most likely to cause a moiré pattern, must be angled at 30° to each other.

Other sets of screen angles are possible, but the separation between the colors must be maintained to avoid moiré.

Mono halftones almost always use the 45° angle. In conventional color separations, the black plate is quite light and it is possible to modify these angles, as long as the relative angles between colors remains the same. In color separations using gray component replacement (GCR) the black is much heavier, and it is definitely preferable to angle it at 45°.

At the correct screen angles, the moiré pattern appears as a tiny rosette where the dots of the four colors cluster together in a ring. If screen angles are not set with great accuracy (around 0.01°) more objectionable moiré patterns will be seen, especially in large areas of even color or flat tints. Moiré in tints cannot be entirely eliminated, but can be reduced by increasing the screen frequency of the tint. Tints can also be generated with stochastic screening, but the results tend to be no smoother than conventional halftone screening.

Dot Shapes

The actual shape of the dot has little effect on the visual appearance of a halftone, other than affecting its tonal gradation in midtones. The coarser the screen ruling, the more visible the shape of the halftone dot will be.

A conventional photographic halftone based on a crossline screen produces a dot shape that is square at the 50% tonal value and becomes circular as the dot becomes larger or smaller. As the dot size approaches 50%, the corners join up with the adjacent dots, creating a jump in tonal value. In the midtones of halftones and graduated fills, these artifacts can be quite noticeable. In flesh tones, for example, a posterized effect with clearly differentiated tonal regions instead of a smooth gradation or a spotty effect as the tonal value oscillates above and below 50% can result.

These problems can be dealt with by using an elliptically shaped dot. Here the dots join up first at the long edge, and then later on the short edge, thus distributing the jump in tonal value over a larger range of dot sizes and providing a smoother tonal gradation. Elliptical dots are preferable for pictures where there is a lot of important midtone detail.

Figure 4-11.
(A) Image composed of square dots.

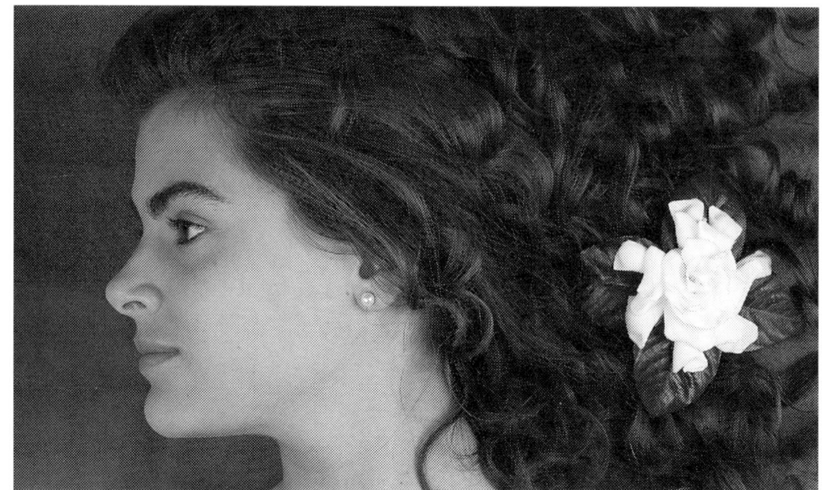

(B) Image composed of elliptical dots.

(C) Image composed of diamond-shaped dots.

Tints

Tints are areas of tone produced by printing halftone dots instead of a solid ink film. Tints are frequently used to incorporate additional areas of color on a page, often as a background to type. They can be used in CMYK to print any of the colors in the CMYK gamut, or they can be used in special colors to extend the range of colors on the page. Tints can be used as areas of flat color, in which the same dot size is printed in the whole of the area defined, or as graduated tints over any specified tonal range.

Graduated tints will have a banded appearance if there are not enough gray levels available for a smooth transition. They also consume a great deal of memory and time on the raster image processor (RIP), so in cases where the design calls for a large number of blends, consideration should be given to either reducing the number of blends or saving the graphic image as a continuous-tone file.

PostScript reproduces a graduated tint as a series of separate lines. The number of lines is equal to the number of gray levels between the highest and lowest tonal value in the blend.

Frequency Modulation

Frequency modulation is an alternative screening method that makes a reproduction more like a photographic original. In a photograph, tonal information is carried by grains of metallic silver, the overall tonal value in any area corresponding to the amount of light it has received during exposure. The exact size and position of each grain cannot be predicted since they are subject to a number of factors, including the presence of nearby grains.

Frequency-modulated (FM) screening uses spots of a constant size that have a variable spacing, in contrast to conventional halftone screens that have a constant spacing and variable size. Spots are widely spaced in highlights and clustered closely together in shadows. The spacing of the spots is determined by the screening algorithm according to the tonal value and the presence of any nearby spots.

A further variation of FM screening (known as second-order frequency modulation) also varies the spot size, although there are limits to the range of spot sizes and the degree of modulation that can be achieved.

FM screens are a major breakthrough in screening technology. They allow any number of colors to be printed without interference patterns such as moiré and deliver many of the benefits of fine screen rulings without the cost.

Figure 4-12.
(A) Image created with the conventional halftone process.

(B) Image created with frequency-modulated, or stochastic, screening.

They also break the link between sampling resolution and halftone screen ruling, making it possible to reduce sampling frequencies without loss of quality or to make use of the information captured at high sampling frequencies that cannot be used in a conventional halftone. The imaging of frequency-modulated screens is discussed further in Chapter 10.

PostScript Halftoning

PostScript halftones are created in two stages. First, the tonal values for each pixel of the image are captured, or created, and recorded as gray-scale values. Next, these gray-scale values are **rendered,** i.e., mapped to the output device. In the rendering stage, transfer functions can be applied to adjust for any distortions to tonal values that may occur in the gradation process or in the output device. Halftoning to apply screen frequency, screen angle, and dot shape also takes place at this time. The image is then ready to be rasterized.

Figure 4-13.
PostScript halftoning.

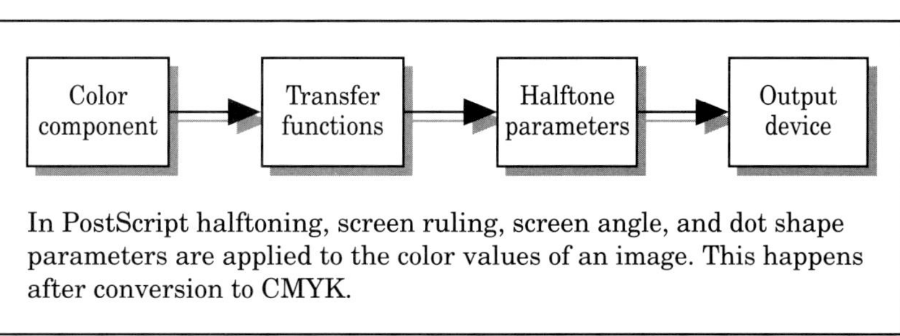

In PostScript halftoning, screen ruling, screen angle, and dot shape parameters are applied to the color values of an image. This happens after conversion to CMYK.

The specification of gray-scale values is completely independent of the rendering stage. This means that images remain continuous tone until they are screened and rasterized by the output device. This makes it possible to scale and rotate the image without affecting the halftoning parameters. It also implies that image processing is carried out in **device-independent** space.

Dot shapes in PostScript are determined by a **spot function,** which specifies the sequence in which the individual device pixels that make up a single halftone dot change from white to black as the tonal value increases. If the spot function specifies that the sequence is to be directly related to the distance from the dot center, then as the gray level changes from white to black the dot will gradually be built up in a spiral. If the spot function relates the sequence to a center line instead of a center point, then a line screen will be built up.

PostScript will allow an application to define the sequence of adding device pixels to the halftone cell with complete freedom, and this property makes it possible to create tonal values without using the traditional concept of a halftone screen. Mezzotints, line screens, and frequency-modulated screening are among the possible alternatives that can be generated.

The halftoning parameters may be a part of the file description, in which case any images in the same file must share the same screen frequency, screen angles, and dot shape; or they may be stored in a halftone dictionary, allowing each image to have different parameters. When the file is output, the halftone characteristics can be defined by the parameters in the file or they can be applied by the output device.

The output device may not recognize halftone parameters that are specified in a PostScript file. If, for example, irrational screen angles are requested and output is sent to a PostScript Level 1 interpreter, the interpreter will use the nearest rational angles. Level 2 PostScript allows the application to define different screening rulings for different colors.

Halftone parameters are defined for a file, but if different settings are defined for objects within the file (such as different dot shapes for different images) they take precedence over the file-level parameters.

Figure 4-14.
Halftoning on a high-end recorder.

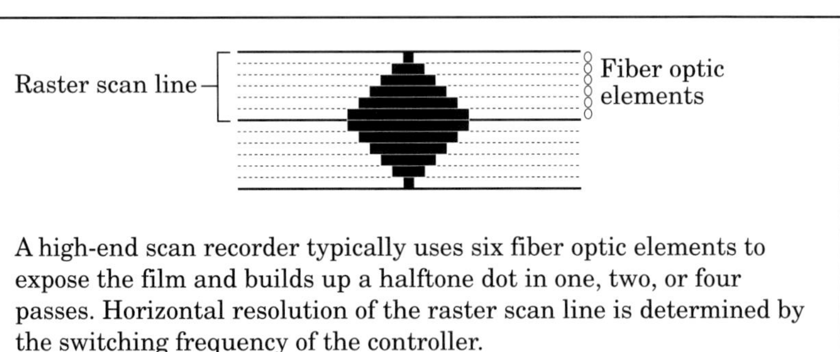

A high-end scan recorder typically uses six fiber optic elements to expose the film and builds up a halftone dot in one, two, or four passes. Horizontal resolution of the raster scan line is determined by the switching frequency of the controller.

Halftone screens are based on the grid of device pixels fixed by the capabilities of the device and its controller. There is a relationship between the halftone screen ruling and the device resolution: a halftone cell (the maximum space available for a single halftone dot) is made up of the smaller device pixels, and the number of possible gray levels is the same as the number of device pixels in the cell.

Figure 4-15.
A comparison of halftoning principles with PostScript Level 1 (A) and PostScript Level 2 (B).

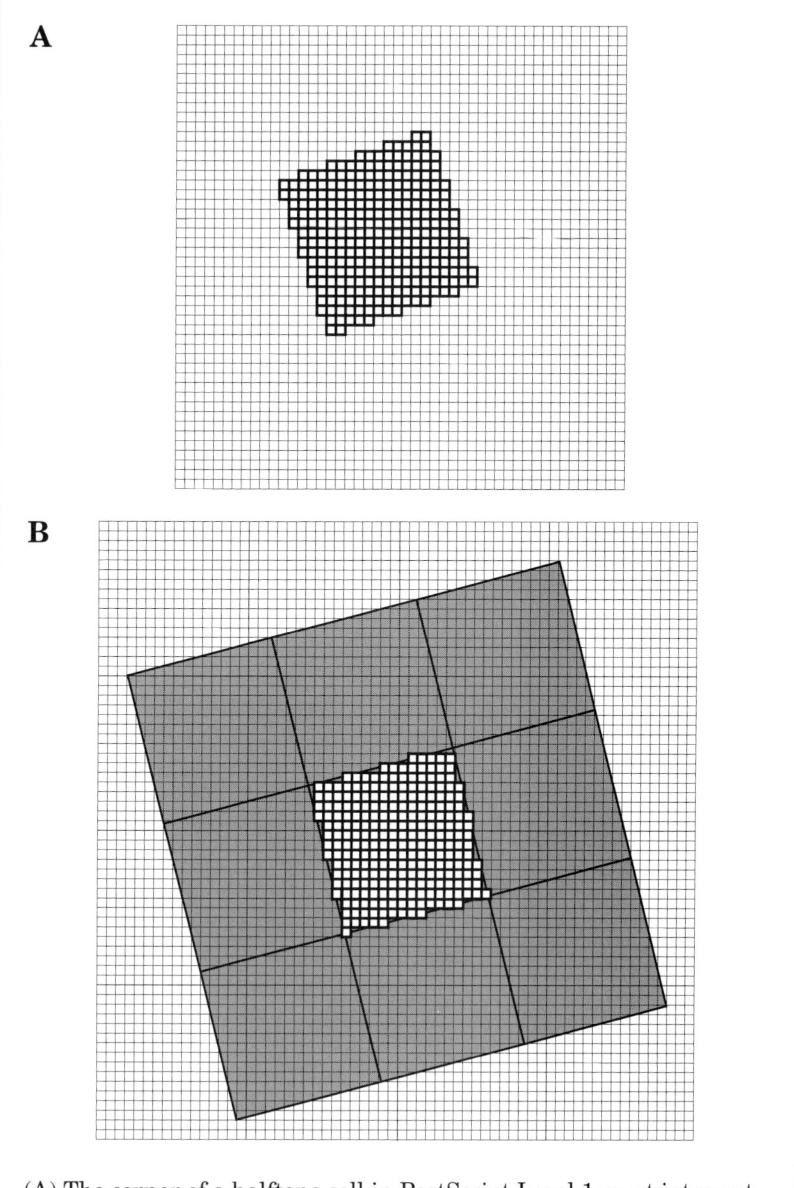

(A) The corner of a halftone cell in PostScript Level 1 must intersect with the imagesetter grid, creating a rational tangent for cyan and magenta (which use irrational tangents). This makes it impossible to achieve accurate screen angles; instead, the nearest possible angle (rational tangent) is substituted.

(B) PostScript Level 2 supports supercells that contain several halftone cells. The corners of the supercell intersect with the imagesetter grid, even though the individual cells do not. Cells may not be exactly the same size, but give more flexibility in building the dot and make it possible to achieve almost perfect screen angles for cyan and magenta.

If the halftone frequency changes, the number of device pixels (and hence the number of gray levels) in the cell will also change. The relationship between them is as follows:

$$\text{Device resolution} = \text{Screen frequency} \times \sqrt{\text{Gray levels}}$$

To achieve a full 256 gray levels, the halftone cell must be based on a 16×16 grid of device pixels. It follows that the maximum screen frequency available is the device resolution divided by 16. A 3,200-dpi imagesetter will thus enable a 200-lpi screen to be output; while a 300-dpi laser printer will only be able to produce an 18-lpi halftone, and will, in practice, make it necessary to reduce the number of gray levels in order to achieve an acceptable halftone frequency.

Because there is the possibility of the PostScript halftoning parameters being discarded during output, files should be marked up with the required information when sent for output by third parties.

Dot Gain

Halftone dots undergo a series of transformations between halftoning and their appearance on the printed sheet, and at each transformation a distortion occurs that affects the tonal value of the final printed image.

Figure 4-16.
Dot gain.

A 40% dot on film

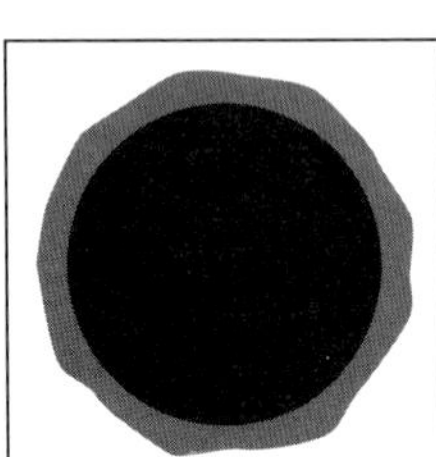

The same 40% dot becomes a 57% dot when printed

The square around each dot shows the area occupied by a "100%" dot.

Dot gain is the change in size between the dot recorded on film and the dot finally printed on paper. In this example, a 40% dot on film has become a 57% dot when printed. The dot gain is 17%. The imagesetter must also be calibrated to produce the correct dot size on film from the digital dot values that are sent to it.

Initially, there will be a small change in dot size when the page is output as film, unless the imagesetter has been perfectly calibrated. When the film is exposed on to the printing plate or onto an intermediate contact film, there will be another change in dot size. A large distortion occurs when the ink film is squashed during printing, causing it to spread out sideways. Halftone dots end up larger on the printed reproduction than on the printing plate. This phenomenon is known as **dot gain,** and it makes halftones look darker as a larger proportion of the paper surface is covered by ink. Midtones are especially affected, and shadow tones tend to fill in and obscure shadow detail.

Dot gain is an inevitable aspect of the printing process. The amount of gain can be minimized in a well-controlled process, but it cannot be eliminated. It is essential to standardize the degree of dot gain inherent at each stage and make allowances for it when the films are output.

The term dot gain is used to refer specifically to the difference between the actual dot size on the film and the dot size on the print. There will also be a difference in dot size between what was specified in the digital file and what is output on the film, unless the imagesetter has been accurately calibrated. The difference between the dot size in the file and that actually output on film is known as **recorder gain.** Appropriate adjustments must be made to compensate for recorder gain to ensure that correct tonal values are printed.

Figure 4-17. The image on the left incorporates an allowance for dot gain on press, while the image on the right does not as indicated by the shift in its tonal gradation.

Dot gain is influenced by a large number of factors, including the design of the printing press, pressures of rollers and cylinders, and the properties of the ink and paper used. Of these, paper has by far the largest effect, and the more absorbent and porous it is, the greater the dot gain will be. The second most important variable is the ink: higher ink weights and lower viscosities lead to more dot gain.

All of these variables can be standardized, and, in fact, there are widely accepted standards that define an acceptable range of dot gain for each paper type. Paper is grouped into four basic types (art, matte, uncoated, and newsprint) and a standard dot gain value can be specified for each one.

The difference between the dot size on the film and the dot size on the print has two components: the mechanical enlargement of the dot through pressure and absorption and the optical effect of light scattering. In an unprinted area, some of the light that strikes the paper is reflected while some of the light is absorbed by the ink film in the area where a halftone is printed. This effect, in which the dot seems to cast a shadow into the paper, is known as optical dot gain, and it makes a printed tonal area seem darker than the physical dot size alone would suggest. In laminate proofing systems (such as Cromalin) only optical dot gain occurs, and the layers of laminate manage to simulate by optical means alone the combination of mechanical and optical dot gain that occurs during printing.

The relationship between tonal value and dot gain can be shown in a tone reproduction curve.

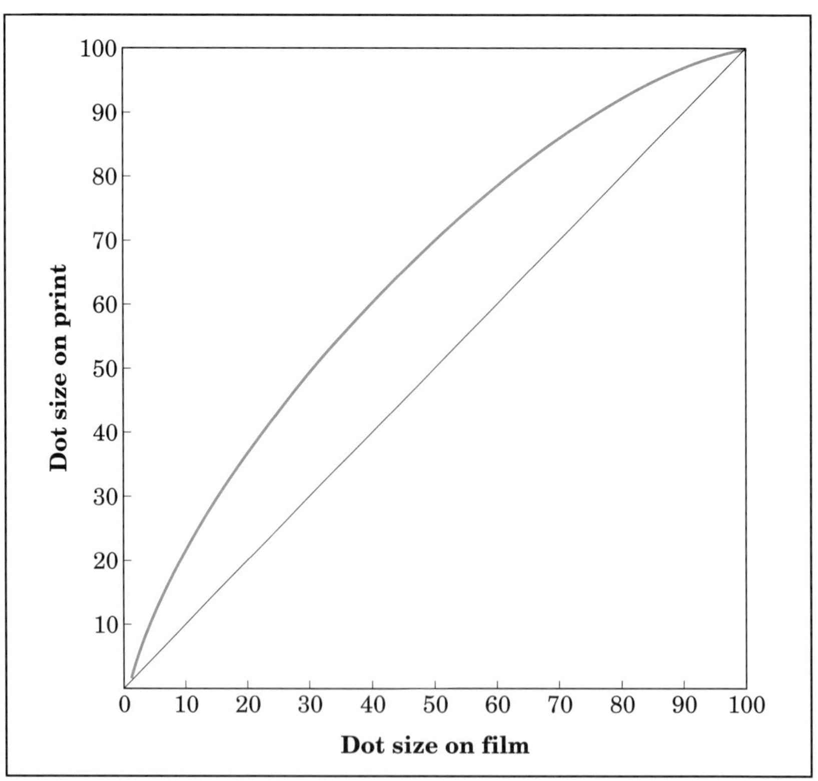

Figure 4-18. A tone reproduction curve shows the amount of dot gain that occurs at each tonal value.

Dot gain cannot be evaluated accurately by eye, so a densitometer is used. It measures the density of a halftone area and calculates the area that is effectively covered by ink. Measurements are usually accurate to within 1%.

The amount of dot gain that occurs depends on the size of the dot periphery, and, for this reason, it is greater in midtones and at finer screen rulings.

This tone reproduction curve for offset litho usually follows the same basic shape (unless there is some distortion caused by abnormal conditions) so that the whole curve can be extrapolated from one or two readings. Tone reproduction curves in gravure, flexo and screen printing also follow consistent patterns, although they are somewhat different from those of offset litho.

Dot gain is normally compensated for during conversion to CMYK dot values, and it should not be necessary to compensate additionally, for example, with transfer functions.

Printers are continually improving their ability to print sharper halftones with less dot gain. Gain on web presses, usually much higher than on sheetfed presses, is gradually coming down closer to sheetfed levels, but, at the same time, good sheetfed printers are themselves achieving even lower levels. This is an advantage since it allows higher ink weights and finer screens to be printed without causing excessive dot gain and filling in of shadows. Reproductions are sharper and have better color contrast. In addition, a larger gamut of colors can be printed.

5 The Color Original

Digital color systems allow the designer to incorporate a huge variety of original images, from both traditional sources and from new media such as digital photography and Photo CD. They can be edited and manipulated in ways that are increasingly powerful, flexible, and intuitive. Selecting the right originals results in better quality printing and saves the time and cost of retouching.

The original images that might be used for reproduction come in many different formats, sizes, and media. Conventional images include photographic originals and artists' illustrations, while electronic images include digitally captured images, Photo CD pictures, and images created in graphics programs.

Conventional Images

The majority of the images that are used for printing are photographic. The ease of capturing an image on film makes photography likely to continue as the dominant recording method for the time being, although the advantages of electronic images will make them increasingly attractive to publishers.

Photographic Originals

Color photographs can be in the form of transparencies, prints, or negatives. Color negatives are rarely used in conventional scanning, as the color values are difficult to judge and many scanners are unable to handle them. They do have the advantages of finer grain and a tonal range that can be captured by a CCD scanner. For conventional scanning, a print should be made from the negative, so that the client and the scanner operator can evaluate it, and, in many cases, it is this print that is scanned. Alternatively, photo labs can create positive transparencies from negatives, or the negatives can be scanned directly by Photo CD.

Both color prints and transparencies are made with dyes in the subtractive primaries: cyan, magenta, and yellow. There are several photographic emulsions in use, all of which the scanner reads slightly differently, even though they may appear visually identical. For many pictures, this difference is not sufficient enough to require allowances in setting up the scanner, but, for high-quality reproductions, this factor has to be considered. The scan parameters can be adjusted for the emulsion type, which is imprinted on the rebate at the film's edge.

The main variables in film emulsions are speed and color balance. As a general rule, slower film speeds (lower ISO numbers) produce finer grain and higher color saturation. Most films are balanced for daylight (5,000 K) conditions, but for situations where tungsten lighting is the main light source, tungsten-balanced (3,400 K) emulsions are available and give better results than the alternative of using filters in conjunction with daylight films. Tungsten-balanced films usually have the letter T after the ISO number in the film name. Fluorescent lighting tends to produce a strong greenish color cast, which can be countered with the use of a magenta filter.

The minor variations in color saturation and color balance between different brands of film, together with the characteristics of different dye sets, make it preferable when commissioning photography to specify the use of a single emulsion type.

Transparencies normally give better results than prints because they are sharper and have a better tonal range and color saturation. Low-end scanners may achieve equally good results with prints as with transparencies because the tonal range of color negatives and prints corresponds more closely to that of the scanner (although there is some evidence that where a transparency or negative is to be greatly enlarged, the best reproduction can be achieved by making a color print at the size of the final image, and scanning from that, rather than scanning directly from the film). Duplicate transparencies should be avoided if possible, as they inevitably lose sharpness and distort color and tonal values. Color contrast also tends to be increased by duplicating.

Artists' Illustrations

Artists' illustrations are created in many different media, from traditional oils and watercolor, through gouache, tempera, chalk, crayon and poster paint, to more recent innovations like color photocopies. Artwork can be scanned directly, as long as it fits on the scanner. It must not be larger than the maximum size the scanner can accept, and, with drum scanners, it must be sufficiently flexible to wrap around the scanner drum without cracking or otherwise damaging the artwork.

Color reproduction of artists' originals can sometimes be disappointing because the pigments and dyes in the illustrations are recorded by the scanner in a manner that does not replicate the way in which they are seen by the eye. An alternative to scanning directly from the artwork is to have a transparency made, ensuring that a color guide is included in the shot if possible. This will not guarantee fidelity to the original, but it will allow the designer to see how the colors will appear and specify any changes.

Other problems that can occur when artists' originals are digitized include:

- The color gamut of the pigments used may be different from the gamut of printing inks.
- Fluorescence occurs with some pigments.
- The surface texture of the illustration can influence the reproduction.

Preparing and Marking up Photographic Originals

When sending color originals out for scanning by a third party, it is necessary to mark them up to indicate the reproduction priorities and to prevent damage. Transparencies should be protected by a plastic sleeve, and color prints should be given a protective overlay. Glass and cardboard mounts should be avoided where possible, as they can cause damage to the emulsion during transport or when the mount is opened to remove the film.

Before you mark up your original illustrations for scanning, evaluate the subject matter and the relative importance of its different elements. The color of the key areas of interest usually has much more importance than the rest of the image. In some pictures, strongly colored elements are an important part of the design, while, in others, neutral backgrounds may be important. If the most critical elements of the picture can be identified, they can be given priority when the picture is scanned and color-separated.

Paper clips or biro marks on the protective sleeve or overlay can damage the surface of the original in a manner that is quite likely to be apparent on the scanned image. Any instructions should be written in felt tip, including such details as:

- The publication and the page number where the image will appear.
- Scaling and cropping details.
- Identification of any priority areas of the original to guide the scanner operator in setting up the tonal gradation.
- Any alterations you want to make to the color balance, including removal of color casts.
- Identification of any specific areas of color in the original that must reproduce accurately, possibly with CMYK values from a tint selector.
- Any other desired reproduction objectives, such as overall sharpness or color contrast.

The scanner operator will clean films before scanning if necessary, but sticky marks or excessive dust may end up on the final image.

Occasionally, it is necessary to use as an original an image that has already been printed. Apart from the obvious degradation of the detail and color values that this will involve, there is the risk of moiré on the reproduction. Most scanner and separation software programs have the ability to apply descreening algorithms to eliminate moiré, although some further loss of detail or sharpness may result.

Electronic Images

Computers and computer peripherals handle graphics in two fundamental ways: by creating a list of drawing instructions or by defining a two-dimensional grid of individual picture elements, or **pixels.**

Sampled Images

Most input and output devices build up graphics in a series of raster scans. Scanners, display monitors, printers, and imagesetters are all raster devices; the only exceptions are CAD plotters that output relatively simple diagrams by drawing a series of lines with pens. Inevitably, raster devices sample or output graphical objects as a series of separate pixels, in which each pixel is assigned a color value defining the intensities of its primary color components. Scanned images are often referred to as **sampled images,** and their resolution corresponds to the **sampling frequency** (the distance between individual samples).

Other terms used to describe sampled images include bitmap and raster images. The term **bitmap** implies the use of

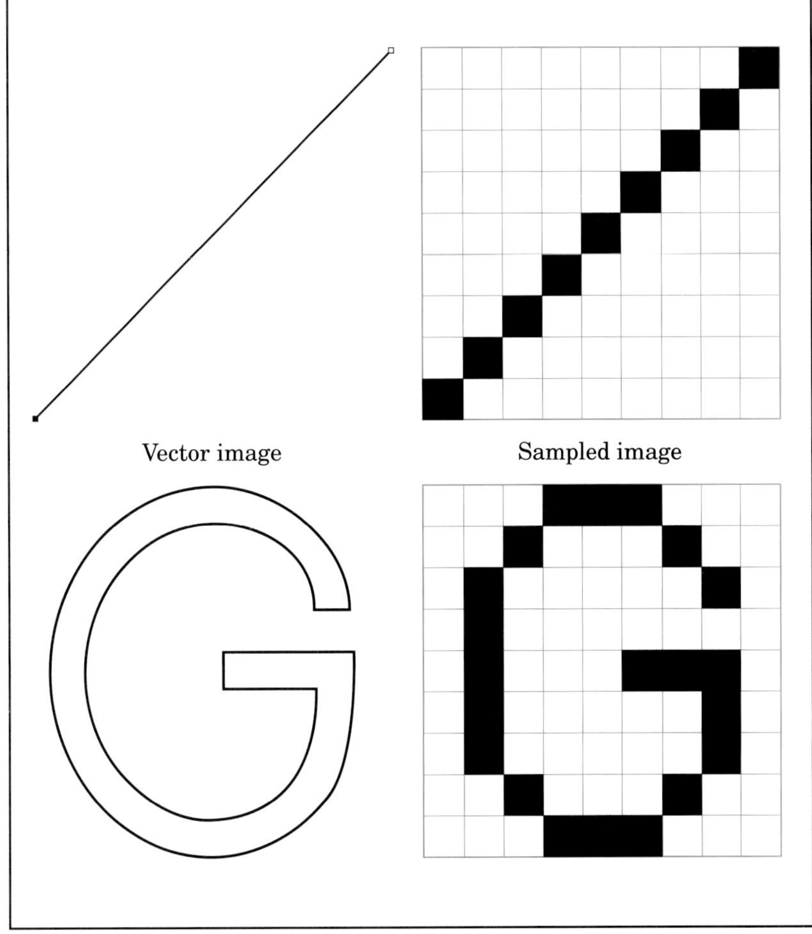

Figure 5-1.
A vector image *(left)* is an instruction to draw a line between two coordinates. A sampled image *(right)* describes the color of every pixel in the image.

a single bit to describe each pixel, and so is more suitable for defining binary images (i.e., images with only two possible values—usually black or white). The term **raster image** is commonly used to refer to pages prepared for output by conversion into a bitmap of device pixels, but it can also be used as a synonym for sampled image.

Sampled color images yield large files, since every pixel requires one byte per color component to define its color value. Thus a 2,000×3,000-pixel image creates an 18-MB RGB file (2,000×3,000×3) or a 24-MB CMYK file. It is usually possible for different applications to read sampled image files, as long as they are able to recognize features, such as the sample frequency and the way that samples are organized into bands or strips.

Image processing, which involves calculating new values for each pixel, can be performed at high speed regardless of the apparent complexity of the image. However, since it is necessary to write new values for every single pixel, spatial operations, such as scaling and rotating, are slow when compared to the alternative vector-based methods.

Vector Graphics

Although most input and output peripherals are raster devices, graphics created by computer systems are usually defined as a list of drawing instructions or **vectors.** Vector-based graphics are much more compact than sampled images and are also largely resolution-independent.

Each drawing instruction in a vector graphic gives the coordinates of the beginning and the end of the element being drawn as well as a mathematical description of the connections between these two points. The elements defined in the mathematical description can be based on straight lines or curves, or on more complex shapes known as Beziers. **Bezier curves** define two control points in addition to the two end coordinates, with the control points providing a description of the path connecting them.

Since vector graphics are nearly always output by raster devices, they must be converted to a raster format before output. Because of the processing that this conversion involves, output time is usually longer than that for sampled images. The processing time required is related to the complexity of the graphic.

Vector graphics are also known as **object-based graphics** (since they are built up from individual objects). The objects created remain separate entities and can be edited at any point until they are rasterized for output.

Because the object description is resolution-independent, objects such as type can be scaled to the exact size required with all lines and curves remaining completely smooth. Bitmapped type cannot be scaled without the risk of **aliasing** effects (or **pixelization**), where individual pixels in a character are enlarged to the point where they become objectionable.

The drawing instructions contained in a vector graphics file are couched in the graphical operators of the operating system, application, or programming language. PICT files, for example, contain QuickDraw operators; others include PostScript files (PostScript operators) and Windows Metafiles (Windows GDI operators). It is often impossible to exchange object-based graphics between applications or platforms.

A series of drawing instructions is sometimes known as a **display list.** As the display list is executed, new objects are always drawn on top of preceding objects. A display list sequence is changed when a graphic is edited to bring an object “in front” or place it “behind.”

Spatial operations, such as scaling and rotating, that affect individual objects or the whole graphic can be performed very easily on vector graphics. On the other hand, alterations to properties, such as lightness values, may not be possible without converting the graphic to a raster image.

Vector/Raster Conversion

Vectors are mainly used to define graphics that are constructed in illustration programs using well-defined graphical operators, while sampled images are typically used to define pictures and complex graphics in which detail is comparatively unstructured.

It is sometimes necessary to convert between these two basic types of graphical objects for the purpose of editing or output. Raster-to-vector conversion is necessary in order to import a raster image into an object-based illustration. This is accomplished by an autotrace routine that finds the edges of all the possible objects by looking for adjacent pixels that have different color or luminance values and separating them into different objects.

A raster image is also converted into a vector image by vector-based image-editing applications like Live Picture and XRes in order to create a smaller file that can be opened and edited without the memory overhead of a raster image. The image is converted back to a raster format after editing.

Vector-to-raster conversion is always necessary in order to transform an image into the device pixels of the output device. It may also be done to reduce the processing needed on complex graphics when they are output. Converting a vector-based graphic to a raster image is a simple task, but once the conversion has taken place the individual objects within the graphic can no longer be edited and any Bezier control points are lost.

File Formats for Digital Images

Numerous file formats have evolved to describe digital images for different purposes. They are differentiated mainly by their resolution, the number of bits that are used to describe each pixel, and the information that can be included in the file headers or tags. EPS and TIFF are the main file formats used for color images in the graphic arts. Other formats, such as PICT2 and QuickDraw on the Mac, and PCX on the IBM platform, are also used for some purposes, but do not support CMYK color.

Encapsulated PostScript (EPS). The PostScript page description language allows objects to be incorporated into pages as Encapsulated PostScript (EPS) files. These contain the description of the object with no page setup information, fonts, or headers. They can also include a low-resolution preview of a bitmap image for display on screen, together with a reference to a high-resolution PICT or TIFF file. EPS files can also incorporate the halftoning parameters for when the image is output, including screen ruling, screen angle, and dot shape, and any transfer functions that have been applied.

EPS files are given header information that is specific to the application in which they are created. They cannot be read by another program unless it has a filter that allows it to import files from the original application. Some EPS files incorporate a CMYK image, either as a **composite image,** in which every pixel has values for cyan, magenta, yellow, and black, or as a **separated image,** in which the CMYK components are extracted and saved in separate files. Two EPS formats are described below.

The **DCS (Desktop Color Separation) format** is an EPS file format that places each color component of an image in a separate file and also includes a low-resolution preview image that can be used for page placement. DCS files are

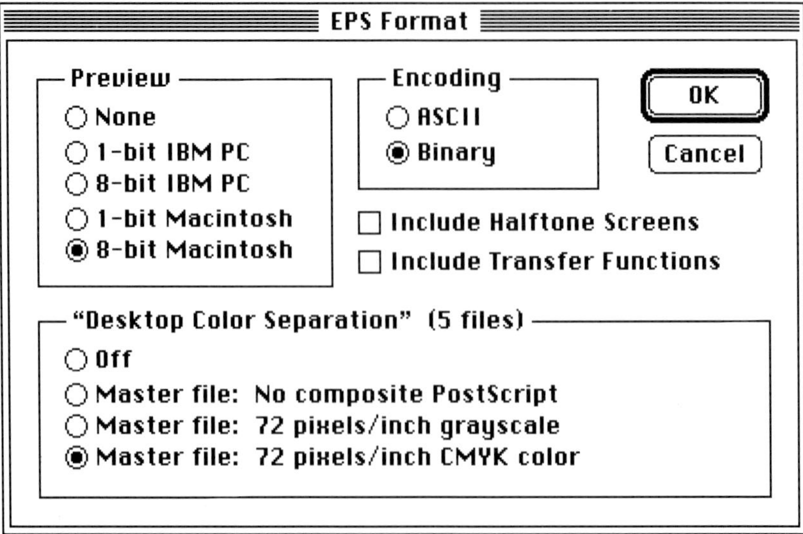

Figure 5-2. Saving a DCS (Desktop Color Separation) file in Adobe Photoshop.

used to output CMYK images as separate films (or plates) for each color on high-resolution imagesetters that cannot process composite files. Since the separate color components do not have to be extracted from a single composite file, output processing can be faster.

DCS files can be created by image-editing and page-makeup applications. Recently, the DCS-2 format has been established to support color graphics and images with more than four component colors, allowing them to be exchanged between applications and output as separate films. The additional colors can be used to define spot colors and extra-trinary color separations.

Scitex PSImage is a composite EPS file format that contains a low-resolution CMYK preview. It is intended for use with Automatic Picture Replacement (APR), a system in which high-resolution Scitex scan files are substituted for the low-resolution versions on output.

EPS files are essential for incorporating objects and images within pages for output. However, because they are, to some extent, application-specific, they are less suitable for the interchange of high-resolution image data between the scanner, the desktop, and the output device. This function is better carried out by TIFF files.

Tagged Image File Format (TIFF). The Tagged Image File Format (TIFF) is a rich and versatile file format that is capable of being extended as new requirements appear. Most bitmap file formats contain a small number of headers that describe the properties of an image, but TIFF images can include up to 60 tags (from an almost unlimited number of possible tags), each defining different properties. Tags are divided into Baseline tags and Extensions. Baseline tags include basic image data such as image size and resolution. Extensions define aspects such as the photometric details needed for the display of color images that are not stored in RGB mode.

Virtually all graphics applications are capable of reading Baseline TIFF images, but the features of the TIFF extensions are supported by a more limited number of applications. Applications such as Adobe Photoshop and Aldus Photostyler are capable of reading all the extensions defined in TIFF 6.0 that are relevant to graphic arts applications and can convert images from one format to another.

TIFF variants defined in the TIFF 6.0 standard for use in the graphic arts include the RGB, CMYK, YCC, CIELAB, and JPEG formats. The TIFF/IT format, created since the TIFF 6.0 revision, is defined in the ANSI IT8.8 standard. It is designed to include the information that a high-end graphics system would use in addition to the basic CMYK information and incorporates earlier standards for information interchange on high-end platforms.

Scitex CT. Scitex CT is a high-resolution composite CMYK format designed for output to high-end Scitex output devices. The format is supported by many image-editing and page-makeup applications.

PCD. PCD is the file format used to store Photo CD images that have been encoded in YCC and compressed. Images in the PCD format cannot be read directly, but must first be extracted from the compressed file.

Photo CD

Kodak Photo CD has become accepted as a serious alternative to other methods of digitizing images. Originally developed for the consumer market, the low cost of scanning Photo CD images has led to its widespread adoption by publishers.

Photo CD images are encoded in the twenty-four-bit Photo YCC model described in Chapter 3 and can be easily converted into other digital file formats. Both negatives and transparencies are scanned with Kodak's Photo CD film scanner, converted to YCC, compressed, and written to disc as a PCD file. The resulting CDs can then be read on any XA (extended architecture) CD player connected to a Mac, PC, or workstation.

The main technical limitation of the PCD scanner is that the maximum density that it can read is only 2.8. As a result, detail can be lost in deep shadow areas in transparencies (although not on negatives, which have a maximum density of around 2.0). Apart from this limitation, Photo CD successfully records virtually all of the information in an original that a high-end scanner would. However, it is not normally possible to color-correct or sharpen the image during scanning. These functions must be carried out later in an image-editing application.

In comparison with conventional scanners, the Photo CD scanner is simple to operate and permits relatively few adjustments. Apart from minor changes to brightness and color

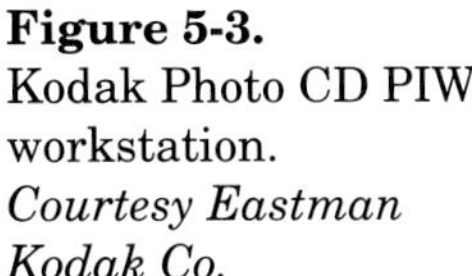

Figure 5-3.
Kodak Photo CD PIW workstation.
Courtesy Eastman Kodak Co.

balance, the main adjustment is the scanning mode. In normal use, the scanner reads the film code from the rebate at the film edge and uses calibration tables and special algorithms to make allowances for the type of film and the exposures used. It then attempts to make the reproduction look like the original scene. This process, known as scene balancing, is akin to the adjustments made automatically by photo finishers to amateur 35-mm negatives, averaging out extremes of lighting and exposure. Scene balance is good at correcting poorly exposed films, but can cause unwanted distortions to professional films that have been selected for their properties of speed and color saturation and exposed to suit the photographer's judgment of the effects desired.

The alternative to the scene balance mode is the **universal film terms mode,** in which the operator enters the emulsion type and the scan faithfully reproduces the characteristics of the transparency. Scene balancing works well with most negatives, but when sending transparencies out for transfer to Photo CD, be sure to specify the emulsion type, ISO rating, and universal film terms unless the transparencies have visible exposure defects.

Despite the relative simplicity of the scanner, not all Photo CD scans are the same. Photo finishers concentrate more on providing a budget service for consumers and do not tend to have the understanding to produce acceptable scans consistently with the correct parameters for reproduction. Trade shops charge more for scanning but are more familiar with the requirements of the graphic arts.

Figure 5-4.
(A) Image scanned conventionally on a Crosfield Magnascan.

(B) Kodak Photo CD scan of the same 35-mm transparency.

The Photo CD image is stored in an **image pac,** which contains the information necessary for five image resolutions. The highest resolution in the standard Photo CD scans 35-mm as 2,048×3,072 pixels, yielding an 18-MB file after decompression; while in Pro Photo CD a 5×4-in. (635×102-mm) original is scanned as 4,096×6,144 pixels, giving a 72-MB file.

Decompression of the compressed YCC image data and translation to RGB is critical to final image quality. The film scanner and the YCC encoding ensure that virtually all the information on the original film is captured (with the exception of some shadow detail on transparencies). However, the decoding utilities that allow users to access Photo CD images do not retain all the image information. In particular, the linear decompression algorithms used in software, such as the stand-alone Access utility and the Acquire plug-in for Adobe Photoshop, do not deal properly with the highlight information in the YCC color model.

Table 5-1. Kodak Photo CD formats.

	Format	Image size in pixels	File size	Maximum repro. size at 150 lpi	Maximum repro. size at 200 lpi	Maximum repro. size with FM screening
Photo CD	Base/16	128×192	72 Kb	—	—	—
	Base/4	256×384	288 Kb	0.9×1.25 in.	—	1.25×1.9 in.
	Base	512×768	1.18 Mb	1.75×2.5	1.25×1.75 in.	2.5×3.75
	4 Base	1024×1536	4.5 Mb	3.5×5	2.5×3.5	5×7.5
	16 Base	2048×3072	18 Mb	7×10	5×7.5	10×15
Pro Photo CD	64 Base	4096×6144	72 Mb	14×20	10×15	20×30

The nonlinear algorithms in Kodak's Color Management System, available for image-editing applications like Adobe Photoshop and Aldus Photostyler, retain more of the original image data. However, because the process of converting from YCC to RGB or CIELAB, and then to CMYK, results in some information loss, it is preferable to transfer directly from YCC to CMYK. This can be done with the use of the device profiles in Kodak's Color Management System, for example. Calibration and color management with Photo CD images are discussed in Chapter 14.

The larger files produced by Pro Photo CD require special access utilities or plug-ins, as they cannot be read by the versions available for standard Photo CD.

Publishers who want to edit or separate color images and then store them must convert to another format like TIFF before writing the resulting file to some form of mass storage.

Print Photo CD is a variation on the Photo CD system designed for use by trade shops. This format allows trade shops to write images to disc both as standard CMYK TIFF files and as YCC files. It is not restricted to Photo CD files and can handle images from a range of different sources including high-end scanners and edited Photo CD files. The Print Photo CD discs can be read by users in the same way as standard Photo CD and can also include other page layout elements such as text and graphics.

Sources of Digitized Images

There is increasing interest in acquiring images in an already digitized form, through media such as digital photography, digitized picture libraries, or Photo CD. There are considerable advantages for publishers, including savings on scanning costs, reductions in production time, increased flexibility and control, and the benefits of an all-digital workflow. It is possible to import pictures into page layouts and prepare visualization proofs before making a final selection, as well as produce color separations directly from the digital file without an intermediate film stage. Photographers and picture libraries are able to add value to their images by supplying them ready for use—already scanned and retouched. Increasingly, the creator or copyright owner, rather than the user of a picture, will be responsible for a photo's digitization.

Issues that need to be considered are:

- **Search methods.** Searching a picture library's stock for physical images currently involves a combination of searching a text database and handling prints or transparencies. Digital images enable fast on-line searching through low-resolution viewfiles and the distribution of low-resolution catalogs.
- **Compression and storage.** High-resolution digital images take up a lot of space and require cost-effective methods of storage. Some form of compression is thus necessary for storing high-resolution pictures.
- **Transmission.** To maximize the speed advantage of digital images, it will often be necessary to transmit them over high-bandwidth communications links, such as **ISDN (Integrated Services Digital Network).**
- **Color management.** Ensuring that digital images appear on different platforms in a consistent way that reflects the photographer's original intentions requires the use of color management systems and calibration tools.
- **Copyright protection.** Fear of unrestricted copying of high-quality digital images can act as a determent to distributing images in this way.

Digital photography. An alternative to recording images on film is to record them in digital form, using a digital camera. This saves on film and processing costs and removes the need for image digitization later in the process. The cost savings for high-volume users can bring a quick return on investment. For the photographer, there is the additional advantage of being able to electronically retouch and composite images, allowing more salable images to be produced with less work. Pictures can be immediately displayed, eliminating the need for Polaroid previews, and can be imported directly into image-editing applications.

Digital cameras use arrays of CCD elements to capture images, but they suffer from technical limits in fabricating CCD arrays with adequate resolution and sensitivity.

Early digital cameras were unable to capture enough information to be usable, the resolution and tonal range being adequate only for visualization or very low quality print purposes. Now a range of high-resolution systems that make use of the advances in CCD design are available. Some of these, such as the Leaf Lumina, are capable of capturing more information than most scanners do, allowing the user to select which elements to retain.

Like conventional cameras, digital cameras come in compact, single-lens reflex (SLR), and large-format varieties. Low-resolution compacts (such as the Canon Ion) are useful for producing classified advertisements and tend to have relatively simple optics, image-sensing CCDs, and controlling software.

Digital SLR cameras, such as the Kodak DCS and the Nikon E2, are based on existing SLR camera designs with the addition of CCD backs and storage subsystems. The capture resolution of these cameras is suitable for news

Table 5-2. Digital cameras and picture formats.

Camera	Image size	Bits per pixel	File size	Maximum reproduction size at 150 lpi†	Maximum reproduction size at 200 lpi
Canon Ion RC560	552×760	8	1 Mb	2×2.5 in.	1.5×2 in.
Nikon E2	1000×1280	8	4 Mb	3.5×4	2.5×3
Kodak DCS 200	1012×1524	8	5 Mb	3.5×4.5	2.5×4
Sony CDK-5000	1144×1520	10*	5 Mb	4×4.5	3×4
Leaf DB400	2048×2048	8	12 Mb	7×7	5×5
Kodak Photo CD	2048×3072	8	18 Mb	7×10	5×7.5
Crosfield Celcis 130	2320×3072	8	21.4 Mb	8×10	6×7.5
Leaf Lumina	2700×3400	12*	26 Mb	9×11	7×8.5
Kodak Pro Photo CD	4096×6144	8	72 Mb	14×20	10×15
Phase One Photophase CB70	5000×7200	12*	108 Mb	17×24	12.5×18
Dicomed 5×4	6000×7250	8	130 Mb	20×24	15×18

*Only 8 bits saved in the file.

†The maximum reproduction size is based on two image pixels for each halftone screen line in the final printed output (see Chapter 6). Increasing enlargement beyond this size will cause gradual loss of definition and detail.

Figure 5-5.
Digital camera back.
Courtesy Phase One.

photography and other applications with similar quality demands.

Large-format systems either take the form of digital backs that can be used in conjunction with existing large-format cameras, providing an interchangeable alternative to a film back, as in the Photophase range, or they are designed from the start as a digital camera, such as the Leaf Lumina and the Crosfield Celcis. These large-format systems have adequate resolution for most graphic arts purposes, and in most cases do not require their own storage subsystems since the image is downloaded directly to a host computer. They are most suitable for studio work and are widely used in catalog production where the volume of product shots means that large savings can be made on film and processing.

The Leaf camera incorporates a Scitex color computer identical to the one used in the Scitex Smart scanner and allows images to be recorded directly into CMYK instead of RGB.

Picture libraries. Many picture libraries are making their collections available in digital form, giving users fast, twenty-four-hour access to high-quality professional images. For the library, supplying digitized pictures eliminates the costs associated with sending out high-value original transparencies, such as transport and insurance, and removes the need to make duplicates. The move to digital picture libraries is likely to be gradual, due to the costs of digitizing a large stock of images. Since digital images are not universally appropriate (for example, many existing users do not have the computer facilities to make use of digital images), libraries will no doubt keep their conventional holdings.

On-line searching provides access to picture libraries all over the world through public telephone networks, allowing picture researchers to search for images in the same way that on-line database users search for text. Thumbnails can be downloaded, and after an image has been selected, the photographer or picture library can be contacted in order to obtain a transparency or high-resolution file of the image.

Copyright-free images. Clip art is a widely available source of images in both vector and bitmap formats, offering access to an enormous selection of images, often at little or

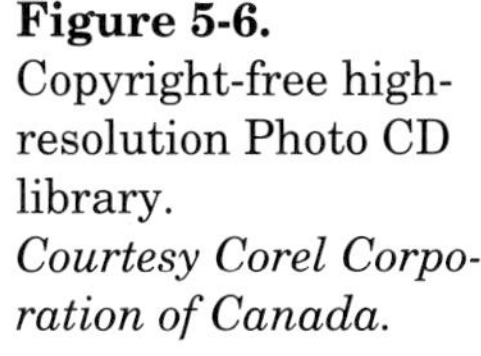

Figure 5-6. Copyright-free high-resolution Photo CD library. *Courtesy Corel Corporation of Canada.*

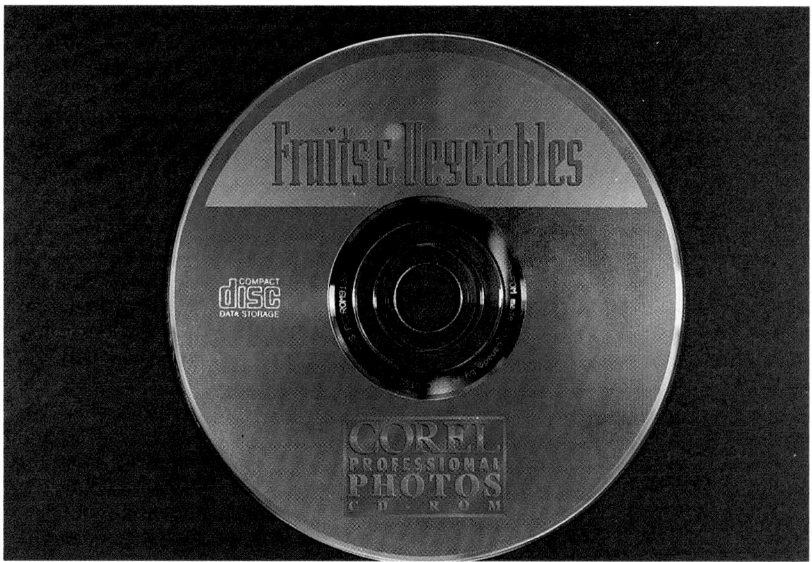

no cost. Many scanned clip art libraries consist of relatively low-resolution images that can look good at the display resolution but are not adequate for printing. However, some collections of professional images are now being distributed on CD, which is a sufficiently cheap medium to allow high-resolution images to be included on the disc. The Corel Professional collection, marketed by Corel Corporation of Canada, contains hundreds of themed CDs, each with 100 pictures in the Photo CD format.

This method of distribution poses a real threat to the picture libraries. The user pays a single fee to acquire the disc and the reproduction rights, and can re-use images without incurring additional costs. The cost of acquiring digitized images in this way is a tiny fraction of the costs involved in using pictures from conventional picture libraries. The returns to the photographer provide an incentive to supply high-quality images, and there is less likelihood of copyright infringement. They main drawback in using images of this kind is that they tend to be of a rather general nature. Their use for promotional purposes is also limited by the fact that users cannot secure exclusive rights.

Creating Color Originals in Graphics Programs

Most illustrations and graphics are originated in graphics programs. They can be created as either vector-based graphics in **draw** programs or as pixel-based images created in **paint** programs.

Draw programs are used to generate the type of illustrations that a graphic artist would create with pens or rulers or by applying color either in flat areas with dry transfer materials or in softer graduations produced with an airbrush. The resultant file describes the image as a series of objects.

Paint programs, on the other hand, are used to produce images that an artist or illustrator might create with oils, water colors, crayons, gouaches, and so on. A file created by a paint program defines the color and intensity of every pixel in the image.

Once an object has been "painted" on to the image canvas, it no longer exists as a separate object but as a series of color values for the individual pixels.

Some programs allow the designer to create both object and raster layers within the same image, so that the most appropriate method of creating the different elements of the image can be used. They may also allow the designer to use an **autotrace routine** to import a sampled image into a draw program and convert it into a series of objects in order to manipulate it.

Evaluating Originals

It is important to make sure that the pictures chosen or commissioned are suitable for reproduction. The most important attributes are sharpness, color balance, and contrast.

Assessing Photographic Originals

When assessing a photographic original it is important to use standard lighting conditions, especially when viewing transparencies (see Chapter 2). When ordinary room light is used to evaluate a transparency, color values will be difficult to judge and any color casts may not be apparent.

Two points should be borne in mind when considering viewing conditions for originals. Firstly, the enlargement and reduction of an original can affect color and tone in ways that are difficult to predict. Color contrast appears to decrease when the picture is enlarged and increase when the picture is reduced. In addition, midtones appear to be lighter on enlarged images and darker on reduced ones.

Secondly, even where the intensity of illumination meets the requirements of the standard, there can be transparency detail in deep shadows that is not visible. Using a magnifier helps to identify shadow detail, but there remains the possibility that some detail can only be seen with the assistance of a more powerful light source. This deep shadow detail will often be lost during tone compression, but if this detail is of particular importance it is possible to adjust the tonal gradation to expand the shadows during scanning.

Sharpness. The sharpness or definition of a picture is especially important, unless it is an intentionally grainy or soft-focus image. Readers of a publication may not be in a position to judge color values or tonal gradation without being able to refer to the original image, but lack of sharpness will be noticeable to anyone. For this reason, picture editors nearly always insist on pin-sharp transparencies.

Images are normally sharpened during scanning by the process of unsharp masking, which is described in Chapter 6. Unsharp masking and sharpening filters can also be applied in image-editing applications, but may not be suitable for some subjects. Remember that there is no substitute for a good original.

Most transparencies are enlarged during reproduction and some of the image definition is lost in the process. To avoid this, transparencies should ideally be as close to the size of the reproduction as possible. Enlargements above 250% will certainly appear less sharp than the original. You can get an

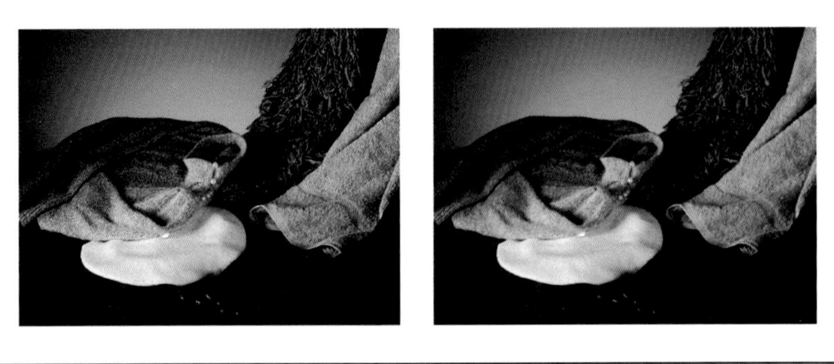

Figure 5-7.
A sharp image *(left)* looks much better than a softer, unsharp image *(right).*

idea how your image will appear after enlargement by inspecting it with a low-power magnifier such as a linen tester.

Color balance. A common problem with color originals is poor color balance, usually in the form of an excess of one of the photographic dye colors throughout the whole image. This effect is called a color cast, and it is especially noticeable in highlights and neutral colors, which show a shift towards the cast color, and in complementary colors, which are desaturated. Overall color casts are caused by poor processing or lighting, or by the use of film that is out of date or has the wrong color balance for the lighting conditions.

Because the eye tends to adapt to any near-neutral color, the cast may not be apparent until it is seen alongside an image with a different color balance. For this reason it is a good procedure to collect together all the illustrations that will print in the same publication and view them side by side in order to identify any differences in color balance.

Slight color casts may not be objectionable, or they may even be a desirable feature of the image. The effect of removing a color cast should be considered carefully, as it will affect the color balance of the whole picture, possibly making it warmer or colder.

Removing a magenta color cast, for example, will make the reds in a picture warmer, the blues and neutrals cooler, and the complementary color—green—will become more saturated. Color casts are easy to remove during scanning or in an image-editing application.

Sometimes a color cast can be seen over a small area of the original. This is known as a local color cast and is usually caused by poor lighting of the subject. It will take much longer to correct than an overall cast.

Figure 5-8.
(A) Normal contrast.

(B) High contrast. High contrast can make the colors in a picture look too strong.

(C) Low contrast. Low contrast can make the colors in a picture look dull.

Contrast. A common problem with transparencies is that shadow detail is lost when printed. If an original has a maximum density greater than the scanner is capable of recording, then detail in the shadows and deep saturated colors will be lost. A good reproduction will compress the tonal range of the original into the tonal range that can be achieved by the printing process, keeping most of the detail but losing a little of the separation between tones.

To get the best from a transparency, a scanner with an adequate density range (or dynamic range) should be used, but in cases where there is important shadow detail at the end of the tonal range, shadow expansion can be specified. This will change the way the tonal range is compressed, allocating more gray levels to the shadow end and less to the midtones and highlights. Highlights and midtones can also be expanded, but expanding any one region of tone causes compression and the loss of gray levels elsewhere in the picture.

Good color contrast is essential for colorful and appealing pictures. Color contrast depends on the saturation of individual colors and also on the balance of saturation in all the saturated colors throughout the image. Colorful pictures have clean saturated reds, greens, blues, and yellows, and it helps if the original has good saturation in these colors. Color contrast can be enhanced in image-editing applications, but if the color is very desaturated the scanner or image-editing program may be unable to restore it. The detail in a saturated color is usually carried by the complementary color, and since enhancing color contrast involves reducing the complementary colors, loss of detail can result.

Grain. Visible grain in a reproduction is usually objectionable, although for some images it forms part of the mood of the picture. Fast films (IS0 400 and above) exhibit more grain than slow ones. When a transparency is enlarged the grain becomes more apparent, and a transparency that seemed acceptable when viewed without enlargement may show objectionable grain when printed.

When enlargement is necessary, the grain of the transparency should be checked carefully with a magnifier. Grain suppression is available in some electronic image manipulation systems. The Despeckle filter in Adobe Photoshop has the same effect.

Blemishes. Any dust, finger marks, scratches, or other blemishes on an original may well appear on the reproduction, often becoming more pronounced. Care should be taken in handling all originals, preferably keeping them in mounts or sleeves except when they are being scanned. A quick wipe over the surface of an original before scanning can save a great deal of time pixel cloning later in an image-editing program. If scratches or other marks in the emulsion appear on an image they can be removed by electronic editing.

Other requirements of good originals include good tonal gradation and good tonal separation between areas of detail (bearing in mind that this tonal separation will be compressed when the image is scanned).

Making color judgments based on the screen display is fraught with difficulty, but two essential requirements are to:

- Ensure that the ambient lighting and display setup conform with the standard viewing conditions (see Chapter 2).
- Ensure that the monitor is accurately calibrated (see Chapter 14).

Assessing Electronic Images

Digital images require different methods of evaluation, since the characteristics of the display can influence the way the image is perceived and some aspects of the image may not be readily visible. If it is not possible to determine the quality of an image from the display, it will be necessary to make a visualization proof at the size of the final print, preferably using a dye sublimation printer and a color management system.

Checking digital images on screen makes use of the software densitometer that is available in most image-editing applications. The cursor is positioned over a pixel and its

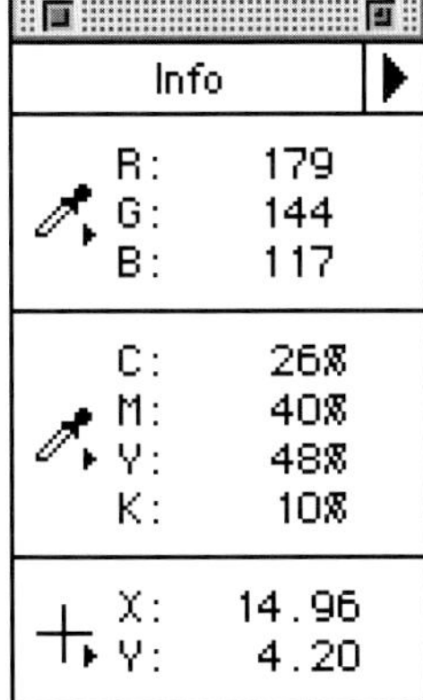

Figure 5-9. Color values generated by a software densitometer.

values appear in an information panel or the application's status line at the bottom of the display.

When checking CMYK color values in Photoshop and the image is in RGB mode, the Info panel will not give the correct CMYK values from the color separation preferences that you have entered. Use the CMYK Preview to examine the color values that will be obtained after conversion to CMYK with the current color separation preferences, but remember that any subsequent changes to either the separation preferences or the color balance of the file will alter the CMYK values.

The recommendations below are not intended to be applied to every image, but can be used as a guide for typical images without special requirements.

Sharpness. Sharpness is difficult to evaluate from a screen display. First, check that the file is large enough to contain all of the information for the output size you want and then check that unsharp masking has been applied to the image. Next, choose the part of the image where the lack of sharpness will be most noticeable, zoom in so that the individual pixels are visible, and check to see that edges do not feather across more than one or two pixels. A fair representation of image sharpness can be obtained by viewing the image at a 2:1 zoom.

Color balance. Check the white point in the image and any neutral colors. In the RGB mode you should see equal values for red, green, and blue, while in CMYK mode you should see cyan, magenta, and yellow in ratios corresponding to a neutral gray (roughly 5:4:4).

Contrast. Check the overall lightness contrast of an image by reading its lightest and darkest points. For high contrast, they should be close to 5% in highlights and to 95% in shadows. Specular highlights (small areas of the image that correspond to light sources or bright reflections) can have values close to 0%.

Color contrast can be checked in a number of different ways. You can read a value for saturation directly by setting the Colors palette to HSL and using the eyedropper to select the most saturated colors in the image: the closer to 100, the more saturated the color. Alternatively, check the amount of the complementary color present in each of the saturated

Figure 5-10. Zooming in on a picture allows you to determine whether it has adequate sharpness. In the top image, the boundary of the detail area does not extend over more than one or two pixels. While in the bottom image, the boundary extends much further and the resulting reproduction will not appear as sharp. Detail from both images has been enlarged eight times.

colors. For example, check the amount of cyan in a saturated red, or the amount of blue in a yellow color. Also check that the saturation of reds, greens, blues and yellows is roughly equal for a balanced appearance.

Tonal gradation. Make a gray scale copy of the image, zoom in on the areas of interest and check that there is good separation between areas of detail (a difference of at least 5–10%). In areas of smooth transition between tones, check that the difference between adjacent areas is less than 2%. Any wanted detail in shadow areas should have values of 90% or less.

Image Retouching

Retouching photographic images is now frequently performed with electronic tools, rather than by traditional manual methods using brushes, dyes, and chemicals. The advantages of electronic retouching are:

- It is easier to see the effects of what you do.
- Retouching can be carried out on a copy, leaving the original intact.

- Image-editing applications are faster, more controllable, and offer many more editing techniques and filters than manual methods.
- Electronic methods of image manipulation are so powerful that it is possible to view the objective of reproduction as achieving the best possible printed image, instead of just the best possible reproduction of the original.

Image-editing applications combine the functions of the photographer, the artist, the retoucher, and the electronic prepress system in a powerful digital darkroom. All the image attributes described above can be altered in an image-editing application, but it is important to recognize that the total amount of information in an image cannot be increased after it has been captured. It can only be redistributed in different ways. It is preferable to start with a good image than to spend time correcting a defective image in an application. Image-editing applications are used most productively for creative design work and for preparing images for output, rather than for the routine corrections of defects, such as poor lighting or spots.

6 Scanning

The aim of scanning is to capture all the information from an original that will be needed in the reproduction. The perceptual mechanism of the human eye actively seeks cues that will give it information about the objects within the visual field, and, for this reason, a reproduction of an image that contains a large amount of detail is usually preferred to one in which some of the detail has been lost. The more information that the reproduction contains about the original scene—the objects in it, their colors, textures, and so on—the closer and more real the original scene appears.

Information that is not captured when the image is scanned cannot be replaced. Any further image processing will discard data but will not be able to retrieve it from the original. For example, if a digital image is lightened throughout the tonal range, highlight detail will be lost. Once this detail has gone it cannot be retrieved other than by returning to the unedited image.

Image processing can add information to a picture, and when an image has become degraded it is possible to employ algorithms that reverse the degradation, if enough is known about the way the image became degraded. Removing moiré and adding sharpness fall into this category. Mathematical solutions of this kind can restore or enhance an image, and make it much more acceptable, but the new information added was not necessarily present in the original image.

A good scan will capture information by sampling it at the right points. For example, a transparency with middletone areas of interest should be scanned in a way that maintains the separation between tones in these areas, so that all the wanted detail will appear in the reproduction. Expanding the midtones later, by adjusting the gradation in an image-editing application, will only redistribute those tones that have been captured, without adding any further tonal steps to contribute to perceived detail. Adding intermediate tones by interpolation will only average the existing tones, making the transition between them smoother, but not actually adding any more detail.

Just capturing every bit of information in an image is not enough, however. There is a limit to how much information can be used in the reproduction, and acquiring more than this simply makes files larger than necessary. Every subsequent file operation will take longer, resulting in a serious loss of productivity.

A good scan will capture all the tone, color, detail, and sharpness of the original image. When scan parameters are not adjusted properly, or if cheaper low-end scanners are used, reproductions are typically flat, unsharp, and lacking in detail, with poor tonal rendering, dull colors, and an incorrect color balance.

When scanning an original, then, the objective is to capture all the information that it will be possible to reproduce, while at the same time making sure that file sizes are as small as possible.

Development of Electronic Scanning

Scanning began to eclipse photographic color separation techniques during the 1970s, bringing automation to what had been a manual operation. The electronic scanner offered control, repeatability, and productivity to those with the necessary skills and capital to purchase and operate the equipment. The economics of using the new equipment led to the development of specialist trade shops that supplied color separations to printers and agencies. Prices of color separations tumbled in real terms, contributing to the increasing affordability of color printing.

The initial advantage of using a scanner instead of a process camera was that color correction was programmed into the circuitry of the scanner and the laborious retouching of films by masking and etching could be almost eliminated (although many companies continue to perform some retouching in this way).

The first color scanners were analog rather than digital, and the image was exposed onto film by the recording unit at the same time as it was being read by the analyze unit. The development of digital scanners, first introduced by Crosfield in 1975, created the possibility of digital storage and processing of the image before output to film. Since then, scanner quality and productivity have increased enormously. Preview stations have been added, modular and multi-station scanners have been developed to maximize throughput, and workstations for color image assembly and planning have been incorporated.

At the same time as graphic arts scanners evolved into highly efficient and consistent workhorses for quality prepress, businesses began to identify a need for small, simple scanning devices that could be used in the office environment. These flatbed scanners use simple charge-coupled

Figure 6-1. Screen SG-7060P drum scanner. *Courtesy Screen USA.*

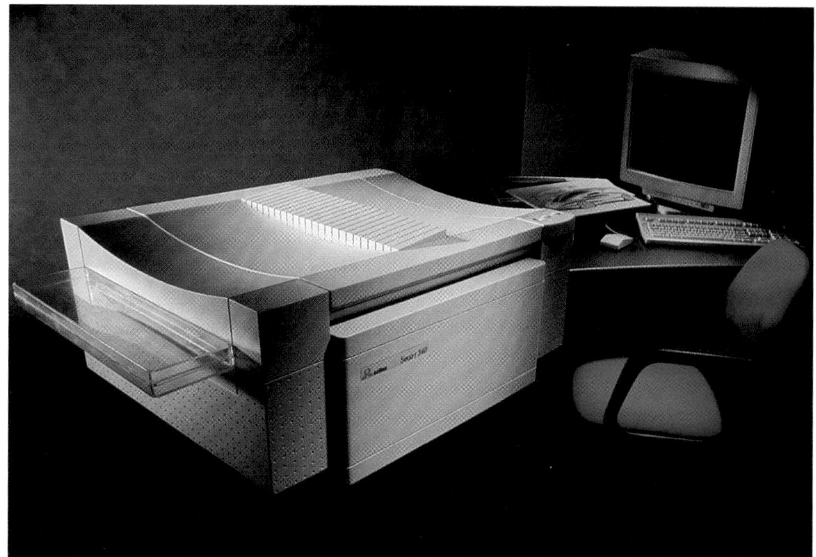

Figure 6-2. Scitex Smart 340 flatbed scanner. *Courtesy Scitex Europe SA.*

devices to record the image instead of the sensitive photomultiplier tubes found in high-end scanners. With their resolution and color capabilities rapidly improving, flatbed scanners soon became of interest to the emerging desktop-publishing (DTP) market. Since then, the quality and price performance of desktop scanners has reached the point where they are able to challenge specialized commercial scanners for an increasing share of the graphic arts market.

Types of Scanners

Scanners can be broadly divided into **high-end scanners** (designed for professional users in trade shops and commercial printers) and **desktop scanners** (used mainly by designers and publishers). High-end systems are normally built as large drum scanners with internal programs for performing CMYK conversions and direct connections to film recorders. Desktop systems include flatbed scanners intended mainly for reflection copy, transparency scanners for 35-mm and medium-format transparencies (occasionally taking transparencies up to 5×4 in. [127×102 mm]), and desktop drum scanners similar to the larger commercial systems that accept both reflection copy and transparencies. Until recently, desktop scanners were associated with "visualization-only" scanning, but now they are capable of handling 90% or more of the quality requirements of commercial color.

Scanning an image involves analyzing the color values of each individual sample. Depending on the type of scanner used, it will then process the color values before storing them in a file or recording them directly onto a photographic medium.

The basic elements of a scanner are similar to some of the elements of the human visual apparatus (see Chapter 2). They are:

- Light-sensitive capture elements.
- An optical system to focus the image onto the capture elements.
- A filter system to allow the red, green, and blue components of the image to be recorded separately.
- A transport system to move the original in relation to the scanner so that it can be sampled at the required frequency.
- Controlling software.
- Processing software to carry out initial image processing before recording.

Image Capture Elements

All graphic arts scanners use either photomultiplier tube (PMT) or charge-coupled device (CCD) systems. When photons strike the photocell in a CCD or PMT, they give up energy as they disappear. This causes electrons to be emitted, turning the energy of the photons into electrical energy. The number of electrons that are emitted can be measured to determine how many photons struck the capture element, and from this measurement the scanner generates a value for the intensity of light arriving from the point on the original analyzed.

Photomultiplier Tubes

Drum scanners are equipped with one photomultiplier tube for each of the red, green, and blue filter signals, together with a separate tube for the unsharp masking signal. The original transparency is mounted on the drum. A beam of light is transmitted from inside the drum, through the transparency, and onto the scanner optics. (In the case of reflection copy, it is bounced off the surface of the copy.) By rotating the drum at high speed and moving the analyze head slowly along the drum's axis, each pixel on the transparency can, in turn, be read.

After being split into red, green, and blue beams, either by filters or by a prism, the light strikes the end of the photomultiplier tube. The photomultiplier tube consists of a photocell inside a vacuum tube, with a light-sensitive cathode at one end and an anode at the other. The photocathode emits electrons as it is struck by photons in the light beam. A series of electrodes amplifies the electron stream until it reaches the tube's anode, and the amplification effect allows the PMT to read small changes in density with great accuracy over a large density range. The smallest number of photons that can be detected (indicating the darkest areas of the original) is limited by the amount of noise present in the system. The maximum density that a PMT can detect is between 3.5 and 4.0, depending on the sensitivity of the tube design.

On a high-end scanner, the input (or analyze) unit is connected via the color computer directly to the output (or recorder) unit. The color computer calculates the correct CMYK dot values for each pixel. On older scanners the link is hardwired, and scaling is achieved by varying the relative rotation speeds and stepping increments of the two units. This limits the range of enlargement and reduction factors and the screen frequencies that can be used. Similarly, resolution depends on mechanical factors, such as the smallest spot size that can be focused and the stepping increments of the analyze head travel.

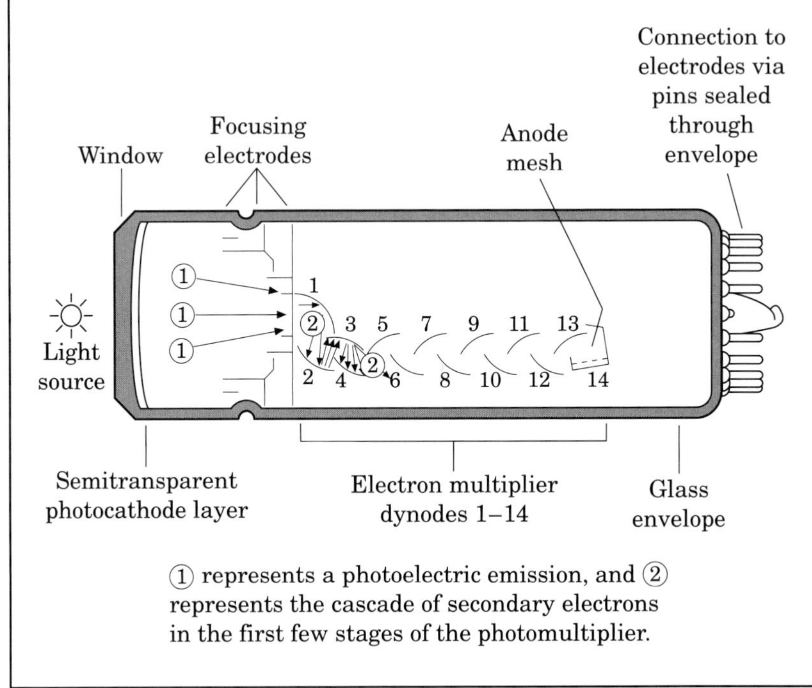

Figure 6-3. Photomultiplier tube (PMT). From *Color Scanning and Imaging Systems* by Gary Field.

On a digital scanner, scaling and resolution can be controlled by software. Most of the adjustments made for different images can also be software-controlled, and, in many desktop systems, the scanner is controlled from a standard platform host computer, either in a standalone utility or from within an image-editing application (such as a Photoshop plug-in).

CCDs

Charge-coupled devices (CCDs) are found in many different kinds of electronic equipment, including camcorders, fax machines, and digital cameras. A CCD consists of an array of tiny electrodes packed closely together on a layer of silicon. When a photon strikes an electrode it causes an electron to be emitted from the silicon layer. Like an airline baggage conveyor, the electrons are "tagged" with their position and transmitted along pathways to an analog-to-digital converter (ADC), where the voltage for each pixel is measured and given a digital value. The tagging of the electrons to the location of individual pixels is called charge-coupling.

Figure 6-4.
Charge-coupled device (CCD).
Adapted from *Digital Image Processing* by Rafael Gonzalez and Richard Woods.

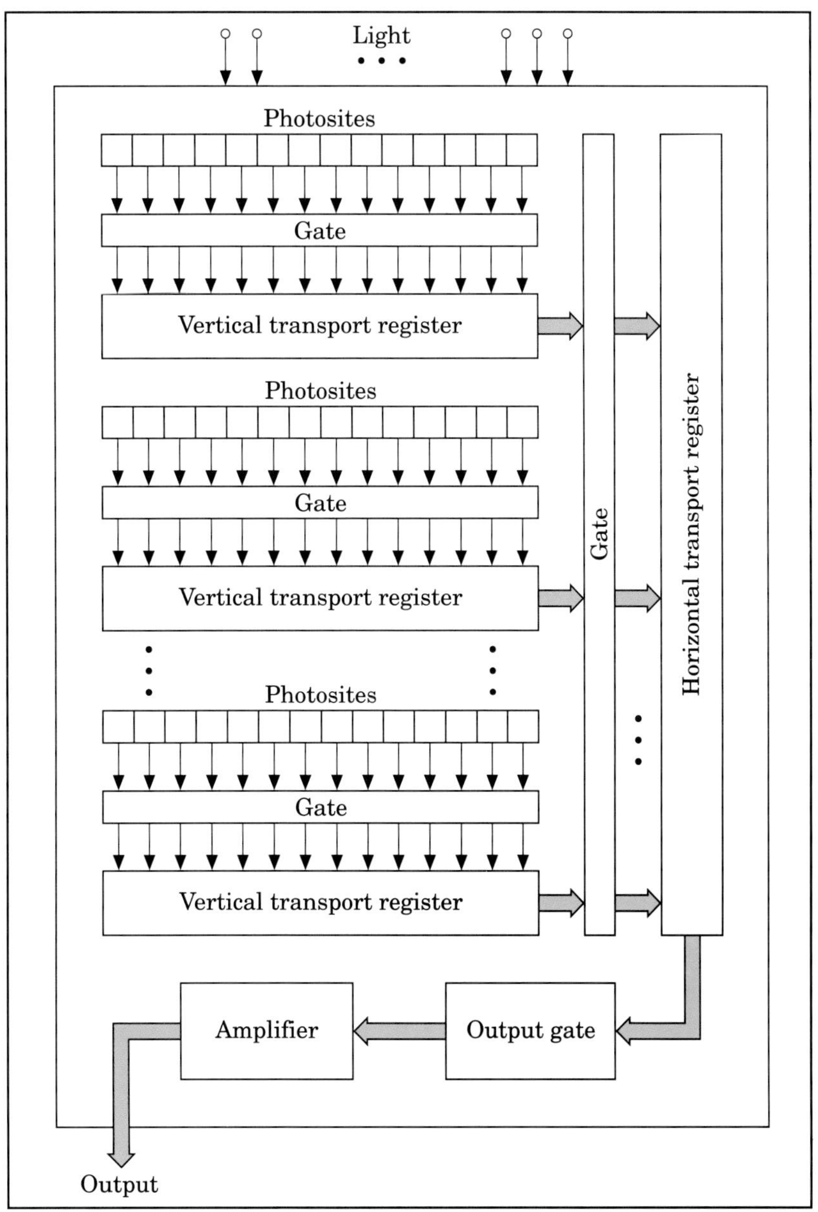

The CCD can detect the presence of a single photon, but the interference caused by system noise and crosstalk (interference between the signals produced by adjacent electrodes) is higher than that of the photomultiplier and thus the ability of CCDs to resolve detail in deep shadow areas is limited. The density range is typically up to 3.0, although a D_{max} of up to 3.5 or even 4.0 is possible. The difference between 3.0 and 3.5 may not seem like very much, but because density is a logarithmic scale it implies that the PMT is roughly three times as sensitive to shadow detail.

The simplest way of increasing the sensitivity of the CCD and reducing the effect of noise so that it has a higher density range is to make each electrode larger. Unfortunately image resolution is dependent on the size of electrodes that can be packed onto the silicon wafer, and hence there is a trade-off between density range and resolution. High-quality CCDs with elements of 10 microns or less and a D_{max} as high as 4.0 have been developed, but are expensive. So as the imaging capability of CCD scanners rises to the level of PMTs, the price advantage of CCDs starts to disappear.

The ADC turns the continuously varying electron levels into digital values, and the number of bits used by the ADC is related to the number of gray levels captured. An eight-bit ADC can output 256 gray levels for each color, but since tonal compression will occur after digitization the ADC should ideally be able to handle more than eight bits per color. Some systems employ CCDs that can capture up to twelve bits and then effectively resample down to eight bits at the ADC, while others retain all twelve bits for later manipulation.

Early scanners were only able to resolve six bits of data for each color. Since then, graphic arts scanners have become capable of resolving from eight to twelve bits per color.

Table 6-1. Pixel depths *(left)* and density ranges *(right)*.

Bits available for each color component	Gray levels available for each color component	Limit of sensitivity (reflectance %)	D_{max}
6	64	0.1	3.0
8	256	0.05	3.3
10	1024	0.025	3.6
12	4096	0.01	4.0

Because a PMT captures data serially, one pixel after another, the scanner design must arrange for every pixel to pass under the optics in turn, and this makes the drum necessary. In a CCD scanner, the data is captured in parallel, and the travel of the scanner head depends on the way the CCD elements are arranged. In a linear array the scanner head makes a single pass over the original (or three passes in the case of scanners that require a separate pass for each filter color), while a two-dimensional array captures the whole image in a single snapshot. Two-dimensional arrays are used in low-resolution devices like camcorders, but are costly to fabricate in the higher resolutions required in the graphic arts. Systems that use two-dimensional CCD arrays include digital cameras and the Linotype Hell Topaz and Kodak Photo CD scanners.

The way in which the electron levels are translated into gray scale information by the ADC is flexible. The gray scale steps do not have to be the same size, and the software can control tonal compression more flexibly than it can with a PMT scanner, which produces a fixed logarithmic relationship between the light intensity and the output voltage.

Likely developments in CCDs include the use of mathematical techniques to filter noise and amplify the response in shadows, as well as continuing improvements in resolution and sensitivity.

Scanner Resolution

The maximum resolution of the scanner determines its ability to capture detail from the original, especially where the original is enlarged. Sampling resolution depends on a number of factors, including:

- The size of the CCD element or scanner beam.
- The size of the stepping increments of the scanning head as it travels over the original.
- The focusing accuracy and depth of field of the optical system.
- The mechanical precision of the scanner's moving parts.

Lower quality scanners do not have the mechanical precision to achieve high resolutions. Those that require three passes to capture all the color information are most likely to lose register between colors.

In a flatbed scanner, the resolution is controlled by software, and unwanted information is simply thrown away. So, for example, if a scanner has an addressable resolution of 1,200 ppi and the user selects 600 ppi for an image, the data from every other pixel is discarded.

In a drum scanner, the analyze head moves along the drum while the drum is rotating. Each revolution of the drum captures a line of data from the image. The resolution is determined by the speed of the analyze head in one direction and by the drum diameter and the way the data is digitized in the other. Input resolution is determined by the mechanical features of the scanner and is normally limited to a small number of possible resolutions.

The limit of a scanner's resolution, as determined by the scanner design, is often referred to as its **optical resolution.** If the scan resolution is not adequate (for example, if the image is being greatly enlarged or the scanner only supports low sampling resolutions) it is possible to avoid "pixelization" (individual samples becoming visible) by creating new pixels through interpolation. Interpolation can be accomplished by the scanner software during scanning or by resampling in an image-editing program. Interpolation does not add any new information to an image and tends to make fine detail appear blurred.

Scanners for single-color line work have no need to capture gray scale information, but require high resolutions. They have small CCD elements with low sensitivity. Some line-work scanners employ two or more linear arrays to achieve resolutions of 3,000 ppi and more. Line work should be scanned at the highest resolution available to prevent the visibility of scan pixels on the reproduction.

Scanner Choice

The decision to use a particular scanner will depend on a number of factors:

Design or production environments. For production environments, the emphasis will be on productivity, quality capability, and functionality in order to be able to meet customers' requirements. There will be a need to transfer files between the scanner and the desktop with standard file formats, but it will not automatically be necessary for the scanner to work internally in these formats. For design environments, the emphasis will be on ease of use, low capital costs, support for creative design work, and the ability to work in open formats that can be transferred to the desktop without time penalties or the need for additional processing.

Technical capabilities. The aspects of the scanner's technical specification to consider include:

- The scan area and the maximum enlargement.
- The bit depth available.
- The scanner D_{max}.
- The sampling resolution in general, and, more specifically, whether this is optical resolution or the resolution achieved through interpolation.

- The scan controls, including unsharp masking, color cast removal, and gradation control.
- Productivity issues, including preview and scan times, storage and buffering, interfaces with other platforms, and the degree of automation.

The volume of work. If scanning volumes are low, the productivity advantages of high-end scanners will be less relevant and can be traded against the convenience of being able to scan directly into the desktop environment without involving external suppliers.

The level of quality needed. It is important to be realistic about the output quality that can be expected from different scanners and to match this carefully to the quality requirements of the work being produced.

An RGB or a CMYK workflow. This decision will need to be taken in the context of the management of design and production generally and is discussed further in the following chapter.

Broadly, high-end scanners are appropriate to trade shops, service bureaus, and printers. Designers and publishers, as well as some printers and service bureaus, will employ mid-range desktop systems, while low-end scanners will be mainly used for visualization purposes and for work where reproduction quality is not important.

The following are advantages of drum scanners:

- High sensitivity and high D_{max}.
- High resolution.
- Low noise.
- High productivity for volume scanning.
- Accept large-format originals.
- Produce color-separated files ready for output.

The following are advantages of flatbed scanners:

- Ease of use.
- Faster scanning of single images.
- Solid-state electronics that do not need replaced or recalibrated.
- Compact construction.
- Good price/performance.
- Accept rigid originals.

The productivity advantage of the drum scanner lies in its ability to scan multiple originals simultaneously and output color-corrected images directly to disk or film without the need for further processing.

For some users, these productivity advantages are irrelevant, as the number of scans they produce does not justify the capital investment. The time involved in dealing with outside suppliers, and in transporting files and originals, can outweigh any savings made during production. The control over image reproduction that in-house scanning can bring may be a far more important consideration.

Internal Color Models

Scanners handle data internally in ways that are most efficient for the scanner hardware and software to process. The output from both CCDs and PMTs is initially an analog voltage that is digitized and then converted into a common format. On high-end systems, these formats are often proprietary and cannot be accessed directly by other applications. If this is the case, some form of translation will have to take place to convert the data into an open file format in order to link the high-end scanner with the desktop. The internal color models of scanners are based on the RGB, CMYK, or CIE color spaces.

All scanners initially capture the color information that is output from the CCDs or photomultipliers as RGB values. The RGB values are device-dependent—they relate to the way in which the individual scanner transforms light intensity into output voltages and codes them as RGB values—and if they are to be printed they must, at some point, be transformed into the device space of the printing system. Most desktop scanners do not carry out this transformation, but simply record the RGB values in a file.

High-end drum scanners usually carry out color separation as the image is scanned, translating the output voltages of the photomultipliers directly into CMYK dot values. The CMYK dot values are stored in the device space of the printing system, giving more efficient image handling but requiring that the target printing system is known at the time of scanning and the image is intended for output to one printing system at a single size and resolution.

If any of these output parameters change, the image will have to be edited or rescanned, with the potential loss of image data and of productivity.

The RGB values that are produced by a scanner are device-dependent values, but if the scanner has been **characterized** (see Chapter 14) it is possible to translate them into "normalized" RGB values or into independent CIE-based color space values. The sampled values are then device-independent and can be stored and converted to device-specific CMYK values as necessary.

Scanner Adjustments

Resolution and File Size

Scanning resolution needs to be set carefully to make sure that all wanted detail is captured without making files larger than necessary. The accepted rule in the graphic arts is that there should be two scan lines for every line of the halftone screen in the printed reproduction. For a reproduction at the same size as the original, this means that the sampling frequency should be twice the halftone screen frequency. For enlargements and reductions, the enlargement ratio is factored in as shown below:

$$\text{Sampling frequency (in ppi)} = 2 \times \text{screen frequency (in lpi)} \times \text{scaling factor}$$

For example, a picture that is to be enlarged by a factor of 1.2, and printed at 200 lpi, should be scanned at $2 \times 200 \times 1.2$, or 480, ppi.

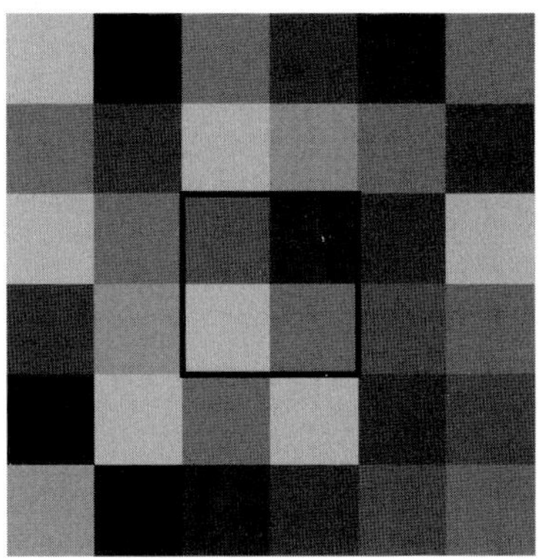

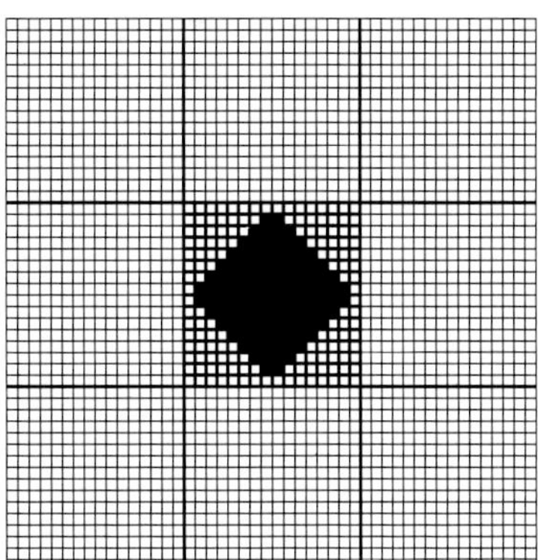

Figure 6-5. The ideal sampling frequency is twice the screen frequency of the output *(left)*. For every four sampled pixels, there will then be one halftone dot *(right)*.

This formula has been found to give optimum reproductions from all kinds of originals. Increasing the resolution above this figure gives absolutely no increase in image quality where normal halftone screens are used, and in fact may lead to oversampling effects and a loss of quality.

There are times when the requirement to make the scan resolution twice the screen ruling imposes demands that the system cannot meet; for example, when very fine screens are used or when a high magnification is required. The "twice-screen-frequency" principle is not a rigid rule, but a guide to achieving the optimum reproduction. Reducing the sampling

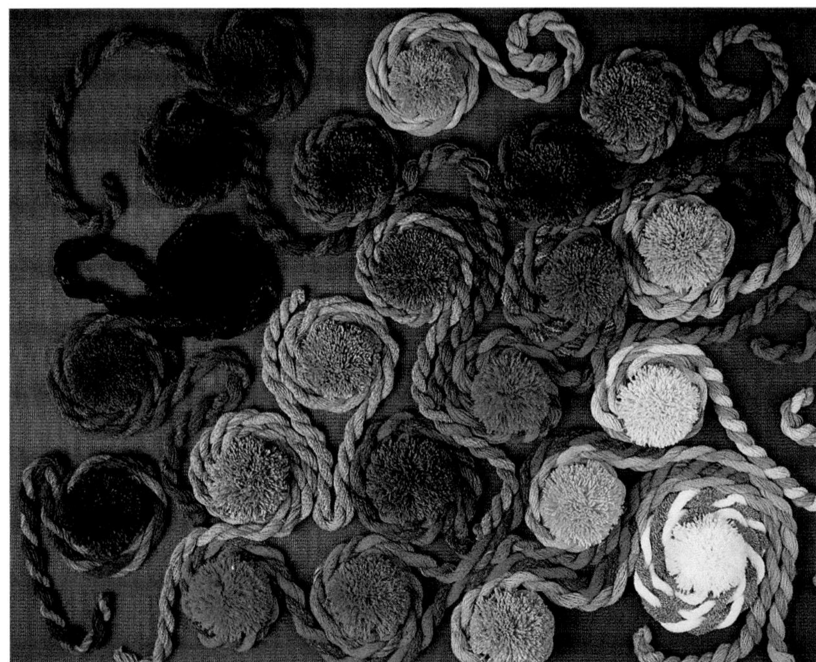

Figure 6-6.
(A) Image sampled at 300 ppi (two times the halftone screen frequency). File size is 6.3 MB.

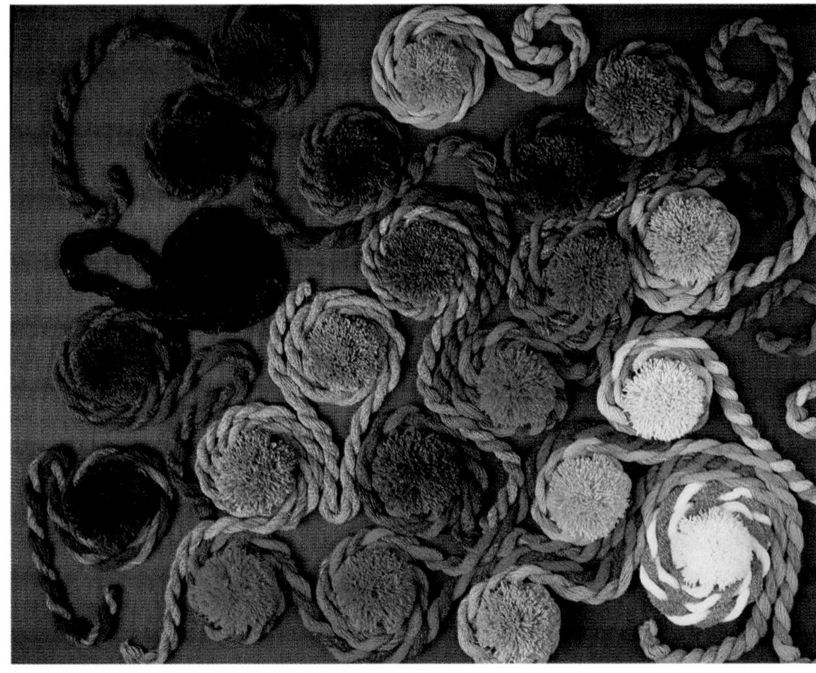

(B) Image sampled at 450 ppi (three times the halftone screen frequency). File size is 14.2 MB.

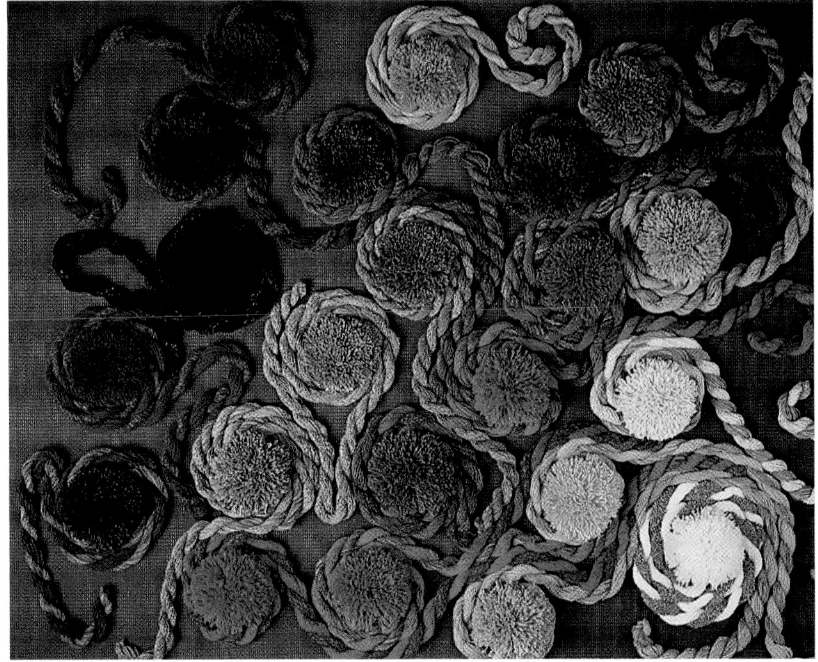

(C) Image sampled at 180 ppi (1.2 times the halftone screen frequency). File size is 2.3 MB. The reduced sampling frequency here has caused the image to begin to lose detail.

resolution causes a gradual loss of detail and sharpness, although even at 1.2× the screen frequency, the loss of quality is still quite marginal, as shown in Figure 6-6.

The use of stochastic screening in place of the conventional halftone screen allows the scan resolution to be reduced without losing any information from the original. File sizes can be reduced by approximately half without loss of quality in comparison with conventional screens. Stochastic screening technology can also make use of any extra information that is captured and the "twice-screen-frequency" principle does not apply.

Where images are destined for archiving instead of immediate use, they should be scanned at the highest resolution that is likely to be required and then resampled down to the appropriate size as necessary. Assuming a limit of 10× enlargement and a screen frequency of 200 lpi, the maximum scan resolution you are likely to need for the majority of work is 4,000 ppi.

As an image is scanned you can crop it to the size at which it will be printed. If the exact crop is not known at this time, cropping can be completed in image-editing or page-layout applications. Cropping the sampled image and discarding the unwanted image areas reduces the image file size.

Sharpness

The sensitivity of the visual mechanism to edge definition makes sharpness a priority for all images, except those that are intentionally soft or defocused. Visual perception in all animals naturally exaggerates the effect of edges, as shown below in the response of the horseshoe crab to a transition between light and dark. The result is a heightened perception of the boundaries of objects, a trait that is useful in identifying food and predators.

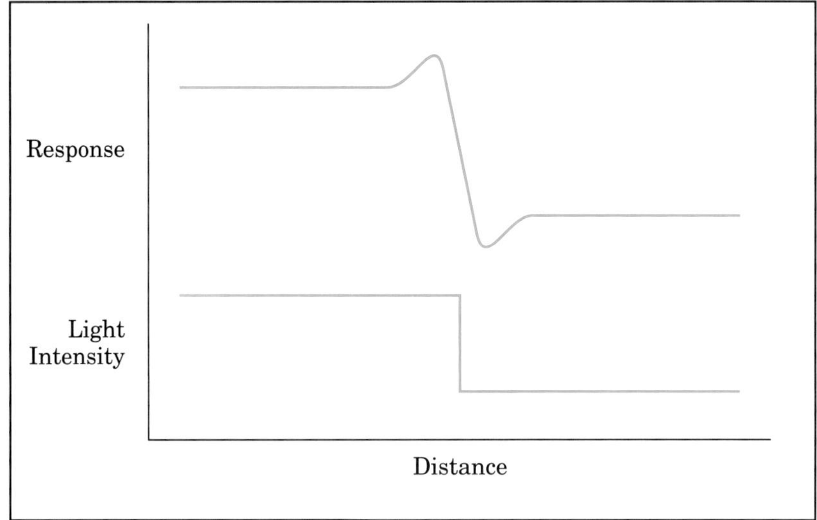

Figure 6-7.
The visual mechanism enhances the perception of edges within the visual field by altering the response to light and dark at a boundary.
From *Visual Perception* by Vicki Bruce and Patrick Green.

Electronic scanners achieve the same effect with unsharp masking (USM). On a high-end system, a slightly out-of-focus signal is captured by a separate photomultiplier and added to the sharp signal, producing the effect shown in Figure 6-8. The result is increased contrast at the boundaries between different parts of the image. Virtually all sampled images gain from sharpening in this way and it can bring out the detail in an image better than increasing the resolution.

On images captured by CCD, unsharp masking is not carried out optically but by computation. A digital file that has already been scanned has USM applied by calculating the difference between adjacent groups of pixels and increasing the contrast between them at the boundary.

Unsharp masking comes into play when there is a significant difference between two adjacent tones, but it ignores minor differences that are caused by small variations of tone within an object. Where all tonal values need to be given increased separation, a sharpening filter should be applied instead.

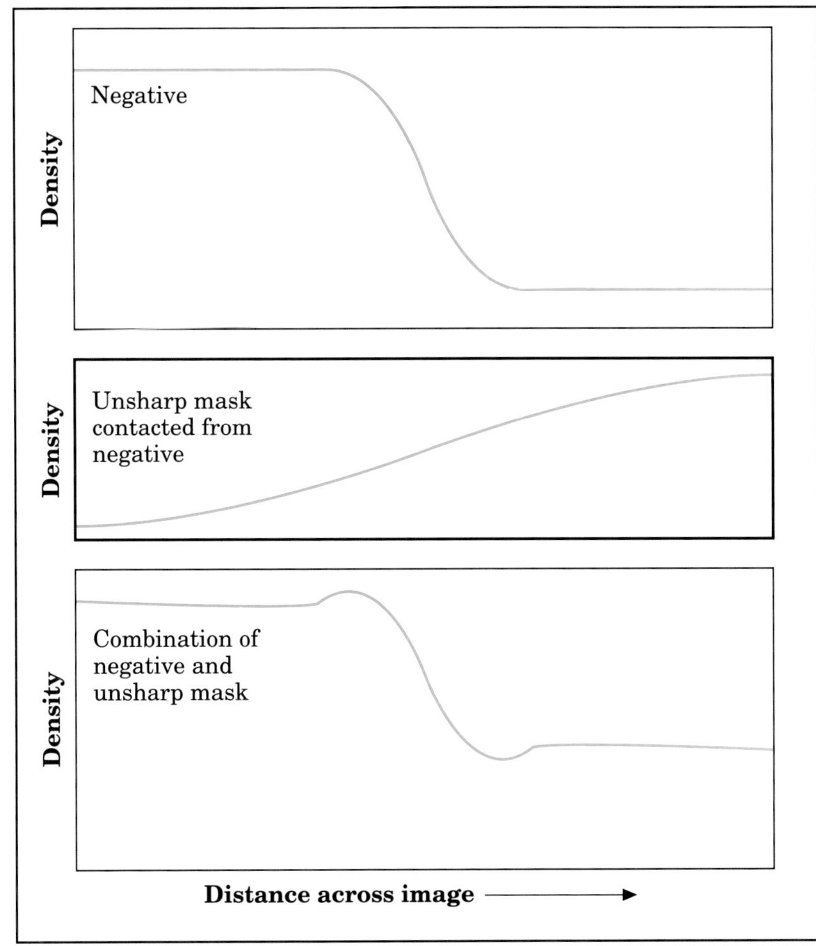

Figure 6-8.
Adding an unsharp signal that is a "negative" of the normal scan causes the definition of the edges to be enhanced in a way that is similar to the response of the eye.

Excessive use of USM can cause unwanted effects, such as random noise and the exaggeration of blemishes in flesh tones. USM settings for different originals include:

- The amount of USM to apply (the degree of contrast enhancement to apply to adjacent areas).
- The USM radius (the number of pixels on each side of the boundary to which it should be applied).
- The USM threshold (the amount of contrast difference between adjacent areas that must exist before they are recognized as an edge and USM is applied).

Unsharp masking or sharpening should ideally be applied after any scaling that is necessary. If the image is to be imported into an image editing application, apply USM after any scaling or editing and immediately prior to converting to CMYK.

Figure 6-9.
Unsharp masking makes scanned images look sharper and crisper.

Unsharpened image.

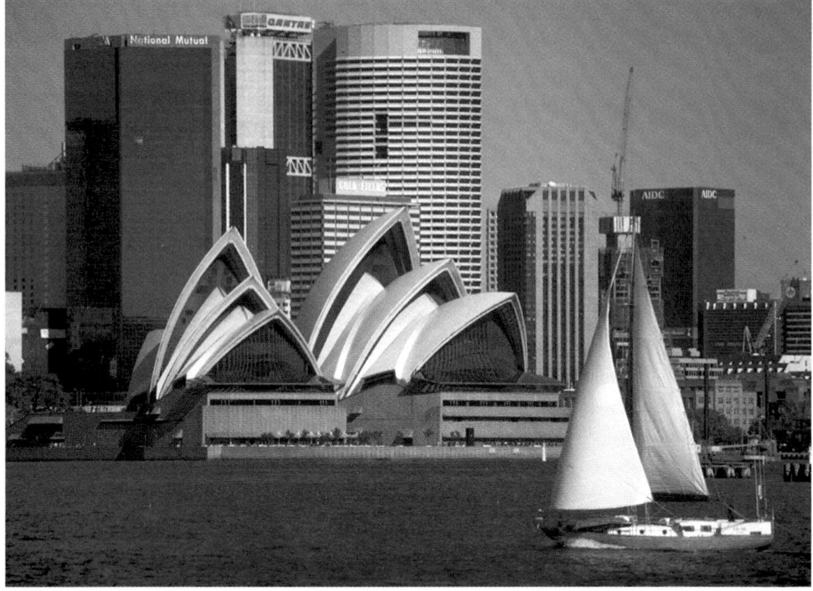

Sharpened image.

Tone Adjustment

The tone controls of a scanner have two basic functions. Firstly, they are used to set the location of the endpoints (the extremes of highlight and shadow) of the original and to control the tonal compression. Secondly, they allow the user to adjust the distribution of the intermediate tones in the original through the tonal gradation.

Both endpoints and gradation can be altered later in an image-editing package, but correct adjustment during scanning will capture more wanted detail from the original. The method used to adjust tone depends on whether the image is being captured as RGB or device-independent color, or is scanned directly into CMYK. Note that when images are not scanned directly into CMYK, the dot placement should be done at the point when the image is converted into CMYK.

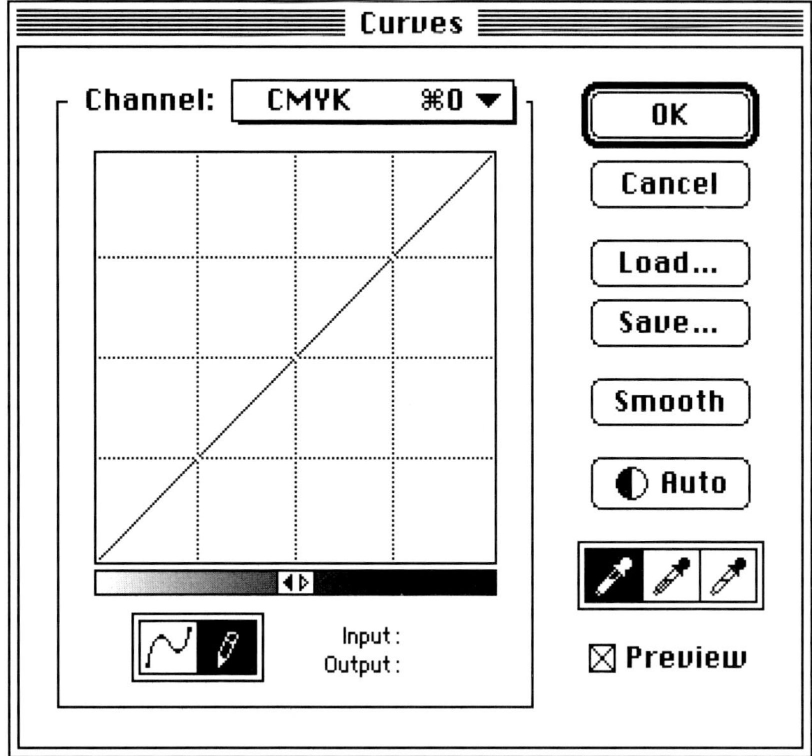

Figure 6.10. White and black points can be set in Adobe Photoshop by double-clicking on the highlight and shadow eyedroppers to set the values for the highlight and shadow dots, and then clicking on the image white point and black point. Midtones can then be adjusted to correct tonal gradation.

White point adjustment. If the image is being captured in RGB or independent color space, the white point is set to the lightest tone in the original. If there is no white in the original, the white point is set from a white patch on a photographic gray scale.

If the image is being scanned into CMYK, the white point adjustment is slightly more complicated, as the objective is to make the diffuse white point on the original correspond exactly to the smallest dot that can be printed:

- If the original has a tone that can be used as the diffuse white point, set the smallest printing dot at this point (e.g., 5% cyan, 4% magenta, 4% yellow).

- If there is no white point, use complementary colors. Set the smallest dot for cyan in a red part of the image, for magenta in a green, and for yellow in a blue.
- Alternatively, choose the lightest tone in the image and set the CMYK values by reference to the closest color in a printed tint chart.

An accurate white point setting is the most important scanning adjustment, and it ensures that there is good contrast in the reproduction, with highlight detail, specular whites where necessary, and good tonal rendering in highlights and midtones.

Setting the white point to a tone on the original with a density that is too high will cause the reproduction to look light and washed out, with a loss of highlight detail. Setting it too low, in a white that should print as a specular, will cause the reproduction to be dark and lacking contrast.

Black point adjustment. Adjusting the black point controls the way that the density range of the original is compressed into the density range that will be printed. This tonal compression will follow the pattern shown in Chapter 4 for most images, with the shadows compressed more than the highlights and midtones to accommodate the eye's greater sensitivity to highlight detail.

Correct black point adjustment ensures that the scanner is capturing only wanted detail and not wasting available gray levels by using them to record tones that will not be printed.

If the image is being scanned in RGB or independent color space, set the black point to the darkest tone in the original. If there is no black in the original, set the black point from a photographic gray scale.

If the image is being scanned in CMYK, set the darkest tone in the original to the largest printable dot, e.g. 95%. If there is no black tone in the original, use a tint chart to set CMYK values for the darkest point available.

Avoid using the black patch on the photographic gray scale (or the black border of the transparency) if there is no black in the original, as it will have the effect of setting the largest dot to a density higher than is needed, thus compressing the shadows more than is necessary.

Saturated colors are also affected by the black point setting. If it is set too high, saturation is reduced and colors look washed out. Conversely, if the black point is set too low, the color contrast of the reproduction may seem excessive.

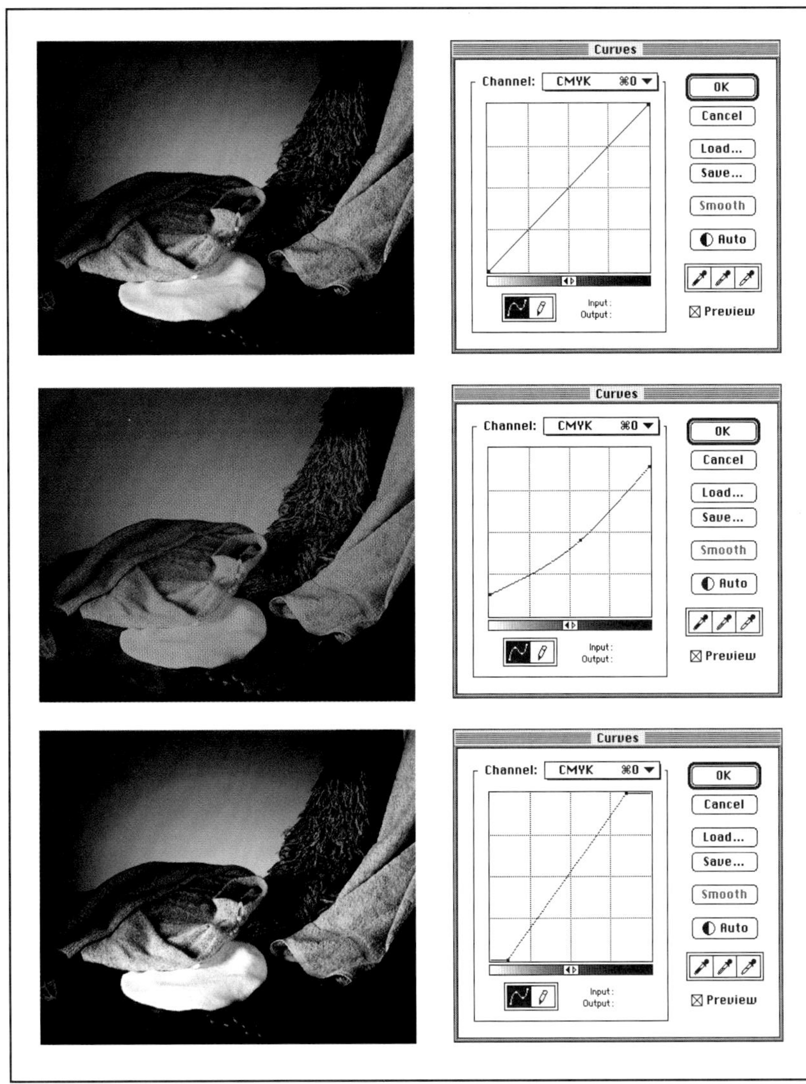

Figure 6-11. The top image, with end points set correctly, exhibits the proper tonal gradation with an excellent rendering of midtones.

Poor adjustment of end points in the middle image has produced inadequate contrast, with veiled highlights and flat shadows.

In the bottom image, poor end point adjustment has resulted in excessive contrast with bleached highlights and filled-in shadows.

The very darkest tone in the reproduction should in fact reproduce (on a sheetfed press on coated paper) as something like 90% cyan, 80% magenta, 80% yellow, and 90% black. These values will be calculated by the scanner depending on the way that values are set for black generation, gray balance, undercolor removal, and gray component replacement. For more information on these settings, see Chapter 7.

If the contrast of the original is too low, adjust the endpoints by setting the white point to a higher original density, and the black point to a lower original density.

Gradation. After the endpoints have been set, the gradation of the scan can be adjusted if necessary. The gradation adjustment can be used to control the setting of the midtones and the distribution of tones on the reproduction. It can expand the number of gray levels in a specific region of the tonal range to emphasize the interest areas of the original or to compensate for originals with unsatisfactory contrast or exposure. Typical gradation curves are shown in Figure 6-12.

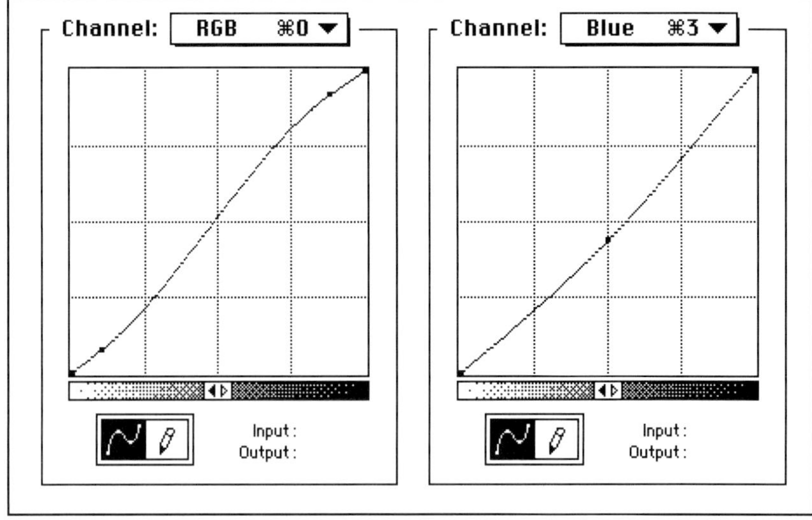

Figure 6-12. Tonal gradation can be adjusted through gradation curves, either during scanning or as a post-scan correction. The curve on the left will increase contrast, while the curve on the right will make an image less yellow (more blue).

The number of gray levels (and thus the amount of detail that is captured) can be increased in a part of the tonal range by making the gradation curve steeper in that area. That part of the density range of the original is then distributed over a wider range of gray levels in the resulting file.

The most efficient way of working with gradation curves is to store a set of basic curves (such as those shown in Figure 6-12) and call them up as needed. Adjustments can be made to a basic curve to suit the particular requirements of the original if necessary.

Color Adjustments

The majority of professional-quality transparencies can be scanned without the need for color correction. On a high-end scanner, correction can take place during scanning, but on desktop scanners color correction is normally applied after the image has been captured. However, if the original has an overall color cast, it should, if possible, be handled during scanning. If a color cast has been identified on an original, the alternatives are to ignore it; reduce it; or remove it altogether.

If the intentions of the designer are not known when the image is scanned, the cast should probably be removed if it gives an objectionable appearance to the image or has the effect of reducing the color contrast. Otherwise, it may be safer to leave it for adjustment in an image-editing application.

Color cast is removed by manipulating the red, blue, and green output of the scanner, either by controls on the scanner itself or in the controlling software. Preview scans are useful in identifying color casts, and a software densitometer can evaluate color components much more accurately than simple visual assessment, since the eye will tend to view any near-white as a neutral white.

If the cast is localized, it will not be possible to remove it during scanning without affecting the rest of the picture. It will have to be dealt with in an image-editing application, but bear in mind that adjusting local color balance can be very time-consuming.

Automating Scanner Adjustments

Traditional prepress scanners demand operators with very high levels of skill, including a familiarity with the printing processes and experience of evaluating color originals. Transferring image capture from the production arena to the domain of design and publishing involves rethinking the operating environment in which the scanner functions.

Table 6-2. Problems with originals.

Problem	Possible solution
Original artwork is too rigid to curve around drum.	• Use flatbed scanner. • Use gallery camera. • Make transparency from the artwork.
Original is too large for the scanner.	• Make a small transparency from it.
The scaling ratio is too large for the scanner.	• Make an intermediate-sized transparency.
Original has been damaged.	• Restore by pixel-editing in image editing application.

Operators can no longer be expected to have a lifetime of experience in color reproduction, and, in the design environment, the scanner has to be transformed from a production device to a tool that supports the creative process. To achieve this, the knowledge of the skilled operator has to be encoded into the controlling software of the scanner so that functions like tone adjustment and color balance are decided by built-in artificial intelligence, but with the provision for operator intervention as needed.

Preparing Originals for Scanning

Before scanning, originals should be assessed and any special requirements noted. They should be cleaned if necessary, as removing dust or marks at this stage will be more productive than pixel-editing in an image-editing application.

Transparencies should be held firmly on the drum or transparency holder so that there is no danger of the distance to the scanner optics varying. The depth of field of scanner lenses is quite small, and focus can be lost if the original is not held flat.

In most scanners, the original is held against a smooth, plastic surface. This helps the original remain flat, but can lead to the appearance of Newton's rings, an optical phenomenon that can occur when two very smooth surfaces are held tightly together. Coating the transparency or negative with mounting oil avoids the formation of Newton's rings.

Normally, a film is scanned with the emulsion up, but if it has been duplicated its orientation may now be reversed, which means that it must be "flopped" during scanning. The emulsion side looks duller than the other side, and when viewed from the emulsion side the film manufacturer's coding appears reversed. The image should read correctly from the side opposite to the emulsion (known as the "film side," the "nonemulsion" side, or the "reading side"), unless it has been flopped during duplicating.

Scanner Workflow

A color scanner is one of the most expensive pieces of prepress equipment, and most users will want to maximize their investment in it. In many instances, the economic case for employing in-house scanning instead of using external suppliers is not convincing, since scanning is a very competitive market and prices are low. Here are some key points on managing the workflow most efficiently:

- Ensure that decisions about how to handle originals are made in advance of scanning to save unnecessary rescans.

- Categorize originals into groups of similar kinds and sizes and use batch scanning where possible.
- Ensure that post-scanning operations, such as file transfer, are not workflow bottlenecks.
- Use intelligent software for adjusting tones and removing color casts in routine images.
- Provide training to scanner operators.

7 Color Separation

There are many instances in which color objects are converted from one color space to another. The term **color separation** is used to describe conversion from any color space into values for the separate CMYK colorants of a specific printing device. This is essential in order to be able to reproduce the object, either by producing films and plates for conventional printing or by sending the data directly to a digital printer.

Conversions between CIE-based color spaces use relatively simple, mainly linear algorithms with no loss of color information. Even RGB and YCC color space conversions are handled mainly by linear algorithms, and as long as information about the input characteristics is available there will be no information loss.

However, conversion to CMYK cannot be handled by such simple algorithms, and there is a real risk that color values will be significantly degraded by the conversion process.

Good color separations are an essential requirement of quality printing. They ensure that the color values of the original are accurately rendered, especially:

- Color balance.
- Color contrast.
- Saturated colors.
- Critical colors that must be matched accurately (such as memory colors, identity colors, and areas of interest).

Poor separations typically have:

- Poor color balance.
- Low contrast.
- Dull, dirty, or washed out colors.
- Color deviations in critical colors.

Although the conversion between two device-dependent color spaces can involve intensive computation, this is all handled by specialized software. Actually making color separations on the desktop is quite simple and usually involves simply choosing a new color mode from an application's menu.

The key to getting good color separations is accurate calibration of the different components of the system and using good software tools. Once a system has been set up, it only needs to be altered to accommodate changes in the source of the color values or in the target output device—when, for example, a different scanner or a different printing device or paper is used.

Figure 7-1. Good separations *(left)* have bright, clean colors. Without optimum color *(right)* a separated image loses appeal and interest.

Color Separation Principles

It is not essential to fully understand the process of conversion from one color mode to another in order to produce color separations. However, an appreciation of the methods used, and the limitations of different approaches, can be helpful in analyzing the reasons for unsatisfactory color reproduction and in developing solutions to these problems. Figure 7-2 illustrates the elementary conversion of RGB values directly to CMY. This method, supported in PostScript Level 1, involves mapping the RGB signals to a scale from 0.0 to 1.0, dividing the value of the signal by the total number of steps in the gray scale) and then applying this simple formula to find the CMY values:

$$C = 1.0 - R$$

$$M = 1.0 - G$$

$$Y = 1.0 - B$$

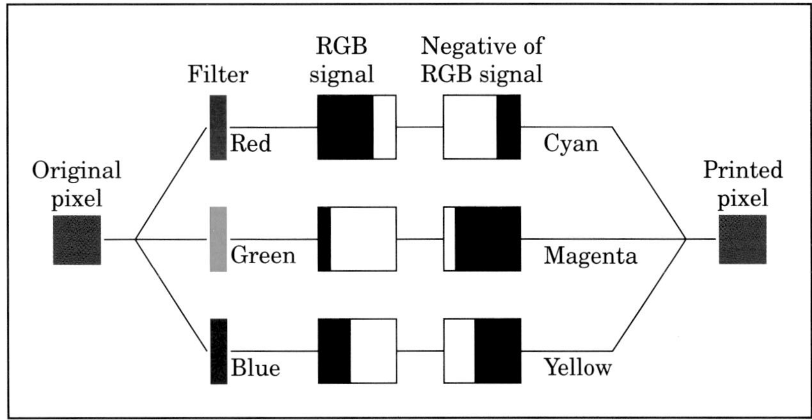

Figure 7-2. Elementary conversion of RGB to CMY. The values for cyan, magenta, and yellow are simply the negatives of the values for red, green, and blue.

For example, converting from the RGB values in Figure 7-2 gives the following CMY values:

$$C = 1.0 - 0.7 = 0.3$$

$$M = 1.0 - 0.15 = 0.85$$

$$Y = 1.0 - 0.4 = 0.6$$

The CMY values can then be remapped to the gray scale of the output (multiply by 100 and you have the CMY dot values). The black can be computed from the CMY values by establishing a logical rule that, for example, generates black whenever the values of CMY all exceed 50%. Black generation is covered in more detail later in this chapter.

This simplified approach assumes that printing inks behave in a perfectly ideal and linear way. It presumes the following:

- Cyan, magenta, and yellow inks perfectly absorb all of their complementary colors and reflect all other wavelengths.
- The inks are perfectly transparent; thus the sequence in which the colors are printed makes no difference in the color appearance of the final print.
- The response of the scanner filters to the colors in the spectrum matches that of the eye.
- Uniform increases in dot value produce a uniform increase in density. In other words, the relationship between density and dot size is linear.
- The density of a pixel where two or three colors overprint is the sum of the separate densities.
- The gamut of the original is matched by the gamut of the printing process.

Unfortunately, not one of these assumptions holds true in practice. Firstly, all these relationships are nonlinear—meaning that uniform increases in a quantity, such as dot value, do not produce uniform color changes in all regions of the tonal range. Secondly, the gamut that can be achieved in CMYK is quite limited relative to additive color systems, especially when mechanical or uncoated papers are used. Finally, the inks used have spectral properties very different from the ideal, and, as a result, a proportion of the hues that should be absorbed are reflected, and some hues that should be reflected are absorbed.

The ideal spectral reflectance of printing inks is compared with their actual reflectance in chapter 2. In effect the inks used are less pure than the ideal, as if they had been contaminated with small amounts of the other colors.

This non-ideal behavior of printing inks is the characteristic that requires the largest correction. Cyan inks are especially deficient, and it is always necessary to reduce yellow and magenta where they overprint cyan.

In the early days of color separation, correction was carried out manually by a retoucher who would hand-etch the separation films. Later, a method of color correction was devised that involved making semi-transparent masks from the separation films and using these to modify the separations. This method became popular as it was faster and more consistent than wet dot etching.

The first electronic scanners replicated the effect of the masking technique with a bank of potentiometers for the operator to adjust. With the advent of digital scanners, a computational approach became possible, and the effect of color masking was defined as a set of mathematical functions that could be used to calculate the correct dot size. A similar function was derived directly from a mathematical model of the interactions between light, ink, and paper. These two sets of functions are known as the masking equations and the Neugebauer equations.

In computing the color values of a pixel using these equations, the "ideal" equation is modified by terms that allow for the effects of some of the variables. In a simplified form, this becomes, for example:

$$C = 1.0 - R + k_1(G) + k_2(B)$$

Where k_1 and k_2 are coefficients that make an allowance for the effect of the magenta and yellow inks and the absorption of green and blue by cyan. The values for M and Y are found in the same way.

In practice, the equations end up becoming rather complex in order to convert between RGB and CMYK at all points in the color gamut. It is not feasible to compute each pixel in an image by using these equations, as it would require billions of computer instructions even for a small image, and processing would take too long. High-end scanners that use computational methods of color separation carry out the calculation just once and store the results in a color lookup table (CLUT) or separation table. When a picture is scanned, the computer just has to find the right entry in the table.

A full twenty-four-bit CLUT is still a lot to store, as it would occupy at least 67-MB and would make recalibration of the scanner a time-consuming process. Instead, a representative sample of colors is stored, and each pixel is compared to the colors in the table. If an exact match exists, the CMYK values are read, but if an exact match is not possible, the nearest value in the table is used to calculate a CMYK value by a process of interpolation. The more entries in the CLUT, the less prone to errors in interpolation the system will be. High-end scanner CLUTs typically contain 8,000 entries.

The values in the CLUT can be determined empirically rather than computationally. The empirical method, which involves measuring the colors that are output from known CMYK dot values and comparing them with the colors of the original image, is a lengthy process because of the number of colorimetric measurements required.

In practice, separation tables are often determined by a combination of empirical and computational methods, values for a small number of colors being determined empirically and the remainder of the table computed with one of the conversion algorithms. Virtually all current systems for color separation use the lookup table approach.

PostScript Level 2 supports the use of lookup tables to convert to device-dependent color and also allows gradations (or transfer functions) to be used to incorporate further nonlinear corrections after conversion.

The time taken to calculate a new lookup table can be considerable. In a trade house with a conventional high-end scanner this operation is rarely performed except as part of recalibration of the scanner to compensate for drift in the photomultipliers. The table is calculated for the relatively small number of paper types that can be accommodated by gradation corrections and the target printing device, usually a litho press operating to SWOP standards.

In a desktop production environment, however, there will probably be several different input devices, and multiple target printing devices. Because separation tables may need to be recalculated frequently, they must be small enough to make the calculation process acceptably short.

The lookup tables used in the desktop environment are smaller than those used in high-end scanners, with typically 512 or 1,024 entries. This does restrict the potential accuracy of color conversions, especially in parts of the color gamut where the eye is more sensitive to shifts in hue. However, sophisticated interpolation algorithms can at least partially overcome this limitation. Smaller lookup tables that support faster image processing can store the multiple tables needed for different devices.

Figure 7-3.
Color lookup table.

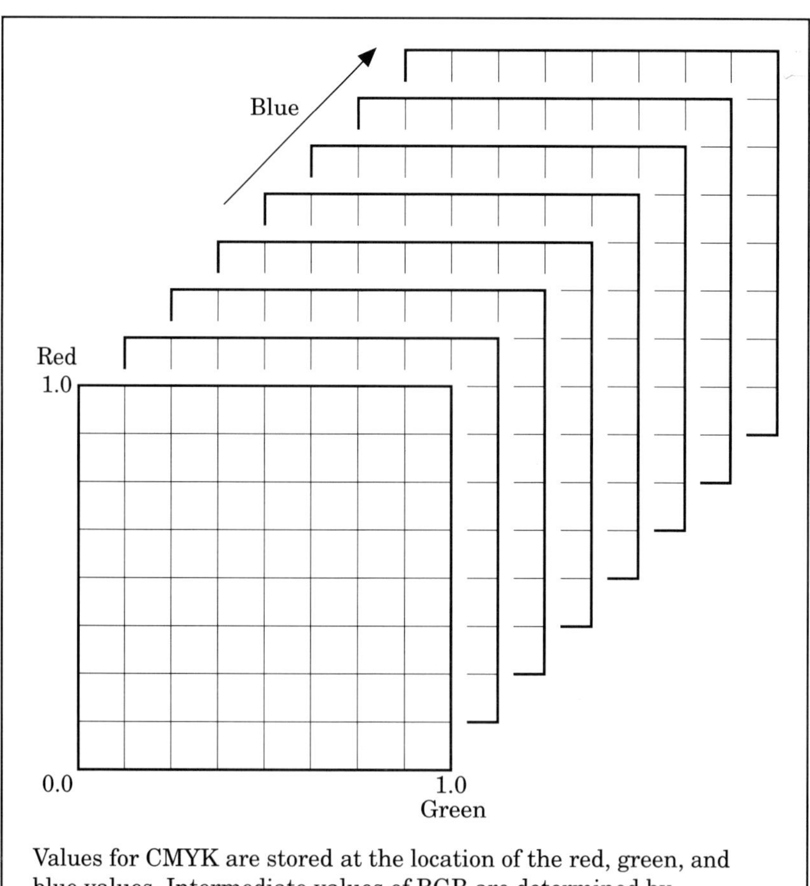

Values for CMYK are stored at the location of the red, green, and blue values. Intermediate values of RGB are determined by interpolation.

Color Separation Software for the Desktop

Two current implementations of color separation in image-editing applications demonstrate the various possible approaches.

Adobe Photoshop. Adobe Photoshop converts objects to device-independent CIELAB (which it uses as a native color model) as it opens or creates them. For conversion to CMYK, it uses a separation table that is built, using a form of the Neugebauer equations, from colorimetric values for the printed process colors. The default CIE x,y,Y values used are those for SWOP litho printing, but others can be substituted by choosing different colorants in the Printing Inks dialog box or by entering user-defined CIE values as custom values.

Black generation can be adjusted by using the Separation Setup dialog box, which allows users to set the UCR and GCR parameters that define the way the values for black are computed from the CMY values.

A new separation table is calculated whenever changes are made to the Printing Inks or Separation Setup dialog boxes. A new table can be saved as a 250-KB file for future use. The interpolation method, which is used to find color values not included in the table, is specified as a general preference for the application and not stored in the table.

Photoshop deals with the complexity of color separation by allowing the user to adjust many of the separation parameters. The default separation table produces moderately acceptable color separations for SWOP printing, but for users who want to adjust the separation parameters no distinction is made in the application between ones that should always be considered (such as adjusting the dot gain for the paper type) and those that are hardly ever altered (such as the gray balance). The consequences of applying some adjustments, such as the interpolation method, are not explained anywhere in the manual or the on-line help.

Many users find the degree of control confusing, and without considerable technical knowledge of the process find it difficult to produce optimal separations. Other users welcome the control over separation parameters and find that the power of the application is enhanced through these means.

Aldus PhotoStyler 2.0. Aldus PhotoStyler 2.0 incorporates a color management system licensed from Kodak's subsidiary KEPS. This also uses device-independent CIELAB to transform colors from one color space to another, but it handles the characterization of input and output devices differently.

Upon installing the KEPS Color Management System, the user selects the input and output devices being used from a menu. Each device has a Precision Transform file that characterizes, or **profiles,** the way in which the device produces color values in terms of the independent color space, in a manner similar to that of Adobe Photoshop. Having specified the input and output devices and defined the way their color values are converted into CIELAB, the CMS then calculates a lookup table to handle the conversion between RGB and CMYK, generating a 290-KB file. When a color image is converted from one mode to another, the CMS uses the entries in this table to find the new values for each pixel.

The KEPS Color Management System is very simple to use. All that needs to be done to make viable color separations is to specify which devices are in use when the system is configured. The CMS is completely integrated into PhotoStyler, and users cannot disable it or adjust the profiles that specify the characteristics of input and output devices, although a profile editor is available as a separate product. Manipulating images has to be done with the image-editing controls. As a result, color separations are potentially more consistent, and while a degree of control over the separation process has been lost, it is still possible to edit as needed. The KEPS CMS, also licensed by Adobe, is available as a plug-in for its Photoshop product. The concept of color management is covered in more detail in Chapter 14.

Creating Color Separations on the Desktop

The basic steps in creating color separations on the desktop are:

- Confirm that the appropriate separation table is available for the input device and the target printing process and paper type.
- Select the CMYK mode.
- Check the highlight and shadow end points and adjust if necessary.
- Save the image.

After conversion, any necessary tone and color corrections can be completed and unsharp masking applied. Individual images should always be adjusted with image-editing controls rather than by altering the separation setup. An image should not be converted back into RGB for editing, as the color values will degrade slightly each time it is converted from one color space to another.

The following are recommended color separation programs:

- For those who prefer to keep separation simple and let the software do the work, color management systems such as Efi, Cachet, KEPS CMS, and Agfa's Fototune.
- For those who want full control over color separation, SpectrePrint Pro from Pre-Press Technologies Inc. is a dedicated color separation plug-in for Photoshop that has a similar interface to a high-end scanner.

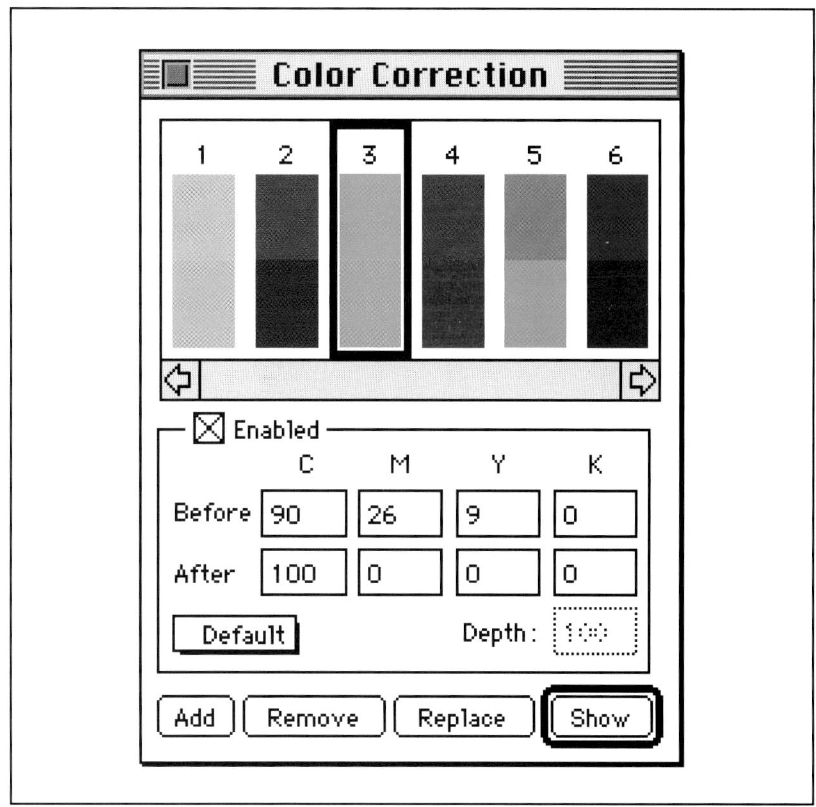

Figure 7-4. SpectrePrint Pro color separation and correction software emulates the interface on a high-end scanner.

Accelerating Color Separation

Although the processing power available in the desktop environment has increased rapidly, color separation remains a computationally intensive task. The need for acceptable table-building times restricts the size of the CLUT that can be used and the complexity of the conversion algorithms. Color separation can be accelerated by dedicated hardware boards available from a number of vendors. These include generic accelerator boards (such as digital signal processors) and dedicated ASICs (application-specific integrated circuits).

Several high-end system vendors have implemented their proprietary color conversion systems as slot-in boards for standard-platform computers and graphics workstations:

- A Scitex board that can be integrated with other color retouching tasks on a Macintosh.
- A Crosfield board for the Mac that performs color separation on data from its Celcis range of capture devices.
- A Barco board that performs bidirectional RGB-CMYK conversion to allow users of its graphic workstations to edit CMYK images and see them updated in real time on their RGB monitors.

Black Generation

The conventional printing processes cannot produce a density high enough in deep shadows by overprinting yellow, magenta, and cyan alone, so black is added to extend the density range of the ink set.

The amount of black to print in any pixel is computed from the values for cyan, magenta, and yellow. Two methods can be used:

- Conventional: Generate black when the values for CMY all exceed a certain level, such as 50%, and increase the black as the CMY total increases.
- Gray component replacement: Generate black from the amount of the complementary color present in each pixel.

Although the black printer was originally introduced to increase the density range, its potential use goes beyond this to the replacement of some of the more expensive colored inks in shadows and tertiary colors.

In the HSL model described in Chapter 3, hue is determined entirely by the balance of the primary colors. Saturation can be thought of as the amount of a primary color relative to the amount of gray, and lightness as dependent on the amount of black present. Thus both the saturation and lightness of a pixel are influenced by the amount of black or gray present.

In a color reproduction, most colors consist of various amounts of all three CMY primaries. In any one pixel, one or two of the primaries dominates and determines the pixel's hue. The remaining one or two primaries make the color duller and darker and are complementary to the dominant color. For example, in a red, magenta and yellow form the dominant component and cyan is the complementary (or tertiary) component.

Since the action of the complementary component is equivalent to adding gray to the dominant hue, the same effect can be achieved by replacing the complementary color with a percentage of black. This is the principle underlying undercolor removal and gray component replacement.

Figure 7-5. Gray component replacement.

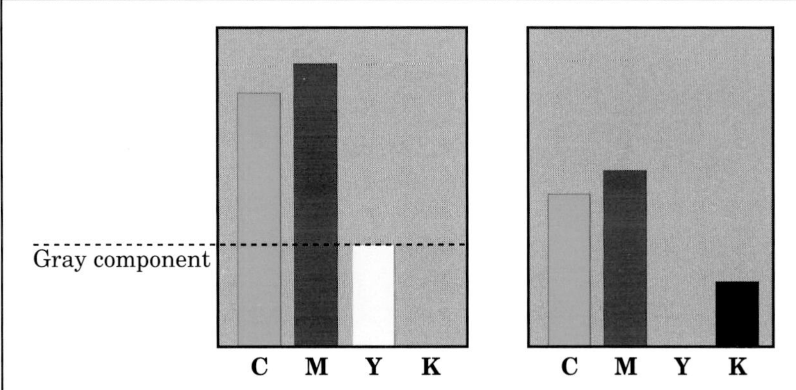

In a tertiary color, all three process colors are present. Equal amounts of the colors effectively make gray *(left)*. It is possible to remove this gray component and replace it with black *(right)*.

Undercolor Removal

Undercolor removal (UCR) involves removing primary colors in deep shadow areas and replacing them with black. The reasons for doing this are:

- To save on the amount of colored ink used.
- To avoid very high ink weights that could cause setoff and marking during printing.

Web offset is especially prone to ink smearing or marking during printing, and so printers specify a maximum ink limit that must not be exceeded. The maximum amount of ink, or **maximum overprint,** is the limit to the sum of CMYK dot values for any pixel. For example, CMYK values of 80, 82, 85, and 100% would produce a total overprint of 347%. Maximum overprints specified by web offset printers are usually around 250%, while for sheetfed printing 300–350% is acceptable. The maximum overprint is also known as the **total ink limit** or the **UCR amount.**

The effect of applying UCR is to cause the gray component in deep shadows to be replaced by black. The tone curves shown in Figure 7-6 illustrate the effect of 350% and 250% maximum overprint settings.

Applying undercolor replacement does reduce the possible contrast of a reproduction and tends to reduce shadow detail slightly. Despite this, UCR aids in the adhesion or trapping of ink layers on top of each other. UCR also makes color balance in shadows more stable during printing since using less of the process colors minimizes the hue shifts that can occur if they fluctuate.

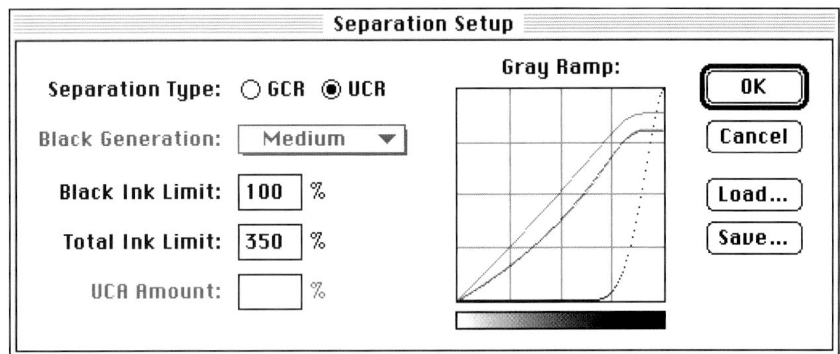

Separation Setup
Separation Type: GCR UCR
Black Generation: Medium
Black Ink Limit: 100 %
Total Ink Limit: 250 %
UCA Amount: %
Gray Ramp:
OK
Cancel
Load...
Save...

Figure 7-6.
The top UCR curve is representative of that needed for sheetfed litho. The UCR curve on the bottom is better suited for web offset.

Gray Component Replacement

While UCR is applied only in shadow areas where the total amount of color printed is high, gray component replacement (GCR) extends the removal of the gray component of CMY throughout the tonal range. Removing the gray component completely creates separations like those shown for 100% GCR in Figure 7-7. The result is a major reduction in the amount of colored ink used and increased control of color balance during printing. However, taking the gray component out completely can have some unwanted effects, such as a slight shift in the hue of some colors and a reduction of saturation and contrast. Removing 50% of the gray component has been found to give optimum results in most images. (This percentage corresponds to the default Medium GCR setting in Adobe Photoshop.)

Figure 7-7.
The three-color, black, and four-color prints for 100% and 50% gray component replacement (GCR) and normal color separations.

	100% GCR	50% GCR	Normal
Three-color			
Black			
Four-color			

The reduction in contrast can be reversed by the use of **undercolor addition (UCA),** which adds color to the deep shadows to extend the density range. UCA should be considered when contrast is especially important, but it is not necessary to apply it to the majority of images. Gray component replacement can actually improve color saturation, especially in deeply saturated colors, if the dominant colors are not reduced too much.

Unfortunately, the algorithms used in most applications reduce the dominant color along with the complementary, and, as a result, saturated colors and deep colors are diminished. Using UCA makes the desaturation of deep colors slightly worse.

Heavy amounts of GCR produce color separations that are unfamiliar to many litho printers, who may then find it difficult to judge the color values. Using such separations also requires careful consideration of the printing sequence, since the heavy black plate should ideally be moved from its usual position on the first unit to a later unit. In other sectors of the graphic arts, such as flexographic printing, GCR has become the norm since it allows the printer to improve color quality.

The more GCR is applied, the more critical the control of the black printer becomes, and the more likely it is that any small fluctuation in ink density or dot gain will have a significant effect on the lightness of the reproduction.

In pages that contain a range of images, three-color tints are notoriously difficult to match because of the conflicting inking priorities. Replacing the gray component of the tint completely and reducing the number of colors to two plus black (using the GCR principle) creates a much more consistent reproduction.

When selecting PANTONE MATCHING SYSTEM colors for a CMYK object, the PANTONE recommended CMYK simulations are mostly two colors plus black and rarely include a third process color. Naturally, the image must be in the CMYK mode for the simulated PANTONE colors to be retained, as they will be changed when the object is converted from RGB to CMYK and the black generation settings specified in the separation setup are applied.

Gray Balance

After tone reproduction, gray balance is the most important aspect of color separation. **Gray balance** assures correct color balance upon image capture or conversion from one

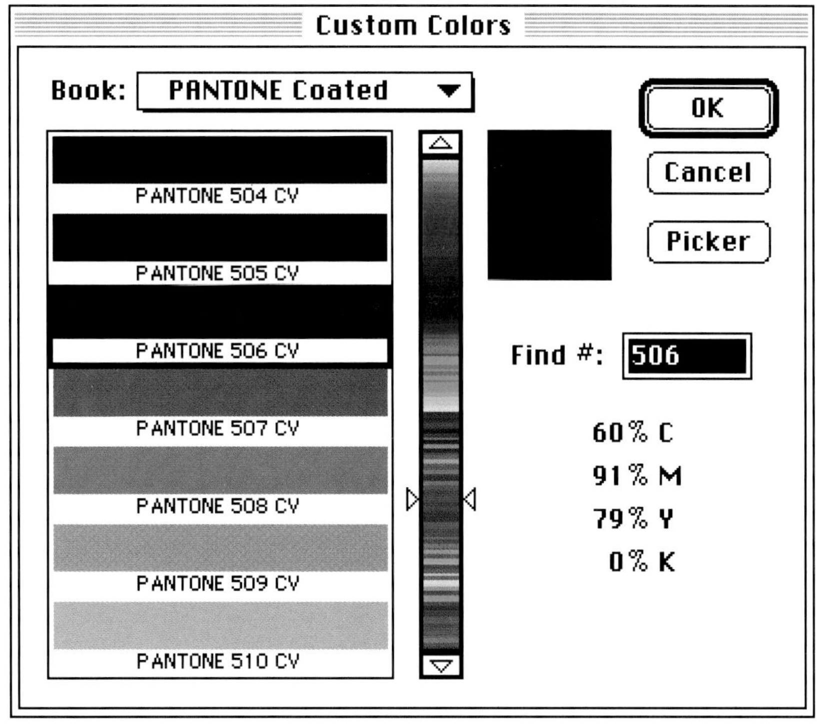

Figure 7-8. Specifying GCR tints. Most PANTONE MATCHING SYSTEM colors are automatically converted to CMYK with no more than two process colors, plus black, if necessary. This helps the printer to match the color more accurately. A small number of PANTONE colors are converted to four-color tints, and if possible, these should be avoided or changed to GCR tints.

color space to another. It is especially important in conversion to CMYK, where the non-ideal spectral behavior of the printing inks must be accommodated.

If a neutral gray on the original is separated according to the simple model described at the beginning of the chapter, the color-separation result is equal CMY dot values. The unwanted absorption of light in the blue and green regions of the spectrum by cyan ink results in a shortage of blue-green reflection and thus a shift towards red. This problem is dealt with by reducing the red component (i.e., reducing the magenta dot values and yellow dot values) wherever cyan is printed.

If gray balance is incorrect, the color balance of the reproduction will seem to have a cast. If the red component has not been reduced enough, the reproduction will appear to be too warm, and the blues and greens will be desaturated. Similarly, excessive reduction of the red component will result in a cool appearance and desaturation of reds and greens.

Neutral gray is the best part of the color gamut to use to analyze color balance for two main reasons:

- Neutral gray lies at the center of the color wheel and changes made at this point affect colors throughout the gamut equally.
- Neutral gray is the color to which the eye has the greatest sensitivity, and small changes in hue can be detected that otherwise would not be apparent in a more saturated color.

Figure 7-9.
The top image illustrates proper gray balance.

In this image, poor gray balance has caused a color cast to appear throughout.

Black is not included in gray balance evaluation because it makes no contribution to the hue of a color or to the color balance of a reproduction.

The aim of calibrating gray balance is to produce a gradation curve or transfer function that shows how the magenta and yellow are to be reduced where they overprint cyan at each step in the tonal range. Gray balance should be adjusted when the color separation setup is calibrated for a particular combination of input (scanner, digital camera, or screen design) and output (printing inks, substrates, and printing process). In addition to the basic characterization of input devices and printing colorants, gray balance adjustment can also be useful for printing off-white or colored papers or when changing the sequence in which colors are printed.

Gray balance can be adjusted either as a gradation correction or a gamma correction. The following procedure, which is described in more detail on the CD accompanying this book, can be used to make gray balance gamma correction or gradation curves for printing inks:

1. Print the CMYK gray balance test element from the CD.
2. Evaluate the printed test element under standard viewing conditions, choosing the most neutral patches.
3. Set up the gamma correction or gradation curves for cyan, magenta, and yellow according to the patches selected.

This procedure can be used to make a gray balance correction for scanner input:

1. Scan a neutral gray scale, such as the one at the bottom of the IT8 test image.
2. Use scanner software or an image editing application to adjust it so that the values for red, green, and blue are equal in all the gray patches. Check the values with the software densitometer.

There is no need to alter the gray balance setup except when the system is being calibrated. Color balance in individual images should be achieved by using image-editing controls rather than by altering the gray balance setup.

In Adobe Photoshop, the settings for gray balance, UCR, and GCR are shown in the Separation setup dialog box. Gray balance adjustment is carried out in the Printing Inks setup dialog box.

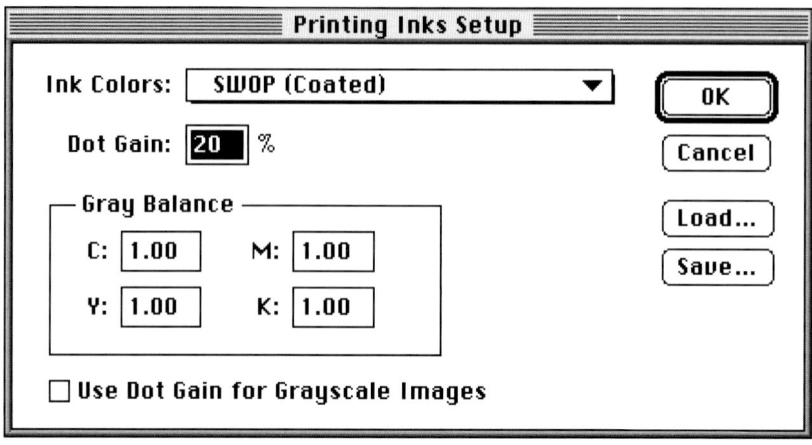

Figure 7-10. The gray balance adjustment in Adobe Photoshop.

Color Separation Workflow

It is important to consider the point at which an image should be converted to CMYK. Conversion can take place at any time from initial capture through final output, according to the working preferences and the technology available. The basic possibilities are:

- Convert to CMYK immediately after scanning and perform any edits on the CMYK file.
- Scan into RGB and edit the RGB file, converting to CMYK immediately prior to output.
- Scan into RGB and include the RGB file in the page sent to the output device, allowing the conversion to take place in the RIP.

All three methods are perfectly feasible, and current desktop separation software makes it possible for conversion to take place at any point in the production process without compromising quality. The advantage of immediate conversion to CMYK on a high-end scanner is that powerful separation routines are available. On the other hand, converting as late as possible keeps image data in a more device-independent color space and makes it possible to use PostScript color processing in the RIP.

Because tints and other graphic elements are usually created in CMYK, it is usually preferable to keep page data in CMYK even when sampled images are in RGB. Conversion to CMYK is a somewhat arbitrary process, and it is extremely important that it is performed only once on any color object. Repeated conversions between device-specific CMYK values and other color spaces will progressively degrade the color values of the separation. Conversion from

CMYK will also change any specified CMYK tint values, often altering the tints specified in two process colors to three or even four colors.

Beyond Four-Color Separations

In Chapter 3 reference was made to the use of additional colors beyond the basic subtractive primaries cyan, magenta, and yellow, plus black. The reason for using additional colors is to extend the gamut available with CMY, which is especially deficient in the orange-warm red, green, and blue-violet regions.

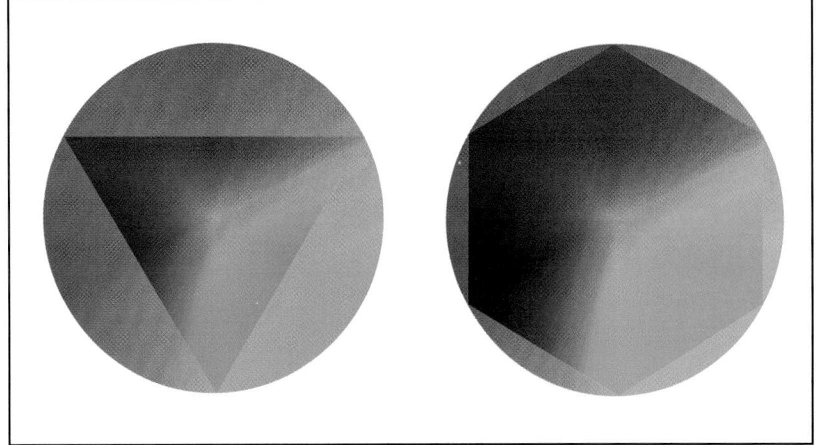

Figure 7-11.
The color wheel on the left illustrates that the gamut available using the process colors cyan, magenta, and yellow is limited in some regions of the spectrum. The color wheel on the right shows how the gamut can be enlarged by adding colors to the primary ink set.

There has been considerable interest in extending this concept further, using up to three additional colors to make a much larger color gamut available. Using more than three process colors in this way is known as applying **extra-trinary color.**

The different possibilities include:

- Color substitution.
- Bump plates.
- Touch plates.
- A larger set of primary colors.
- Custom palettes.

Color substitution is widely used in packaging. The job is printed with four colors, but one or more of the standard set of primaries is replaced with colors that are a closer match to the interest areas in the original. The dot values of the other colors are adjusted accordingly. Barco's InkSwitch System performs color substitution for any of the special colors selected.

Bump plates add additional cyan, magenta, and yellow plates to the four-color set. This increases the range of densities possible with the standard process set. Crosfield's HyperColor software produces color separations for bump plates, analyzing the original to determine where to add the extra layer of color. The first layer prints as a solid in overprinted areas so there is no screen clash between the two layers.

Touch plates are created by adding one or more special colors to the CMYK set to emphasize areas of interest or match specific identity colors within the original. Several software plug-ins are available to create touch plates, including TransCal's HiFi ColorSeps.

Additional primary colors can be used to extend the process set from four to six or seven colors. Many organizations have developed extra-trinary colorant sets, including Scitex (red, green, and blue), Linotype Hell and others (orange, green, and violet or blue-violet), and PANTONE (orange and green).

PANTONE's Hexachrome System is a six-color set that modifies the existing cyan, magenta, and yellow colorants in addition to adding two new colors. The use of six instead of seven colors makes it possible to take advantage of the many existing six-color presses that print all of the colors in a single pass. The Hexachrome System is designed to make close matches possible with 90% of the PANTONE MATCHING SYSTEM colors, in addition to extending the process gamut. Hexachrome color separations can be created in PANTONE's POCE (PANTONE Open Color Environment) and Kodak's PrecisionColor Management System.

Custom palettes are in effect an extension of touch plates. Multiple extra colors (including special colors, metallics, and fluorescents) are chosen according to the specific requirements of the original and added to the process set. TransCal's HiFi ColorSeps supports the creation of up to eighteen colors. Creating a custom palette allows the color reproduction of an original to be optimized, but is only feasible in printed pieces, such as packages or posters, that do not include a range of different illustrations.

To add additional colors to the process set, the separation software has to use a different color lookup table, and the quality of the resulting color separation is very much dependent on the lookup tables used. Color substitution, touch plates, and custom palettes require a new separation table for every set of colors chosen, while systems based on standardized colorant sets utilize re-usable separation tables. Color separations with more than four colors are normally saved as DCS-2 files for import into page-makeup programs.

Additional colors should be created during color separation when a file is converted from RGB or CIE-based colors to the colors of the printing process. Adding extra colors to a CMYK file will risk distorting the color values.

Screen clashes (moiré patterns) are a potential problem with extra-trinary colors. Only three colors can be accommodated at the ideal screen angle separation of 30°, and moiré becomes more noticeable with the use of additional colors. The complementary color in each area should be removed (by using high GCR settings for black generation) if conventional halftone screens are used. Because frequency-modulated screening removes the possibility of moiré altogether, it is the preferred method of halftoning when more than four colors are printed. Alternatively, it is possible to use high screen frequencies (over 200 lpi) with some variation between the screen frequencies of the individual colors.

Cost is an important factor in evaluating which colors to use on which jobs. Jobs with extra-trinary colors need a plate for each additional color and must be run on a multicolor press with seven units—four for CMYK plus three for the extra-trinary colors, or they must be printed in two or more passes through the press. Since this can add significantly to the cost of production, careful judgment is needed to establish which jobs will benefit from the additional colors. In many jobs, it is possible to enhance the areas of interest with just one or two extra colors.

It is also feasible to enlarge the available color gamut by using CMY inks with a greater spectral purity. Such inks would be more costly to produce, but the cost should be weighed against the expense of printing additional colors.

Not all printing processes support the use of more than four colors. Many printing presses, such as webs for publication printing and digital color presses, are restricted to four printing units. As a result the use of extra colors is realistically limited to jobs produced by sheetfed litho, screen printing, and those digital printing systems that can be fitted with extra printing units, such as the Indigo E-Print.

Similarly, proofing for colors outside the normal process set can be difficult, since many proofing systems are based on the use of CMYK only. Among the alternative possibilities are:

- Digital proofs using the Indigo E-Print.
- Cromalin prepress proofs that support the use of PANTONE colorants.
- Press proofs using the inks specified for the final job.

Color Correction

Color correction may be necessary for the following reasons:

- To correct for the characteristics of the input device.
- To correct for the characteristics of the printing process, including the inks and paper used.
- To correct for a poor original.
- To apply customer preferences to an image.

Correction for the input device and the printing process is normally incorporated into the color lookup table used for conversion to CMYK. Device profiles are increasingly being used to create a portable definition of characteristics that can be used in building lookup tables. However, it is occasionally necessary to apply additional color corrections—for example, many Photo CD users find it necessary to remove a slight yellow cast from the scan and increase the contrast.

Most professional transparencies require no correction, but sometimes the only originals that are available for a given job have defects in color balance. Customer preferences are a more common reason for alterations to color balance, for example to ensure the acceptable reproduction of skin tones or to increase the brightness or color contrast within the image.

Color corrections can be applied to an entire image or to selected areas or colors within the image before or after conversion to CMYK. Adjusting gradation curves for the individual colors gives the greatest degree of control, although simpler controls are also provided in many image-editing applications, such as the Variations option in Adobe Photoshop.

Image-editing applications offer a wide variety of methods of selecting and adjusting different parts of an image. Some corrections are easiest to perform on the individual color components, while for others it may be useful to convert the image to the HSL mode and work on the hue, saturation, and lightness channels independently.

8 Color Systems

Underpinning the revolution in digital color is the huge increase in performance and affordability of the computers used. Today's desktop machine is as powerful as the university mainframe of twenty years ago and has far superior color display capabilities.

Nevertheless, the demands imposed by color DTP and color prepress in the graphic arts stretch even the most powerful desktop system to the limit. Large files and intensive computations are the order of the day: a color page can consume 100 MB of memory and contain 10 million or more individual pixels all requiring frequent recalculations. Heavy demands are also placed on color displays, as every time the color values of image pixels are changed they must be converted to RGB signals and displayed on screen. Users have high expectations for the color fidelity of the screen image and expect to make critical color judgments on the basis of what they see.

Thus the two key requirements that graphic arts users have for their systems are fast and efficient processing of color images and fast and accurate renderings of color on displays. Powerful, well-designed computer systems in which all the elements function together smoothly without bottlenecks are needed to deliver these requirements.

A computer system has both hardware and software components. The basic hardware building blocks of a computer system are:

- The processor.
- The system memory.
- The display.
- Mass-storage devices.
- Other subsystems and peripherals.

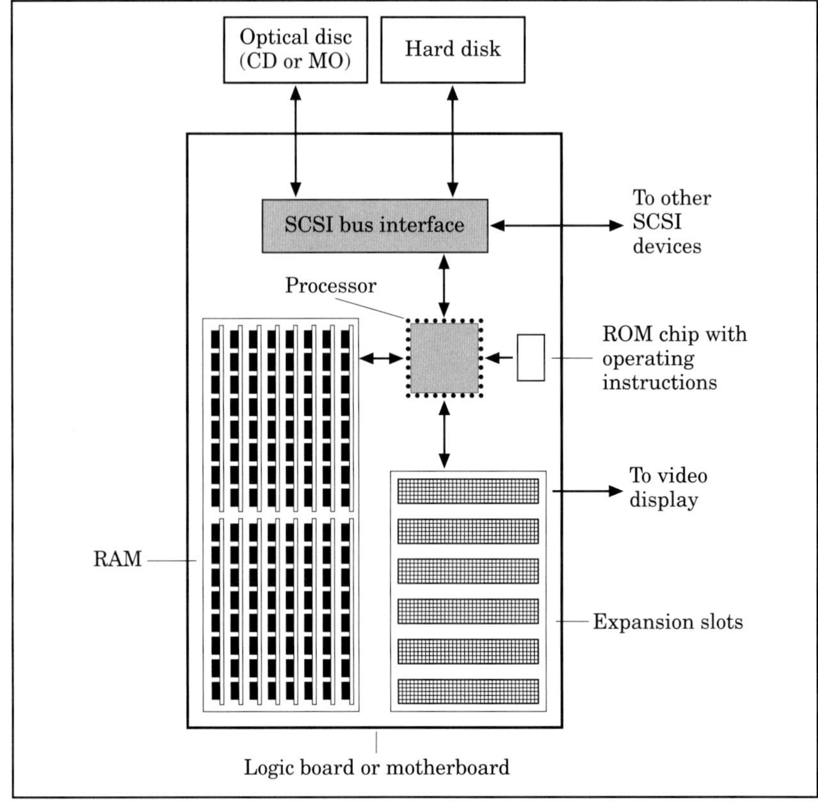

Figure 8-1. Basic elements of a desktop computer system. On a PC, the SCSI interface is on a slot-in card.

The **processor** is the heart of the system, executing the instructions sent by the application. Its architecture controls the way in which different parts of the system communicate and determines the platform's speed, memory limits, and other constraints. The processor is in constant communication with the **memory,** which holds application code, files in current use, and operating-system resources.

The main software components are:

- The operating system.
- The user interface.
- The application.

The **operating system** is responsible for executing the instructions of the user **application** and the control of the hardware resources. The operating system and the **user interface** are increasingly integrated together as a single set of routines that handle interaction among the user, the host computer, and the application.

All the platforms used in the graphic arts communicate with the user through a **graphical user interface (GUI)** that allows interaction with the system by direct manipulation of objects, such as icons and menus, instead of typing commands at a **command-line interface (CLI).** Graphical interfaces are easier to learn and more intuitive in use, but do impose a processor and memory overhead on the system. Some tasks, such as batch processing of files, can be carried out more efficiently from a command-line interface.

While the hardware resources are provided by the computer platform, it is the software application that embodies subject-specific knowledge and expertise and is responsible for the optimal use of the resources available. Software is evolving at a faster rate than hardware and is viewed by many as a consumable that needs to be renewed at regular intervals.

A computer system is not simply a static set of building blocks, but is actually in a state of continuous development. As the power of computer systems continually increases, it is important that users are able to exploit the additional speed and functionality that become available. The hardware platform should provide a clear upgrade path and evolve in response to user needs as painlessly as possible.

Platforms

The main computer platforms used in the graphic arts are:

- Desktop (or personal) systems—the Apple Mac and the IBM-PC and its compatibles.
- Workstations—such as the Sun SparcStation and the Silicon Indigo.
- Proprietary high-end systems.

The Apple Macintosh was an essential part of the desktop publishing revolution and continues to dominate graphic arts design and prepress, largely due to its user interface and the availability of applications and interfaces to key peripherals such as color scanners and output devices.

The IBM-compatible, more widely used in business applications outside of the graphic arts, became capable of running graphics applications with the development of Windows 3.1. The main advantage of the PC has been eroded by the falling prices of Macs, but it is used by a significant minority of designers and publishers. The PC is also widely used by trade shops and printers as a front-end to high-resolution devices, such as imagesetters.

For large volumes of color work, interaction with RIPs and OPI servers, and particularly for applications where speed is critical, such as high-resolution color retouching, the workstations offer a significant increase in performance. The major applications used in page layout and image editing tend to be developed for both desktop and workstation platforms.

In the PostScript environment, proprietary systems have been largely eclipsed, since the importance of having a standard platform that can run a range of applications outweighs the ability to optimize hardware resources for specific tasks.

Processors

Processor speed, usually measured in MIPS (million instructions per second), ranges from a few MIPS on desktop systems up to supercomputer speeds of several hundred MIPS on the most powerful workstations.

The architecture of both PC and Mac platforms, originally designed for much lower speed and memory requirements, places some limits on the future upgrade routes possible. It is likely that most graphic arts users will eventually migrate to a workstation-type architecture, either a PowerPC or one of the Unix-based systems such as Indigo or Sun. These systems are based on a **RISC (Reduced Instruction Set Computing)** processor design, which uses a smaller number of simple basic instructions as the building blocks of computation. RISC architectures are capable of faster execution, although they need more memory than the **CISC (Complex Instruction Set Computing)** architecture utilized in the PC and the Mac.

One of the features of RISC architecture is the ability to execute more than one instruction for each clock cycle through the use of **"pipelining"** (moving instructions into fetch and decode stages while the preceding instructions are being executed) and **"superscalar"** (multiple pipeline) designs. Both the Motorola 680x0 processor on the Mac and the Intel 80x86 processor on the PC are increasingly incorporating these aspects of RISC architectures.

The classical Von Neumann architecture, still the basis of desktop systems, has a single processor handling all aspects of computation. However, in more powerful systems, it is being replaced by distributed architectures in which multiple processors work in parallel to handle different parts of the computation task.

The speed of a computer system can also be enhanced by delegating some processing tasks to specialized subsystems. Some examples of such subsystems follow.

Video graphics. High-resolution color images and graphics place heavy demands on the processor to calculate screen updates during editing. The traffic generated by screen updates also slows communications between other parts of the system. Much of this load can be kept off the processor by using dedicated graphics subsystems. Video boards can handle the processing involved, and (on the PC) local bus systems ensure that screen redraws bypass the main system bus.

Application-specific integrated circuits (ASICs). These are "slot-in" boards that carry out a specific function in conjunction with the software on the host computer. Operations that make heavy demands on the processor to carry out repetitive calculations, such as image retouching, halftoning, and color conversion, can be greatly accelerated if they are implemented in silicon instead of in software. This is especially true if they have their own memory resources or are able to access main memory directly. Adobe's PixelBurst coprocessor, for example, executes the high-speed rendering of PostScript data with screened images processed at up to 100 million pixels per second.

Since ASICs are dedicated to specific tasks, their life spans tend to match that of their associated applications. The alternative to using an ASIC is to improve processor performance, either with a digital signal processor or multiple processors working in parallel.

Digital signal processors. A digital signal processor (DSP) is an add-in board that handles repetitive arithmetic operations at very high speeds. It is very useful for many image-editing operations. Unlike ASICs, which are hard-wired in silicon to accelerate a specific set of instructions, DSPs can be programmed to carry out a wide range of functions and can work with several applications concurrently. A DSP yields a performance similar to using two processors working in parallel.

The PowerPC processor incorporates the arithmetic operations of signal processing, but since these operations and many other tasks must share this processor, it does not have the same performance capabilities as a dedicated DSP working alongside a processor.

The processor and the operating system design are closely integrated, and while it is possible to emulate an operating system in order to run applications on different platforms, there is always a heavy performance price to pay unless an efficient silicon-based method of translating emulated instructions into native instructions is implemented.

RAM

Random-access memory (RAM), usually known simply as "memory," stores the operating system, application programs, and data files that are needed by the processor. Only part of a large application's code is stored in RAM during program execution. The rest remains on the hard disk until it is needed. Many systems make use of **virtual memory,** or "scratch disk" space, on the hard disk designated for RAM overflow. Image files that are being edited are also held in RAM, together with the last unsaved version to allow the application to "undo" any changes. To hold the current image in RAM, together with one level of "undo" and space for edits, available memory needs to be three or more times larger than the size of the image. It is possible to use virtual memory to hold part of the image on the hard disk, but this is not recommended as it causes processing to slow down as the image is read from and written to the much slower hard disk.

On systems where only low-resolution images are being loaded into memory, the amount of memory needed can be as little as 8 MB. Where high-resolution images are being edited, the memory requirements are much higher.

Organizations that handle large volumes of high-resolution images will probably have 128–256 MB of memory installed, but there will always be a need for more memory. The typical 24-bit image of today, with a CMYK file size of perhaps 20 MB, requires at least 60 MB of available memory for efficient processing. The digital image of tomorrow, possibly sampled at twelve or even sixteen bits per color, could produce a file of 40 MB for the same output size, demanding a minimum of 120 MB of RAM. Higher sampling resolutions for better image resolution (with frequency-modulated screening to overcome the limits of the conventional halftone process) would push the demand for memory even higher.

Video

Monitors used in the graphic arts have cathode-ray tube (CRT) displays. Three electron guns (one for each color) scan the display screen and selectively fire electrons at the screen, causing the colored phosphors to emit light.

The display image is built up by the electron guns repeatedly scanning across the screen. The **dot pitch** (the size of one screen pixel) of the monitor is determined by the width of the raster scan line and the spacing of the shadow mask. The intensity of the emission from each pixel is controlled by the exact voltage potential between the electron gun and the screen. A **digital-to-analog converter (DAC)** in the host computer converts the digital values used to describe the pixel into the analog voltages needed to create the display.

The following important display properties are determined by the graphics board and the video driver:

Addressable resolution. The number of pixels that can be displayed on screen depends on the dot pitch and on the amount of video memory available. Display resolution is also determined by the spot size of the electron beam and any light scattering that occurs.

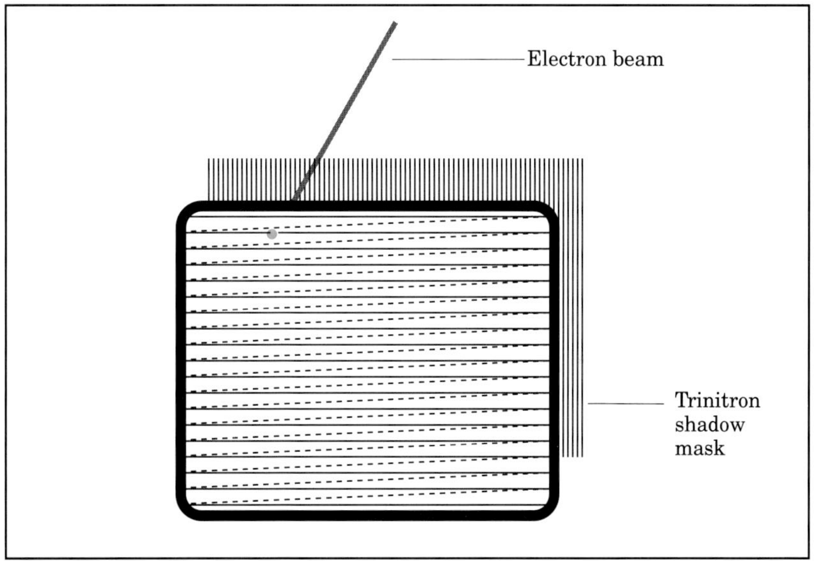

Figure 8-2.
The video display. The vertical sync rate is the number of times per second that the whole display is scanned and the beam returns to the start again. The horizontal sync rate is the number of times per second that the beam makes one horizontal scan of the screen.

Color depth. To display twenty-four-bit color, the DAC must support eight bits per color and the video board in the host computer needs to have three bytes of memory available for each screen pixel in the display. Alternatives are sixteen-bit (65,536 colors) and eight-bit (256 colors). Much is made of the importance of twenty-four-bit color, although, in practice, a sixteen-bit display is almost indistinguishable from a twenty-four-bit display and is a good compromise for users who find the accelerated twenty-four-bit color boards too expensive.

An eight-bit system displays a twenty-four-bit image by dithering the available colors. If the image is intended for display only, a better rendering can be achieved by converting the image to an eight-bit index color image. If the conversion to eight bits is completed adaptively, an acceptable screen display can be generated. A sixteen-bit system displays a twenty-four-bit image by converting each pixel to the closest value available. In this case, no dither pattern is visible.

Refresh rate. If the rate at which the electron beam repeats the raster scan of the display (i.e., the refresh rate) is too low, the screen will appear to flicker. A refresh rate of seventy cycles per second (70 Hz) is the minimum for flicker-free screens, although even at 80–90 Hz a degree of flicker can be apparent. Flicker becomes more noticeable at higher brightness settings and can also be a result of a strobing effect from fluorescent room lighting.

Interlacing. Early monitor designs were based on TV standards, in which alternate rows of pixels are scanned in turn. This is acceptable in moving images but results in screen flicker in static images. Noninterlaced displays are normally used in the graphic arts, although, in some systems, the highest refresh rates and addressable resolutions are achieved by interlacing the display.

Graphics Boards

Since a color monitor is an analog device, the colors it can display vary continuously between the minimum and maximum luminance levels for each color. The constraints on addressability and color depth are the limitations of the graphics board and the driver software responsible for converting the digital image to analog voltages, rather than the monitor itself. A good graphics board will utilize the monitor to the best effect, speeding up screen redraws and enabling more accurate color judgments to be made.

The three types of graphics boards are:

- Standard boards in which all processing is carried out on the host computer, the board simply transforming the pixel values to analog signals and passing them to the monitor.
- Accelerator boards that have built-in basic graphics operations and drawing primitives.
- Graphics coprocessors that store graphic objects and instructions and calculate the way in which graphics commands from the host computer are to be executed.

Accelerator boards enhance the display speed considerably, but graphics coprocessors are a better solution as they reduce the demands made on the host computer's resources.

Most graphics boards support user-selectable color depth and resolution within the range supported by the amount of video memory available. Expanding color depth and resolution increases the amount of computation needed, and thus brings about a drop in performance unless the extra processing is carried out entirely by a fast graphics board.

Display Factors

The apparent brightness and contrast of the display is very subjective. The eye adapts to the overall amount of light available, and as ambient illumination declines the display appears brighter. Room illumination should be as consistent as possible, and natural daylight must not be allowed to fall directly on the screen. Where critical color judgments are made, the monitor surroundings must be considered very carefully and the standard viewing conditions (described in chapter 3) taken into account.

Ergonomic factors should also be taken into consideration. Eye strain and headaches among monitor users are linked to the brightness of the display and to strain on shoulder and back muscles. Users should take occasional short breaks, focusing the eyes away on a distant spot away from the screen. If problems are encountered, it can help to reduce the display brightness when working on jobs that do not require color judgments.

Screen-display intensities may be adjustable to compensate for different viewing conditions and color balance requirements. The display brightness is adjusted though the monitor's gamma adjustment control. Separate controls for the intensities of the red, green, and blue signals may also be provided, either on the monitor itself or through the driver software or graphics applications.

Working with a large monitor is essential for graphic arts work in order to have a full view of the page and any other on-screen items. The common 14- and 15-in. screens (as measured diagonally across the screen) are appropriate for business applications, but when used for page-makeup or image-editing, the user is forced to continually scroll the display.

A 19-in. monitor will display a page full-screen in portrait orientation, while a 21-in. screen also makes room for other items like menus and toolbars to be displayed.

Alternatives to CRTs

The CRT display is large and heavy, with a front-to-back dimension greater than the screen diagonal. For portable computers, flat-panel displays are used as an alternative to CRTs, but the display quality is inferior.

Flat-panel displays exploit a variety of display technologies, the most widely used being the liquid crystal display (LCD). Liquid crystals occupy an intermediate state between liquid and solid and can be given unusual optical properties. Crystal molecules group together in nematic (thread-like) forms, and when a voltage is applied the threads rotate and alter their opacity to light. When lit from behind, a display image can be formed by selectively altering the potential of individual threads. Flat-panel LCDs are not widely used in the graphic arts at present. Contrast is lower than CRTs since the crystal threads cannot be made completely opaque.

More promising technologies include thin-film transistors (TFTs) and electroluminescent displays in which metallic salts emit light after receiving an applied voltage. It is possible that flat-panel displays could be an option for graphic arts users in the future.

Mass Storage

With storage volumes now frequently measured in gigabytes and even terabytes, the large files produced by scanned images need to be safeguarded in an accessible, but cost-effective manner. When comparing different storage devices and media, the most important features are:

- Speed of file transfer and access.
- Capital cost of devices.
- Cost per megabyte of storage media.
- Compatibility with different platforms.

The basic types of mass storage used in the graphic arts are primary, secondary and archival, interchange, and backup storage.

Primary storage. This will in most cases consist of a local hard disk, possibly used in conjunction with a network server or secondary local disk. Access and transfer speeds are critically important, since both application programs and data will be continually transferred between primary storage and memory.

Primary storage should be large enough to accommodate the suite of applications and utilities needed by the user, together with user page-layout and image files (including

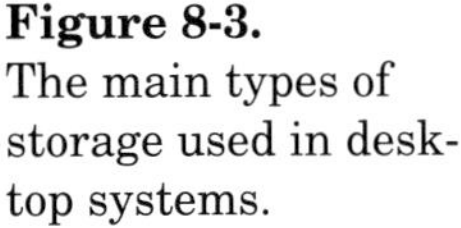

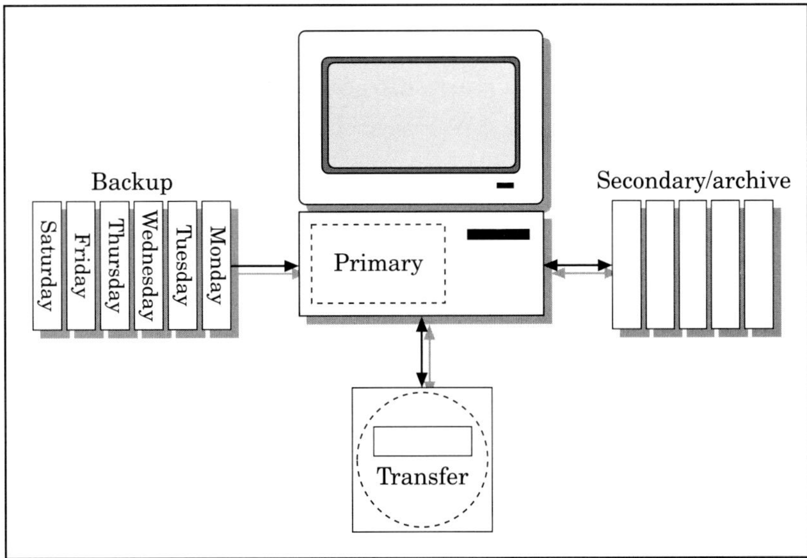

Figure 8-3. The main types of storage used in desktop systems.

intermediate copies that may be made during editing) and any virtual memory that is needed due to lack of RAM. A practical minimum is around 200 MB, although to work efficiently 1 GB or more is necessary. This will no doubt increase by orders of magnitude as applications and operating systems continue to grow, image files become larger, and storage costs continue to fall.

It is possible to transfer some primary storage to fast external subsystems (such as removable cartridges), and this can be a useful way of extending primary storage without having to install new hard disks every time there is an incremental increase in user requirements.

Secondary and archival storage. Typical uses of secondary and archival storage include:

- Work in progress that is not currently required.
- Libraries of images digitized for future use.
- Page and image files that have been output and are being kept for reference purposes or for possible reprints.
- Rasterized high-resolution data that has been used to output pages on an imagesetter or platesetter and is stored temporarily in case alterations or reprints are required.

These uses for secondary and archival storage may involve regular access to data and so speed of access, while not as critical here as for primary storage, is still significant. In most organizations, the volume of archival storage is many times greater than the primary storage media, often extending into **terabytes** (1,000 GB) of data, and thus the price/performance of the media chosen for archiving is important.

Archiving large numbers of image files makes some form of image database essential so that low-resolution thumbnails can be viewed and the image retrieved without requiring the user to trawl through the high-resolution files. Useful applications of this kind include Aldus Fetch and ImagePals.

Interchange. Publishers, designers, and printers regularly need to exchange large volumes of data, and the most important requirement is compatibility. Unreadable media and data formats cause serious problems in time-critical work. Both the drives and the software drivers can cause data to be written in a way that other similar devices cannot access, and it is advisable to confirm that your disks can be read by the target device before sending data.

Data interchange can be achieved more rapidly and reliably, and without the cost of storage media, by using direct data transfer through a local or wide-area network or through communications facilities.

Backup storage. The importance of regularly backing up data should not be underestimated. Hard disks fail on average once every four years, and even though component reliability is improving, platter speeds and track densities are also increasing, and failures continue to occur. Backing up should be thought of as a risk management activity. If data loss is unimportant, there is no reason to invest resources in it, but if your data has value and its loss would be costly, then backup is essential. User files, preference settings, and other current data are the priority for backing up (preferably on a daily basis), since applications and other resources can always be reinstalled, if necessary.

Types of Mass Storage Media

For storage purposes, data transfer rates are much more important than access (or seek) rates, since, with large files, far more time is spent transferring data than locating the file. When running applications, by contrast, access times take on greater importance, as small sections of code must be continually located and transferred into memory.

Hard disks. With the fastest access times of all media, the hard disk is the most suitable medium for primary storage.

Fast hard disks with a SCSI interface have access times of under 10 ms.

Hard disks are normally mounted internally in the host computer, but it is also possible to use an external hard disk that is connected through a SCSI or parallel port interface. External hard disks can be used for the efficient transfer of large amounts of data.

Removable hard disks. In a removable disk system, the disk platter is independent of the drive mechanism that contains the writing heads. There are two types of removable in use in the graphic arts: the **cartridge disk** and the **shuttle disk.** A cartridge disk has a single disk platter contained in a plastic case, and storage volumes range from the widely used 44-MB SyQuest cartridges up to the 105-MB and 270-MB SyQuest Marlin. The main competitor to SyQuest is Iomega's Bernoulli system.

Removable hard disks are widely used as a transfer media. The low device costs also make them a possibility for archiving data, although the relatively high cost per megabyte of the media can make them more expensive than optical discs when the volumes of data are high.

Shuttle disks have proprietary drive mechanisms and store upwards of 1 GB of data, often on multiple platters. They are used for transferring high-resolution files from one system to another in a trade shop where a high-bandwidth network is not available.

Optical discs. Optical and magneto-optical discs are available in a range of sizes and storage capacities, the most widely used being the 3.5-in. 128 MB and the 5.25-in. 650 MB and 1.3 GB. Although not as fast as hard disks, they offer lower media costs and are a good choice for large-volume storage.

Jukebox systems holding multiple optical discs make it possible to access data volumes as great as one terabyte. The present 1.3-GB standard for 5.25-in. optical discs will give way to increasing data densities, with a 30-GB disc forecast by the year 2000.

CD-ROM discs. A CD is an optical disc with two special features: (1) the data, written with a higher-powered laser, cannot be erased and (2) the way in which this data is written is highly standardized.

The advantage of standardization is that data can be read on any host computer with access to a compatible drive. The ISO 9660 XA multi-session (Mode 2, Form 2), as used in Photo CD discs, is by far the most widely applied CD standard in the graphic arts. The drawback of standardization is that the evolution of the medium is held back and data densities cannot increase beyond the present 650 MB without a completely new standard, but it is likely that one will be developed in the near future.

Access and transfer speeds are similar to other optical discs. Writing to CD is somewhat more complicated than with other media, with a mirror image of the CD being created on the host computer's hard disk during the writing process. The falling prices of CD recording devices and their increasing ease of use make the medium a viable option for data storage and interchange. Users with large volumes of data can quickly recover the costs of a recording device as the price/performance of CD is high.

Tape drives. Tape drives are available in a range of volumes up to 25 GB, with the highest volumes in **digital-audio tape (DAT)** drives. Since tape access is sequential, it must be wound to the correct position before data can be read, like an audio cassette. This makes access times extremely slow, and, as a result, tape is suitable only for applications where the data will be needed infrequently. It is used for security backups, to which access is only required in the event of unexpected failure of primary storage, and for storing large volumes of work in progress such as rasterized page data. Tape cannot normally be used as an interchange medium.

Floppy disks. The floppy scores poorly on the speed of access and transfer and the cost per megabyte. It is a convenient medium for storing and exchanging relatively small files, such as text, fonts, EPS graphics, and page-layout information.

Other storage media. Other media that may offer cost-effective storage solutions include the PCMCIA credit card-sized device and the Sony MD Data optical disc (based on the Sony Mini Disc used in the music industry), although so far these have made no real impression in the graphic arts. The MD Data disc, which stores 140 MB of data on a 2.5-in. disc with data transfer rates similar to that of other optical discs, has the potential to replace removable disks and the smaller optical discs as a storage and interchange medium.

Future storage requirements will be measured in terabytes, and present research is focused on increasing data densities and improving access and transfer. Among the techniques under consideration for optical discs are:

- Modulating the laser spot size instead of writing a standard binary spot.
- Reducing the track width to allow more tracks to be written.
- Recording with blue light instead of red. The wavelength of blue light is half that of red, so twice as much information can be recorded in each dimension.
- Recording multiple layers of data (a technology currently under development by IBM).
- Storing data holographically, with the possibility of writing multiple holographic images in the same physical space by using a range of different wavelengths.

A proposed three-dimensional medium records multiple layers, with each slice being read in parallel so that data is transferred at around 1,000 times present rates.

Handling Color Images on a Network

In a production environment, color files may be handled on different machines dedicated to specific parts of the production task from scanning, editing, and separating through final output. Files are transferred among various machines as they move through the different phases of production.

In some instances, the fastest and cheapest method of image transfer is to simply use some form of physical storage media, such as removable cartridges and external hard disks. This method, often known as "sneakernet," avoids the need for high-bandwidth networking systems and the complications of managing network traffic.

For other organizations, there are advantages in linking all the different machines together in a **local area network (LAN).** However, some conventional networking systems such as LocalTalk carry as little as 20 kilobits per second (Kbps), and the large files used in the graphic arts can overwhelm the available capacity. Network traffic can be managed by using routers that examine packets of data and ensure that they are transmitted over the necessary parts of the network, using the maximum bandwidth available. Bandwidths can be increased by using higher-capacity systems such as Fast

Ethernet, which can handle up to 100 Mbps. Incidentally, note that communications speeds are usually measured in bits (binary digits) per second, or bps; elsewhere, file transfer is measured in bytes (units of eight bits), abbreviated with a capital letter "B."

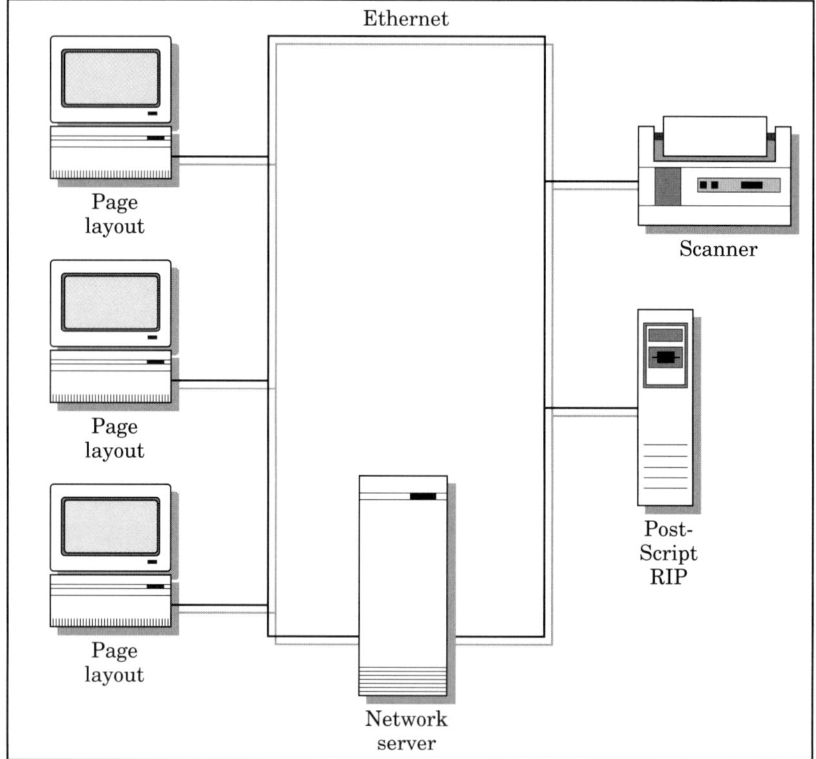

Figure 8-4. A simple, relatively low-bandwidth Ethernet network based on a file server.

Files and applications that all machines need access to are held on a file server, which also controls printers and other shared devices. Servers can be based on faster PCs, Macs, PowerPCs, or workstations. Organizations with existing corporate networks and a mixture of PCs and Macs are most likely to opt for PC or workstation-based servers.

In a graphic arts production environment, most data transfer involves sending files from one specific machine to another, rather than sharing files among many machines. It is possible to keep traffic on the main network to a minimum by connecting the machines that send and receive high-resolution images with high-bandwidth (SCSI or fiber optic) cables. The fiber optic standard FDDI (Fiber Distributed Data Interface) has been used by high-end systems for data transfer and is supported by many PostScript systems.

Figure 8-5.
A high-bandwidth connection with a direct SCSI interface between devices keeps large files (high-resolution images) off the main network.

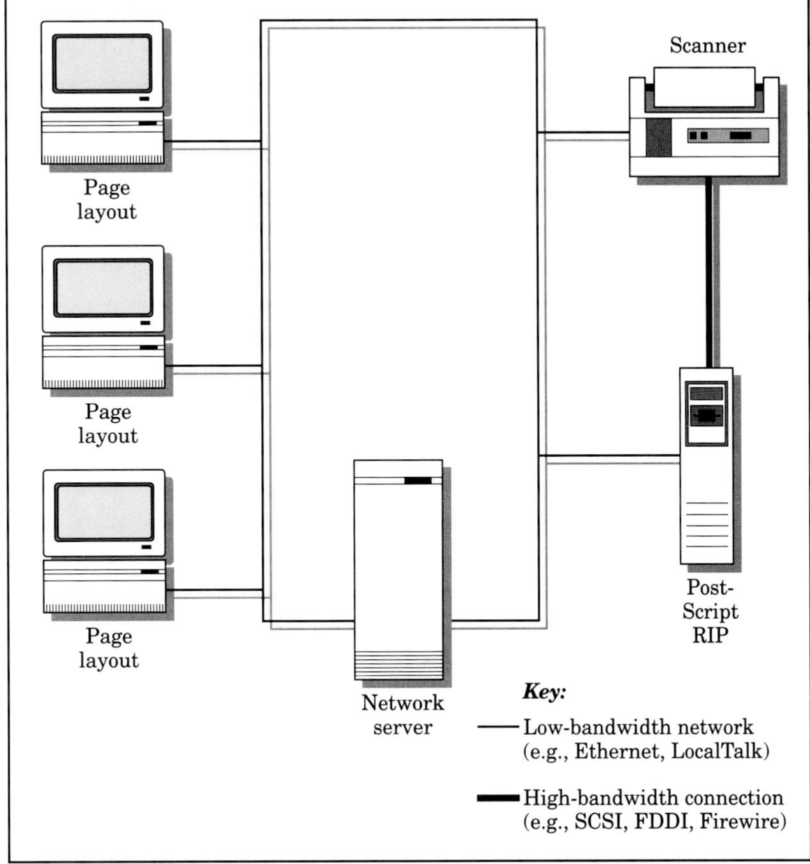

Open prepress interface (OPI) servers also minimize the traffic on a network by holding the high-resolution files on the server and sending low-resolution versions for placement within page-layout applications.

There are several different versions of the SCSI interface. The highest bandwidth (up to 20 Mbps) is available in fast and wide SCSI-2. In the longer term, Apple's Firewire and IBM's serial storage architecture (SSA) interface are intended to replace serial, parallel, and SCSI interfaces to peripheral devices. Firewire is designed to handle up to sixty-three devices and a maximum transfer rate of 400 Mbps. Fiber optic and Ethernet are both evolving systems that will be able to handle higher bandwidths in the future.

Open Prepress Interface

The open prepress interface is a key element in managing the flow of high-resolution images from one area in a production network to another. OPI was developed by Aldus Corporation as a way of transferring information about color

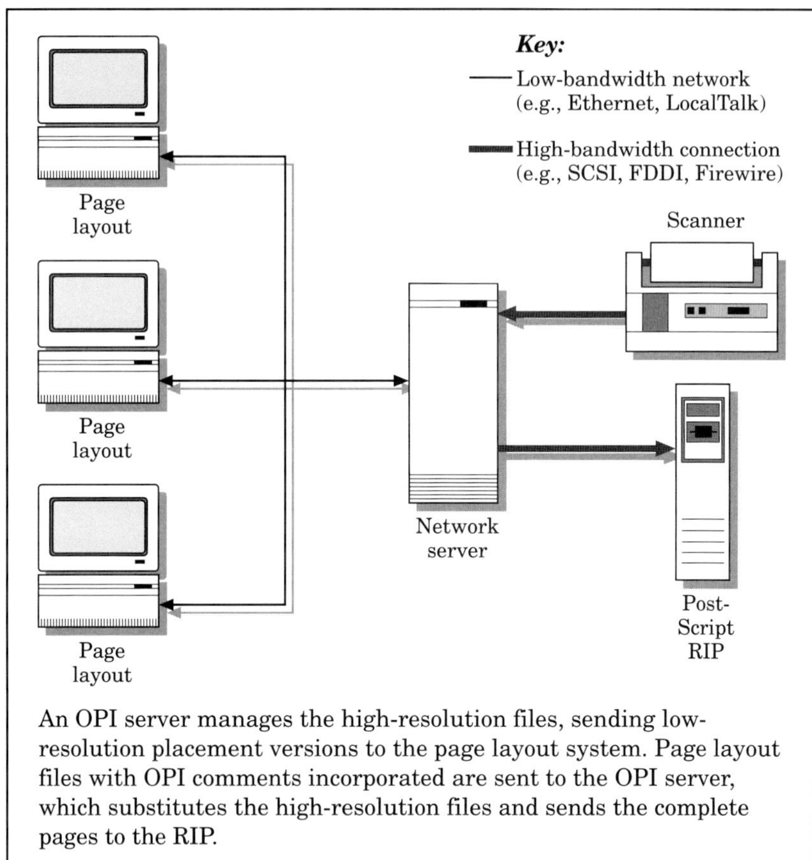

Figure 8-6. OPI workflow.

An OPI server manages the high-resolution files, sending low-resolution placement versions to the page layout system. Page layout files with OPI comments incorporated are sent to the OPI server, which substitutes the high-resolution files and sends the complete pages to the RIP.

images from page-layout and illustration applications to output devices. Low-resolution versions of scanned images are placed in a page, and OPI comments tell the OPI server how to position the high-resolution versions that it substitutes when a page is output.

OPI allows the scaling and cropping defined in a page-layout program to be applied without the user needing access to the high-resolution files. This makes it possible to keep the large high-resolution files off the main network, limiting transfer to the links among the scanner, the OPI server, and the output device, with a possible branch for color retouching and editing high-resolution images.

The application's PostScript driver inserts the OPI comments into the PostScript code generated when the publication is sent to an output device or printed to a file.

OPI comments describe the following image details:

- Name of the TIFF file.
- Dimensions of the printed image.

- Image position on the page.
- Crop area.
- Sampling resolution (in pixels per inch).
- Color resolution (in bits per color).
- Information about whether a color is a special (spot), a composite, or a separation.
- Information about whether a color is set to overprint.

OPI comments can also be included within EPS image files. Additional OPI comments available for gray-scale images describe the values for each pixel and allow quadratone, or "false-color," images to be printed by specifying a percentage of cyan, magenta, yellow, and black to be used in place of black alone.

Aldus recommends the use of composite rather than separated images with OPI, since the file conventions for separated images are not sufficiently standardized.

OPI placement and cropping are limited to rectangular shapes. If a clipping path has been used to apply a cutout to an image, it is executed by the interpreter before the OPI instructions.

OPI comments only allow you to include image-editing information, such as adjustments to contrast and color balance, for gray-scale images. Information about imposition and trapping cannot be included either; it must be handled elsewhere in the workflow. Because the OPI specification is an evolving standard, it is possible that future versions will enable more information to be passed to the interpreter.

An OPI server reads the comments and replaces the low-resolution images contained in the publication with the corresponding high-resolution files before final output. The OPI server consists essentially of OPI-capable software running on a workstation (or a reasonably powerful alternative) that holds the high-resolution files. A PostScript RIP can also act as an OPI server.

OPI is designed to work in both PostScript and non-PostScript environments. When used in a fully PostScript environment, the workflow is as shown in Figure 8-7. A TIFF image, usually a low-resolution version, is placed on the page in a page-layout application. The resulting file is then separated into the individual color components (CMYK), and, if necessary, the high-resolution version of the file is inserted before the image is rasterized and sent to the output device.

Figure 8-7.
In an all-PostScript production environment, the high-resolution files are held on the OPI server and inserted into the pages when they are output.

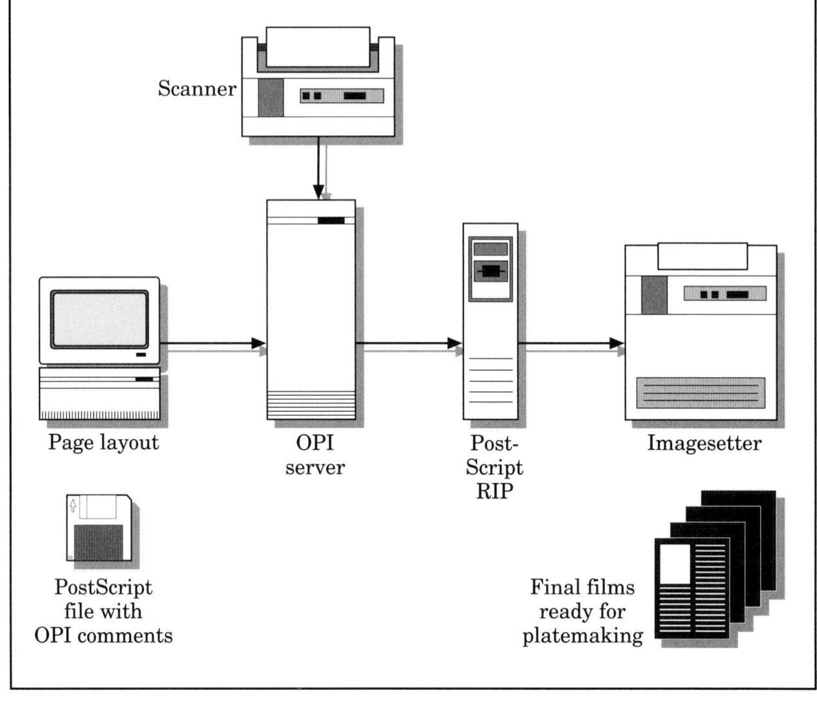

Figure 8-8.
OPI workflow in a mixed environment.

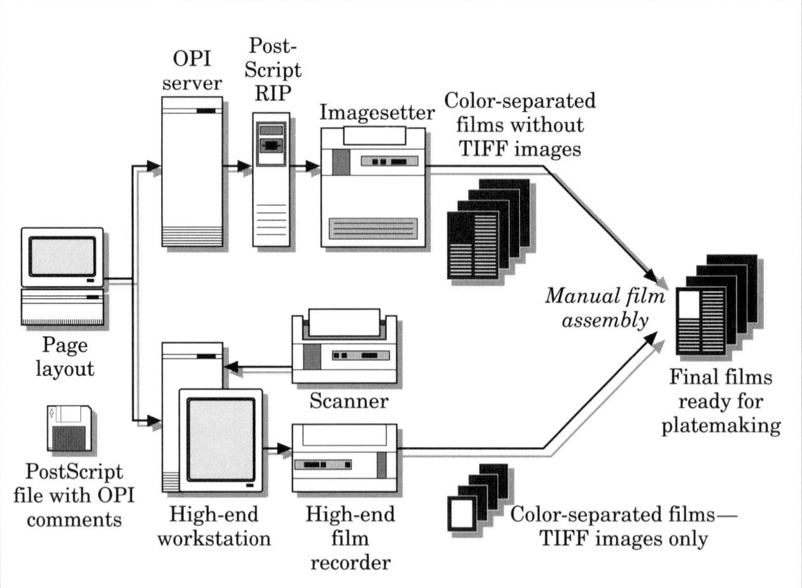

In a mixed environment, a hybrid workflow is necessary. Pages are output to film as in the PostScript environment but without the high-resolution images, which are scanned and output directly to film on a high-end system. The two sets of films are stripped together manually or by an automated step-and-repeat machine before platemaking.

In a non-PostScript environment, the high-resolution files and the page-layout files are output independently of each other (as shown in Figure 8-8) and combined at the film stage prior to making plates.

The insertion of high-resolution files into the workflow is a processor- and memory-intensive operation and a potential bottleneck in production. Workstation-based OPI servers are essential to maintain a flow of high-resolution data to the output device.

Communications

Files can be exchanged more efficiently by transferring them over communications links rather than transporting physical storage media. Sending digital files electronically saves the costs of storage media and transportation and can make the transfer process much faster. Because files are received at the destination computer almost immediately, it is possible to work on them interactively in real time, instead of waiting hours, or even days, every time a file is sent from one location to another.

Figure 8-9. Communications links among publishers, advertising agencies, output services, and printers can be used in a variety of ways.

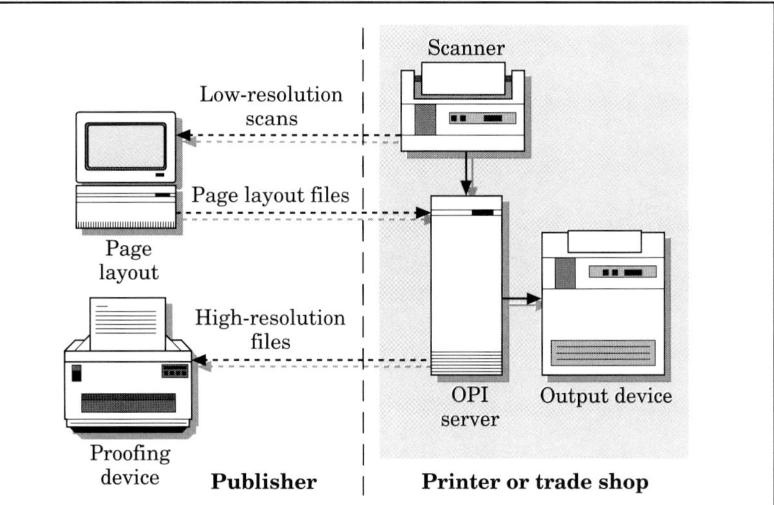

This is a link between a designer and a trade shop. Transparencies are scanned at the trade shop, and low-resolution versions are sent by modem to the designer. The pictures are placed by the designer, and the resulting page layout files with OPI comments embedded are sent back to the trade shop for the high-resolution files to be inserted. An ISDN link transmits the complete pages with the high-resolution files back to the designer's high-resolution color printer, which is being used as a remote proofing system. When the designer has approved the hard copy proofs, the pages are sent to the imagesetter for the films to be output.

Communications links are widely used to transfer high-resolution data to output services and printers for output to film, plate, or proof. They can be also used to transfer data, such as scanned images, back to the designer or publisher for approval or for inclusion in page layouts.

Complete pages can even be sent over communications links directly to a digital proofing device or printing press. Remote imaging will become more widely used as communications links become faster, more cost-effective, and more reliable.

The large files used in the graphic arts pose special problems for communications links. Data integrity is extremely important, since, unlike a text file that can easily be repaired if corrupted, an image file will simply fail to transfer if any data is lost.

The communications options are:

- Analog connections, such as ordinary telephone lines and high-bandwidth fixed links.
- Digital connections such as ISDN.

Analog connections using modems and ordinary telephone lines tend to be too slow when large volumes of data are sent. Files must first be modulated into an analog signal, and the resulting bandwidth is less than that available with all-digital links. The faster modems now available (transmitting at up to 28.8 Kbps in the V.34 standard) are approaching half the transmission speed of a single ISDN line, but unavoidable line noise makes it difficult to make significant advances beyond this.

Fixed analog links (including land lines and microwave links) are suitable for printers and publishers requiring constant communication between a small number of sites, but are not appropriate for the majority of graphic arts users who require high bandwidths for relatively short periods and need to send files to many destinations.

Dial-up digital services use existing telephone networks, but replace the analog links to exchanges with direct-digital connections. The transfer rates on the fixed-bandwidth ISDN system are 64 Kbps per line (although the use of transmission protocols can reduce the actual transmission rate slightly), and lines can be multiplexed to create bandwidths of 2 Mbps and above. Variable bandwidth services offer transfer rates of up to 155 Mbps.

An ISDN installation is usually connected by an interface card or an external adapter to a host computer, but it can also be connected directly to a compatible device such as a color printer for remote proofing. After installation, the user pays only for the time actually spent on-line and for the rental of the service.

Specialized communications software is necessary to manage ISDN communications. Additional options available include software to handle unattended file transfer and to manage communications from within applications such as QuarkXPress.

Communications links can act as a means of distributing the final document, as well as a method of transferring data among the different organizations concerned with its reproduction. Publishers of electronic documents need to consider ways of ensuring consistent appearance on different platforms (through techniques of color management, font mapping, and document delivery systems such as Adobe's Acrobat) and fast delivery of documents (using file compression).

Image Compression

Capturing and storing an image as an array of separate pixels is something of a brute-force approach when compared to the elegance of the human visual mechanism. A high-resolution image file inevitably contains a quantity of redundant data that can be removed so that transfer and storage can be made faster and more cost-effective. Image compression algorithms use one of two approaches to remove redundant data:

- **Lossless algorithms** search for similarities within the captured data that they can code more efficiently.
- **Lossy algorithms** discard data that is least perceptible to the eye.

When lossless algorithms are used to compress an image, no information is discarded, and, after decompression, the image is identical to the original. Lossy algorithms provide higher compression ratios at the cost of some loss of information contained in the original image.

Lossless compression algorithms make use of the fact that most images do not contain all 16.7 million possible colors in a random arrangement, but include objects with areas of identical or similar colors that are formed into regular shapes that do not vary suddenly except at boundaries. The likely value of a pixel can thus be inferred from the values of the surrounding pixels.

Run-length encoding (RLE) and PackBits algorithms simply encode a continuous run of identical pixels with the value of the first pixel and the number of identical pixels that follow. Very high compression ratios are achieved on images with large areas of flat color, but the technique is less effective on the varying tones and detail found in a typical sampled image.

Huffman compression is a two-stage process that first divides the image into the different sequences of pixels that occur, and then generates a lookup table that assigns a code to each sequence of pixels (the shortest codes being assigned the most frequent sequences). The LZW algorithm (named after its creators Sempel, Ziv, and Welch) creates a similar lookup table (known as a string table) to allot a code to each sequence of values that it encounters. The string table is built on the fly, and is cleared after reaching a predetermined maximum number of entries.

Huffman and LZW handle repetitive patterns as well as solid areas of color, but like RLE, they achieve higher compression ratios on smooth images as opposed to ones with a large amount of noise or detail.

Lossy compression algorithms are based on the assumption that some high-frequency data captured by the scanner (corresponding to rapidly varying image detail) will not be perceived by the eye and can be discarded without the loss of data being perceptible.

Of the different lossy compression algorithms that exist, the **discrete cosine transform (DCT)** has become the most widely used and is the basis of the JPEG scheme. DCT is a type of Fourier transform (a class of algorithms widely used in image processing), in which a linear transformation is applied to an image to produce a set of transform coefficients which are quantized and encoded. Very small coefficients, corresponding to high-frequency information, can be discarded or coarsely quantized.

The amount of information discarded during JPEG compression, and the resultant compression ratio and reproduction quality, can be controlled by the user at the point when the file is compressed.

Even at very high quality (low-compression ratio) settings, some information is inevitably discarded in lossy compression. The degradation of an image may be almost insignificant but nonetheless there will be some loss of detail, and lossy compression should be used with care or avoided altogether if quality requirements are high. The observable image quality degradation effects of the DCT algorithm typically include:

- Smoothing of detail.
- Fringing at edges.
- Shade-stepping in smooth areas of tone.

The DCT algorithm can be modified to reduce these effects and to make the quantization process work adaptively according to the requirements of different regions of an image.

The JPEG scheme is a standard for image compression developed by the Joint Photographic Experts Group in collaboration with the International Standards Organization (ISO) and the Consultative Committee of the International Telephone and Telegraph (CCITT). JPEG is based on the DCT algorithm and can also include other compression algorithms, which can be selected according to the needs of the application. The Huffman algorithm is included in the standard for cases where lossless compression is required.

A set of default DCT quantization and compression codes are specified in a "baseline" JPEG standard, but application vendors can substitute their own values or make the process work adaptively according to the needs of the image. In practice, most images can be compressed with baseline JPEG at a ratio of up to 5:1 without a perceptible quality loss. Most applications only support the baseline version of JPEG and do not employ Huffman compression.

All four compression algorithms described above are supported in the TIFF file format. In the case of JPEG, a TIFF extension allows image compression parameters to be defined in tags (although such parameters are not essential for baseline encoded images, as they are included in the image data). This allows images to be compressed and decompressed successfully by different applications. Only baseline DCT and Huffman encoding are supported in the current TIFF JPEG extension.

PostScript Level 2 includes filters that can compress and decompress JPEG (baseline) and LZW images. The JPEG compression filter incorporates defaults such as setting a quality level and converting the image from RGB to the YUV color space, although applications can use their own defaults. (Y, U, and V are arbitrary letters used to denote a color space similar to CIELUV.)

Figure 8.10.
Image compression: the image at the left is not compressed, the middle image has been compressed 10:1 using baseline JPEG in Adobe Photoshop, and the image at the right has been compressed 10:1 using Highwater Systems' JPEG adaptation.

Since the JPEG standard is loosely defined and different implementations are possible, images compressed by one application may not be recognized by other applications. If an alternative implementation is used, the same application must usually be employed both to compress and decompress the image.

Fractal compression is an alternative method of image compression. Fractal compression looks for complex similarities of pattern rather than relatively simple similarities of individual pixels and groups of pixels. Fractal compression is very powerful, but too "lossy" for graphic reproduction (although if someone absolutely must put a 50-MB image on a floppy disk, it may well give them the best results).

Ideally, image compression should take place in the background, transparent to the user except when it is necessary to specify preferences, such as the level of quality. Systems that automatically compress files on the fly, such as communications devices, should also detect files that have already been compressed and not attempt to compress them further, as in doing so the file is likely to become larger.

The compression methods discussed so far are usually applied to images with either RGB or CMYK components and are applied equally to each component. However, if the color components are organized in terms of hue, saturation, and lightness (see chapter three), it is possible to discard some of the hue and saturation data from the image without altering its appearance, since more information is carried by the lightness component and the visual mechanism gives much greater priority to lightness information.

This principle is used in the encoding of Photo CD images. Subsampling is carried out on the YCC data so that only one bit of color information (CC components) is kept for every four bits of lightness information (Y component). Huffman encoding is then used to compress both lightness and color. When the image is decompressed, interpolation is used to restore as much of the lost color information as possible.

Using different amounts of data for different color components makes it possible to achieve maximum compression while preserving the appearance of the image, but it does make the decoding process more complex. Similarly, it is possible to compress some areas of the color gamut and the tone scale more than others, as more information is captured than is needed in these areas. However, the resulting nonlinear compression and decompression algorithms then become far more complex. Compression/decompression algorithms that operate on the hue, saturation, and lightness components must be also designed to maintain the color balance of the original and preserve the highlight and shadow endpoints.

These factors are largely responsible for variations in image quality when using different utilities to access Photo CD images.

It is not possible to edit images compressed with PackBits, LZW, Huffman, or DCT algorithms. However, some image-editing programs (such as Fauve's xRes) have the ability to compress a large image file into a proprietary vector-based format and create a set of edits that can then be automatically applied to the uncompressed image.

9 The PostScript Language

The PostScript page description language dominates the world of desktop prepress. It has become the “defacto” standard method of communicating pages created on the desktop to an output device and is increasingly being used as a way of transferring graphics and documents between different applications and platforms. While a detailed understanding of the language is not essential to these activities, an awareness of the main concepts is useful to be able to work productively and avoid output problems.

PostScript is essentially a graphical programming language used to create precise descriptions of graphical objects for accurate transfer to an output device.

A fundamental strength of the language, and the main reason that it has eclipsed alternative page description languages, is its concept of device independence. Graphical objects are defined within a limitless coordinate system, and it is not until the page is output that it takes on the finite resolution of the specific output device. Device independence allows pages to be printed at the highest resolution available on the printer or imagesetter that is used to output them.

Code that is written in a programming language is turned into a series of low-level instructions by either a **compiler** or an **interpreter**. Compilers are used by programmers to translate code directly into low-level instructions and the resulting programs can be executed on any compatible computer platform.

An interpreter is normally part of the environment in which the program is executed. It accepts the code produced in a programming language and translates it line by line into low-level instructions. As the interpreter comes across a valid instruction that it has all the necessary information for, the instruction is executed.

Compiled programs execute slightly faster, since there is no need for line-by-line interpretation, but they are less able to exploit device-specific features when they are executed.

PostScript language code is written not by a human programmer but by another program (the user application). When the application's print function is invoked, PostScript code is generated and sent to an output device. Here the device's interpreter translates the code into low-level instructions which it executes, producing a raster image of the page. Compared with more general-purpose programming languages such as C++, PostScript is a relatively simple language.

PostScript was first developed in 1985 by Adobe Systems, as one of several languages then available for controlling printing devices. Other printer control languages, such as Hewlett Packard's Printer Control Language (PCL), still exist, though they are of little interest to the graphic arts as they are unable to support high-resolution output devices.

PostScript was widely adopted by the nascent desktop publishing market, but as DTP matured the weaknesses of the original PostScript language in controlling color and halftone screening became a barrier to further adoption, until language extensions were developed for these purposes. In 1990, Adobe published PostScript Level 2, which incorporated these extensions and added a number of sophisticated functions. Implementing PostScript Level 2 is not an easy task for hardware and software developers, and so far not all applications exploit the full functionality that it offers. The number of applications and output devices that support the features of Level 2 is gradually increasing.

The main features of Level 2 are:

- Better memory management.
- Better color handling.
- The introduction of forms caches and patterns.
- Increased use of dictionaries.
- The ability to handle file decompression during output.
- Improved control of the output device from the front end.

Memory management reduces the chance of a memory limit being encountered when a file is being output, a frequent problem with Level 1 interpreters.

Color handling includes color conversions based on color lookup tables and CIE-based color space.

A **forms cache** stores repeated page elements (such as borders, logos, tints, or other graphics that are common to a number of pages) in memory, so that they do not need to be reprocessed for each page.

A **dictionary** is a lookup table that holds a set of parameters used in defining a graphical object. An example is a halftone dictionary that holds the screening parameters (screen frequency and angle and dot shape).

PostScript Fundamentals

PostScript achieves device independence for page descriptions (and all the separate elements that comprise them, such as graphics, fonts, colors, and so on) by maintaining a clear distinction between user space, where documents are created, and device space, where they are output. Page descriptions remain in user space until they are actually output.

Creating and printing a document using PostScript can be divided into four separate phases, as illustrated in Figure 9-1. First, the user creates a document (usually in a page-layout application) and saves it in the native format of the application or the host computer. Next, the document is "printed" from the application (either directly to an output device or to a file on disk) when the application's PostScript driver translates the document into PostScript code.

The resulting code is then sent to the output device, where the interpreter executes the code and translates the page

Figure 9-1. Conceptual PostScript model.

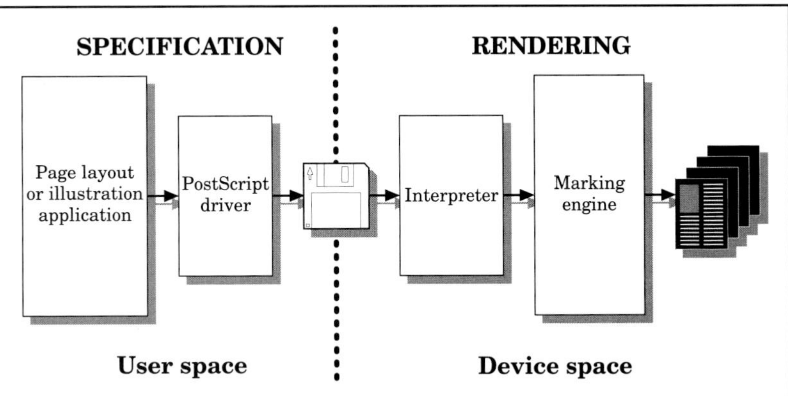

An application's PostScript driver (or generic PostScript driver) translates from the host computer's native graphics format (such as QuickDraw or Windows GDI) into the PostScript language code. The resulting code is sent to an interpreter that examines the code, generates a raster image for each page, and passes it to the printer or exposing mechanism.

into a raster image in the coordinate system of the output device. Finally, the raster image is sent to the marking engine, which reproduces it onto film or paper.

Creating the page and translating it to PostScript code both take place in user space, while code interpretation and printing take place in device space. This distinction between user space and device space is fundamental to PostScript's device independence.

Although a PostScript interpreter will process all of the valid instructions it receives, a page description is more device-independent if it conforms to the Document Structuring Conventions published by Adobe.

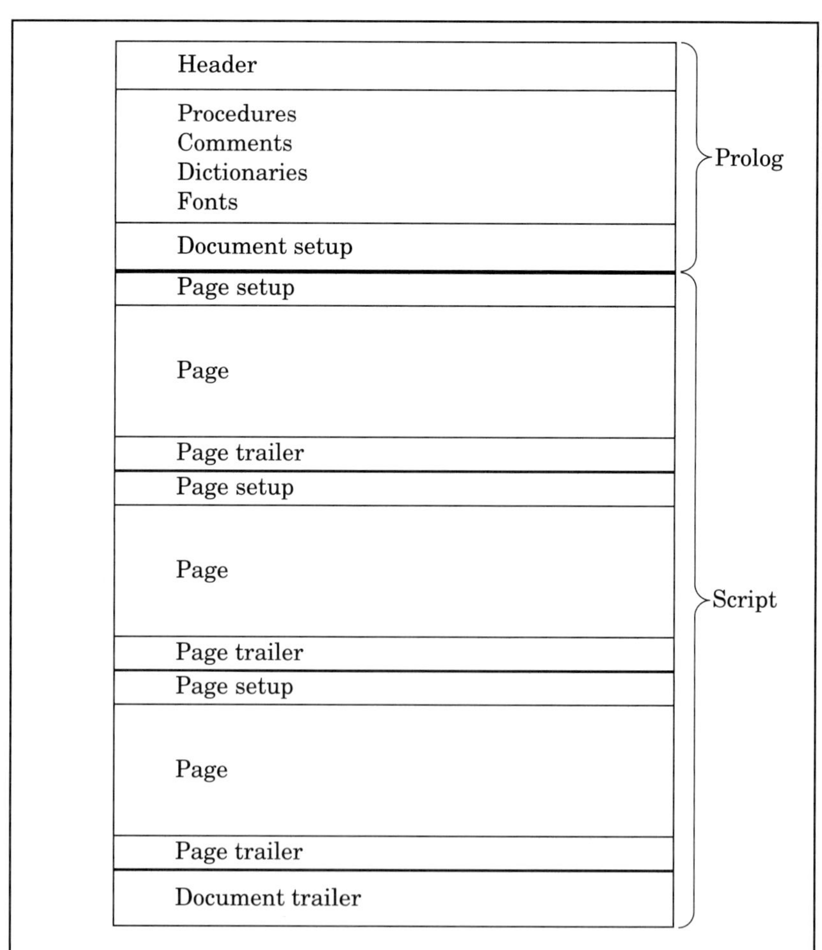

Figure 9-2. Structure of PostScript language file.

These conventions specify an overall structure for a PostScript page description and define structure comments (prefaced by %%) that are incorporated into the page description. These comments are not actually processed by the interpreter but allow other programs to read and display the file and to carry out operations such as imposing the individual pages in a publication, managing the resources it needs, and handling any errors.

A PostScript program that conforms to the document structuring conventions has two parts: a **prolog** and a **script.** The main purpose of the prolog is to identify any procedures that will be used when the program is executed. It will also include a header that contains comments naming the document's creator and any resources, such as fonts that are used.

The script consists of a document setup section, followed by the individual page descriptions and a **trailer** that announces the end of the document. The trailer may also include some comments deferred from the prolog. Each page in the publication is defined in turn through a series of instructions to the interpreter to perform graphics operations. At the end of each page in the script, the instruction ***showpage*** tells the output device to output the page. Each page may also have its own setup section.

PostScript instructions are known as **operators,** and they are used in conjunction with the procedures defined in the prologue and with specific data or **operands.** For example, in Figure 9-3 the ***lineto*** operator has been given the operands 440, 550, and a line is drawn from the last position to this new coordinate. There are over 200 operators, each with a specific function and usage. Operators carry out tasks like:

- Constructing paths.
- Controlling the specification of type.
- Controlling the specification of images.
- Drawing lines and objects.
- Controlling the way that colors are output.
- Controlling the way that the page is output.
- Defining the **graphics state** (such as the current color or line width).
- Defining transformations in user coordinates (allowing scaling and rotation to take place).

Definitions of a graphical object used in a publication can be held in a separate resource file instead of being embedded into the page description. The resource is then simply named in the page description. Named resources must, of course, be

Figure 9-3.
The PostScript code *(top)* that produced the 60-pt. Helvetica Bold letters "GATF" and the 10-pt. rule *(middle).*

```
%!PS-Adobe-3.0
%%Title: GATF.PS
%%Creator: Phil Green
%%Pages: 1
%%BoundingBox: 18 23 577 819
/Helvetica-Bold findfont 60 scalefont setfont
%%EndProlog

10 setlinewidth
200 550 moveto
440 550 lineto
stroke

240 585 moveto
(GATF) show
showpage
%%Trailer
end
```

GATF

PostScript code is not difficult to understand. In this simple example, the prolog identifies the bounding box of the page (the area inside the page margins) and defines the font that will be used.

The ***moveto*** operator moves the current drawing position to the coordinates 200, 550, and then the ***lineto*** operator creates a horizontal line to the coordinates 440, 500. The ***setlinewidth*** and ***stroke*** operators define the line width and paint it on the page.

The font name and size have been defined in the prolog, so the letters "GATF" are simply identified (in parentheses) with the ***show*** operator. Finally, the ***showpage*** operator is the instruction to print the page.

available to the interpreter. If they are not (as often happens in the case of fonts) an error will occur.

Resources defined in the PostScript language include:

- Screening parameters (halftone dictionaries).
- Character-drawing procedures (font dictionaries).
- Color lookup tables (color-rendering dictionaries).
- Input device profiles (color-space arrays).
- Output device features (page-device dictionaries).

A resource can be kept in memory by the interpreter and used whenever it is called for by the page description, or it can be stored on disk and fetched as needed. Multiple instances of a resource can be used in a page description, allowing, for example, halftones on the same page to have different screen rulings or frequencies.

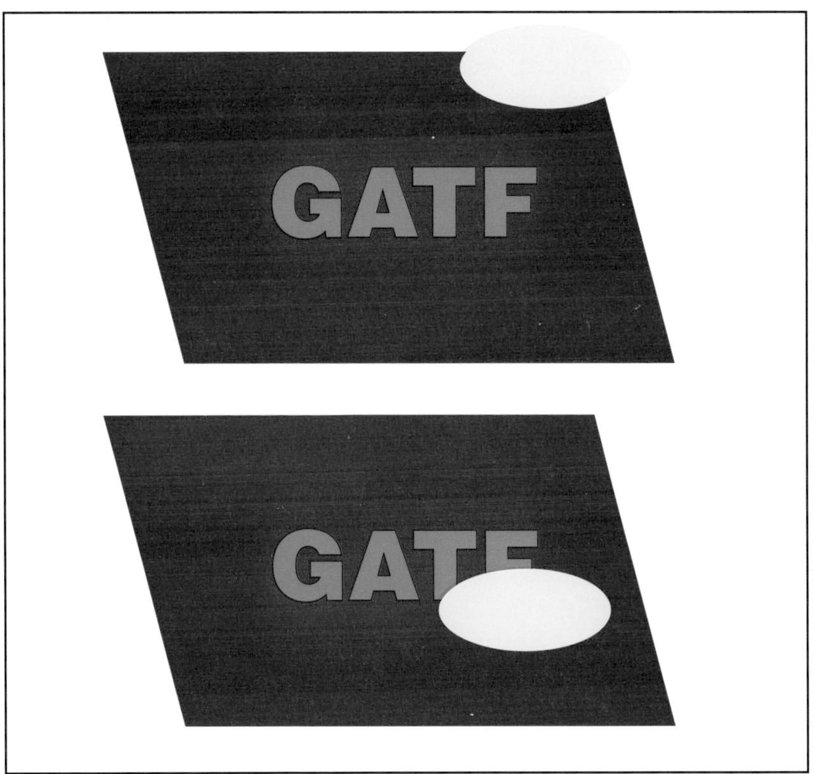

Figure 9-4. When one color is painted on top of another, it is opaque. The underlying color is knocked out and does not print.

The PostScript imaging model is analogous to opaque paint being applied to paper. Paint can be applied in one of three ways: as a line, as a fill, or as a bitmap image. Because paint is always opaque, every instruction to paint an object will paint over whatever was last painted at the same coordinates and make it invisible. This makes it important to paint foreground and background objects in the correct sequence.

PostScript's opaque painting model does not allow painting one color over another additively. The only exceptions are:

- When an object is set to overprint the underlying object.
- When a mask operator is used.

Figure 9-5.
The exceptions to PostScript's opaque painting model.

A. When the painted object is set to overprint, the underlying objects are not knocked out. In this example, the ellipse was filled with yellow and set to overprint the cyan type (resulting in green type where they overlap) and the magenta background (resulting in red where they overlap).

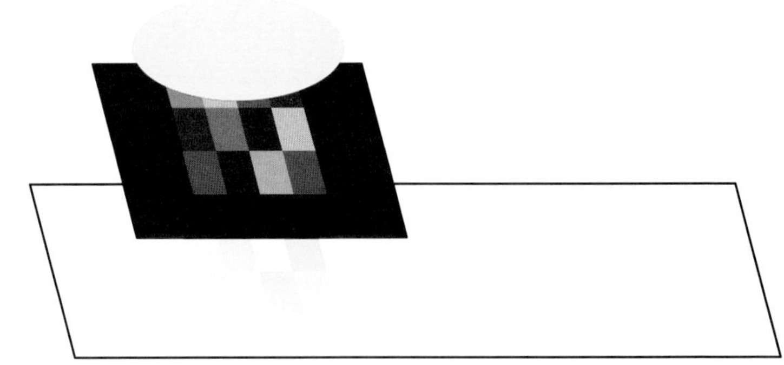

B. When a mask is used, paint "falls through" the mask in proportion to the transparency of the mask.

When colors are set to overprint, both the underlying object and the overprinting object will be printed. Only colors in the Separation color space can overprint.

A mask operator is used to make an object transparent. A PostScript mask works like a stencil, allowing a second object to be painted over the first in the open areas of the stencil.

The User Space

Pages are created in user space, which is a device-independent coordinate system with its origin at the lower left, as shown in Figure 9-6. User space is a limitless space with coordinates

Figure 9-6.
User space.

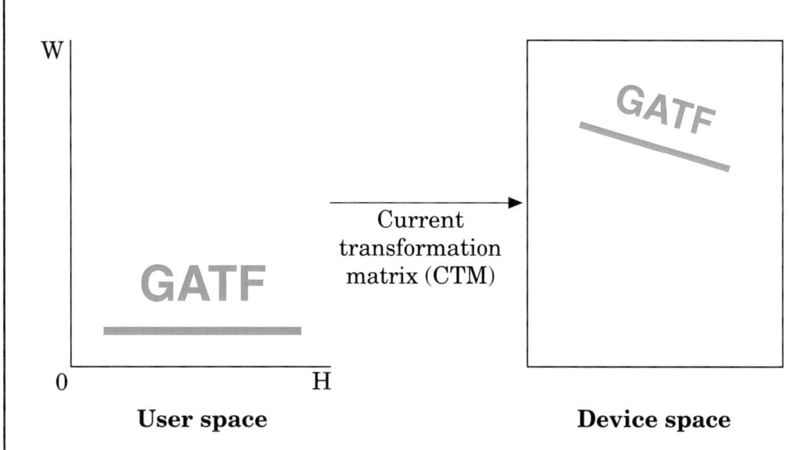

Graphic objects are created in user space, an unbounded coordinate system with 1/72-in. units. A **transformation matrix** defines how a page created in user space is to be positioned on the actual printed page, with any scaling and rotation that is needed.

based on units of 1/72 in. (0.353 mm). Coordinates are translated into device space by the interpreter, and a **transformation matrix** determines how the user space coordinates will be mapped to the output device, allowing scaling or rotation as the page is output.

PostScript's native measurement system is 1/72 in. (0.353 mm), which corresponds closely to the point system used in the graphic arts. Applications can specify measurements in whole units or any fraction of a unit, so there is no limit on the precision available. Applications display measurements that are based on the PostScript unit of 1/72 in., converted to points, inches, or metric units.

Graphical Primitives and Paths

Most programming languages have difficulty in imaging both text and graphics together, since the methods used to draw characters are very different from those used for graphics. The only way of combining them successfully is to render type as a graphic object, by turning it either into a bitmap or into a vector drawing procedure. PostScript describes everything (with the exception of scanned images) as vector graphics.

Vector drawing in PostScript is based on three fundamental procedures or graphical **primitives:** straight lines, arcs, and curves. These are the basic building blocks of every type of graphic object, regardless of how complex it is. The use of such simple and well-defined building blocks makes their behavior highly consistent and predictable, regardless of the different applications and device spaces that may be used to create and output them. **Lines** have just two coordinates defining the position of each end of the line, **arcs** are based on a portion of a circle, and **curves,** which are based on any other kind of path, are described in PostScript as Bezier splines. A **Bezier** is a path defined by a pair of equations that are created when the user sets the curve's endpoints and control points.

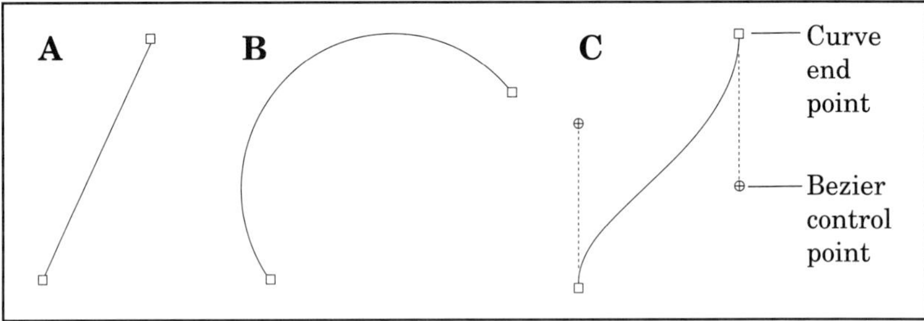

Figure 9-7. PostScript has three basic graphical primitives from which all objects are built: the straight line (A), the arc (B), and the curve (C).

To draw an object using these graphical primitives, PostScript first defines a **path** that describes the object's outline. A path in PostScript is essentially a series of points that are linked together. Paths can be open or, if the coordinate of the last point is the same as the first, closed. As well as defining lines and shapes, paths are also used to create clipping templates for other graphics. A path can also be thought of as a virtual line, since nothing is actually drawn until color is applied to the path by either **stroking** or **filling** it. The path coordinates and the stroke width can be specified with great precision, giving the user complete control over the creation and output of graphic objects.

To draw a character, a series of straight and curved paths are constructed to form the character outline, which is then filled with the current color in the graphics state.

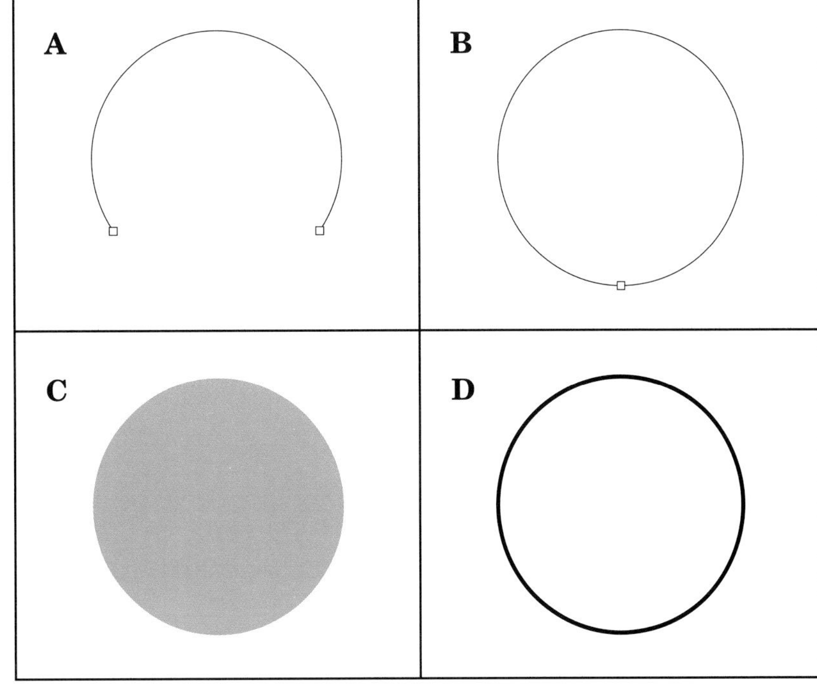

Figure 9-8.
A **path** in PostScript is a virtual line that can be open (A) or closed (B). It can also be filled with a color (C) and **stroked** with a line of any thickness (D).

Once a path procedure has been interpreted by the output device, it can be stored in memory and reused when required, saving on the processing needed for repeated elements within pages. Paths can be made up of multiple segments and can incorporate subpaths. The only limit on the number of paths that can be used is the amount of memory required to store them during output. This limit is rarely encountered in Level 2 devices, except with very complex graphics.

Encapsulated PostScript

An EPS file is a special kind of PostScript object that can be embedded into a page. It can contain text, graphics, images, and even other EPS files. It is not sent directly to an output device, as it has no device setup operators and no ***showpage*** command. An EPS file will include:

- A header identifying it as an EPS file.
- Bounding box coordinates defining the area of user space that it will occupy.
- An optional bitmap preview of the object.

Previews can be either PICT (for the Mac) or TIFF (for the PC), or they can be in the device-independent EPSI format. EPS files are often application-specific, and they may not be editable in other programs unless a filter for the original application is present.

Images

PostScript describes the position and color of scanned images using the ***image*** operator. ***Image*** defines the following image properties:

- The image format (its height and width, its spatial resolution, and the number of colors).
- The coordinates of the user space where the image will be placed.
- The source data for the image (in other words, the color values for each pixel).
- A definition of how the source color values are to be translated into the current color space.

Figure 9-9.
Image matrix.

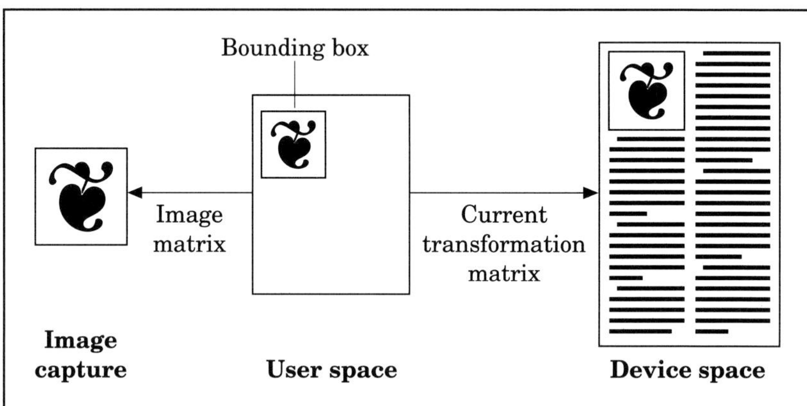

An **image matrix** defines the way that an image is scaled when it is placed on a page in user space. The image retains the same number of pixels (unless it is resampled), but the size of the pixels is altered by scaling. When output, the image is scaled along with the rest of the page according to the transformation matrix.

Scanned images are given a vector outline called a **bounding box** that defines their position in user space and a set of values for each pixel in the image. Just as the user can scale and rotate an object as it is mapped from user space into device space, PostScript allows the user to define how the original image source coordinates are to be mapped into user space with an image matrix. In most cases, the color values for the individual pixels will be contained not in the page layout file but in a separate TIFF or EPS file. When the printer driver turns the page into PostScript code it inserts the color values.

PostScript Level 2 provides a method of handling all aspects of color specification and output. In practice, many applications and devices use their own methods of turning RGB values into CMYK output, but PostScript offers a standard way of converting color values between color spaces that works consistently on all platforms. It uses device-specific parameters to control the way that color is rendered to output devices such as color printers, film recorders, and display monitors.

Level 2 caters to all the different color spaces that are likely to be used in the graphic arts. The three basic categories of color space that are available through the use of the ***setcolorspace*** operator are:

- Device-dependent color spaces (RGB, CMYK, monochrome, and HSB).
- CIE-based device-independent color spaces.
- Special color spaces (including separations and patterns).

Note that HSB (hue, saturation, and brightness) as used in PostScript is an alternative way of representing RGB colors and not a color space in its own right.

CIE-based colors are always defined in terms of XYZ values. This means that color values can be converted between different CIE-based color spaces by the use of standard mathematical algorithms.

Color values can be converted to the output device color space by a PostScript color lookup table, known as a **color rendering dictionary.**

PostScript can achieve device-independent color by translating device-dependent color into XYZ. To do this, it needs information on the way in which the source color values can be converted into XYZ values, in the form of a **color space array.** The color space array is supplied together with the image, while the color rendering dictionary resides in the output device. Device-independent color processing is covered further in Chapter 14.

Among the data specified in a CIE-based color space are the diffuse white and black points. This allows the color balance and density range that are characteristically captured by the input device to be mapped as accurately as possible to those of the output device.

Figure 9-10. PostScript Color Processing

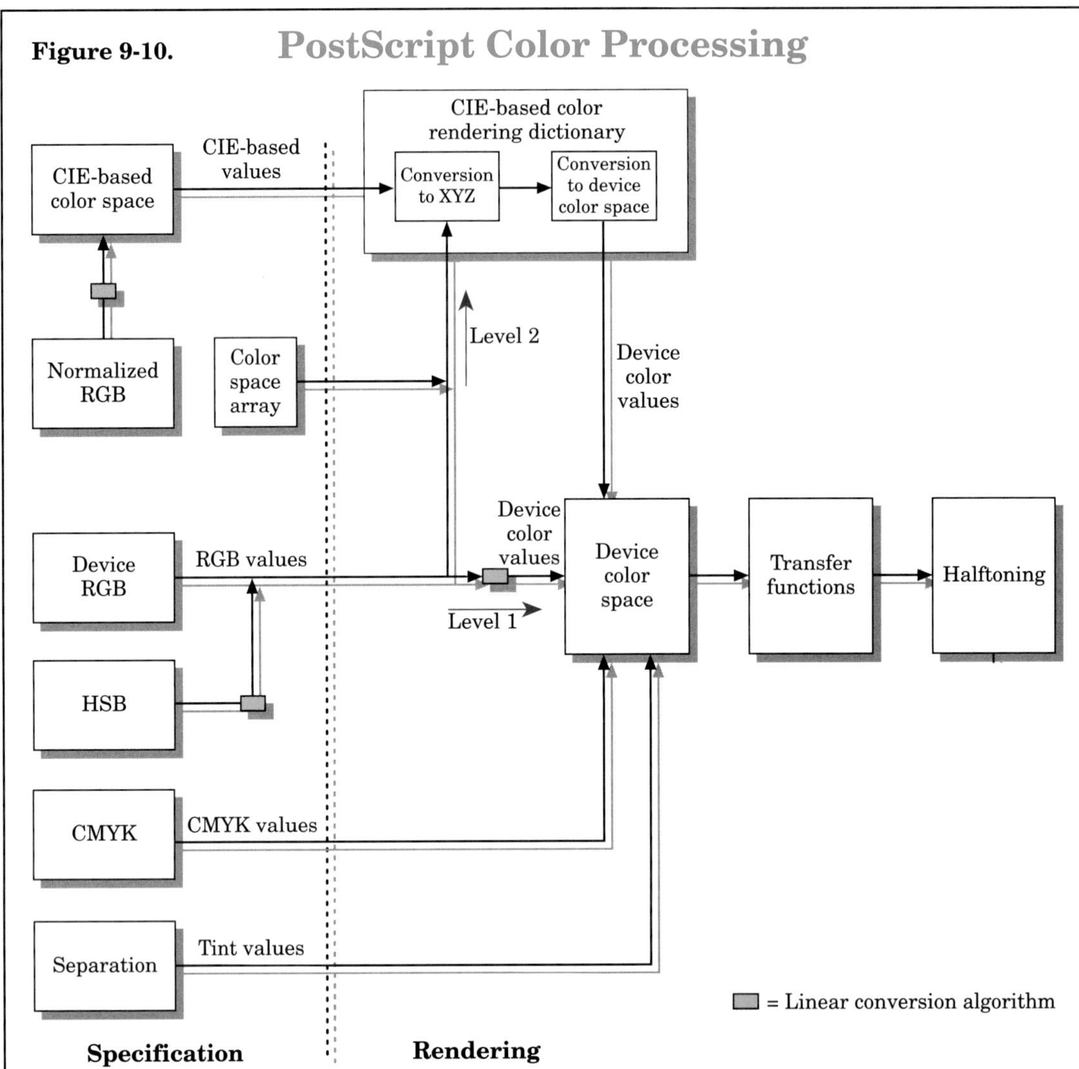

Color values of an image are specified within user space and its color space defined with the ***setcolorspace*** operator. Color values can be converted to output device color values either by the simple Level 1 conversions, or by the more sophisticated Level 2 conversions. After conversion, transfer functions and halftoning can be applied.

To use Level 2 processing, the interpreter must have:

- The color space of the source color values defined with the ***setcolorspace*** operator
- A color space array that defines how the source color values are to be converted to XYZ values
- A color rendering dictionary that acts as a lookup table to convert from XYZ values to device color values

Notice that the process works for conversion into any device color space, including both CMYK for printing and RGB for monitor display.

The separation color space is available to define colors that will not be output as composite CMYK. It has two main uses:

- To send color images to output devices that produce a single film or plate for each color and do not support composite output.
- To output special colors that are being used in addition to the CMYK set, such as bump colors and extra-trinary colors.

There is no limit on the number of colors defined as separations that the PostScript language will permit, although different applications impose their own limits on the maximum number of special colors that can be incorporated into a publication.

Level 2 images can have up to twelve bits per color instead of the usual eight bits per color. This feature is not at present supported either by user applications or by output devices, although the increasing use of PostScript in commercial color reproduction makes the introduction of twelve-bit components possible.

The Printer Driver

The role of a PostScript printer driver is to generate PostScript code when a document is printed. The driver creates code by translating from the host computer's native graphics format, such as QuickDraw routines on the Mac or Windows GDI functions on the PC. The driver is also responsible for downloading any resources, such as fonts and dictionaries, that are needed and incorporating any EPS files specified by the user into the output.

Unlike other kinds of printer drivers, a PostScript driver is not specific to the output device, but to the host platform or application. PostScript printer drivers are often written by the developers of the host application, and this tends to vary in how they handle the creation of PostScript code. Generic Level 2 drivers are also available from Adobe for all platforms.

Although PostScript code is created in user space and is therefore independent of the characteristics of the output device, it must be appropriate for the target output device. The driver does this by using printer description files that supply information specific to the output device, including the paper size, the maximum image size, and the available resolutions.

Code can be output either as ASCII characters, which can be viewed and edited in a word processor, or as binary code, which will be processed faster by the interpreter. Printer drivers and output devices that support Level 2 features can generate and accept binary code, but in most cases it is not an available option in Level 1.

The code is usually sent directly to the output device, but if necessary can be output to a file using the "Print to File" (or "Print to Disk") option. The resulting file can be examined and edited in a word processor file, but cannot subsequently be transferred directly to an output device. Instead it must be sent by a downloading utility, such as Adobe Font Downloader.

PostScript Errors

PostScript is rather prone to generating errors during execution that prevent files being output correctly. The result can be a complete refusal to output, or alternatively the wrong fonts may be printed, scrambling line breaks and page breaks. Interpreters on high-resolution output devices normally log any errors and the offending operators, but it can still be difficult to see exactly what has caused the error.

The most common PostScript errors are caused by:

- The correct fonts not being available to the interpreter.
- Interpreter memory limits being exceeded.

Font errors can be fixed easily enough by making them available to the interpreter. Memory limits are much harder to predict or resolve and can be the most difficult to decipher from the error information provided by the interpreter.

PostScript itself does not impose any limits on the number or size of things that consume memory during output, such as the number of paths that are used in a document. The output-device interpreter, however, has just a fixed amount of RAM available, and this RAM must hold all the fonts, procedures, paths, and so on used in the document, as well as graphic objects, halftone and color-rendering dictionaries, and programming constructs like stacks. High-resolution devices additionally use hard disk space to store the current page during output.

If the amount of memory available is insufficient to process a document, a ***limitcheck*** error will occur and processing will cease. Limit errors are much less likely to occur with a Level 2 interpreter, which allocates memory as it is needed. Level 1 interpreters have a fixed memory limit for each item. Typical limits in Level 1 interpreters are shown in Table 9-1.

Table 9-1. Typical limits on resources that can be held in memory in a PostScript Level 1 interpreter during processing. *Source: PostScript Language Reference Manual, p. 568.*

Quantity	Limit
userdict	200
FontDirectory	100
operand stack	500
dictionary stack	20
execution stack	250
interpreter level	10
path	1,500
dash	11
VM	240,000
file	6
image	3,300

Unfortunately, ***limitcheck*** errors cannot be predicted by user applications. Running a file-checking utility (see Chapter 10) will trap many likely errors, but unless it is able to simulate the memory management of the interpreter it cannot absolutely guarantee that a document will output successfully. The chance of a ***limitcheck*** error occurring can be minimized by:

- Splitting very long paths into multiple paths.
- Cropping images in image-editing programs, instead of using a clipping path in an illustration or page-layout application, especially where complex paths are used to define the crop area.

To minimize the possibility of errors, the printer driver should ideally generate code that conforms to Adobe's Document Structuring Convention. It should also make optimum use of memory resources during processing by bringing into memory only those items that are required by the document and removing them when they are no longer needed.

Output problems can of course be caused by user errors, such as supplying incorrect fonts or specifying composite output for a publication containing special colors. In such cases the file may be printed without PostScript errors, but does not produce the output wanted.

PostScript Limitations

PostScript is an extremely powerful graphical imaging method, and its dominance is unlikely to be challenged by any other page description language in the foreseeable future.

This method does, nevertheless, have a number of limitations, the principal ones being:

- The inflexible nature of the opaque painting model, which makes relatively simple operations, such as trapping and adding transparent color, either very complicated or completely impossible.
- The lack of true vignettes, which makes it necessary to construct tint gradations and blends from a large number of separate objects.
- The lack of page independence within the structure of the PostScript file, which makes page imposition more difficult.
- The difficulty of editing a document once it has been translated into PostScript code.
- The inability of printer drivers (including those developed by Adobe) to generate compact, error-free PostScript code.
- The frequency of execution errors when PostScript code is output.

Some of these limitations will no doubt be overcome in language extensions, while others, such as the lack of transparency, are due to basic language characteristics that are unlikely to be modified. The copious amounts of code that are generated by PostScript drivers, and the time it takes to process this code, is becoming less of an issue as RIPs become faster.

Adobe Acrobat

Adobe Acrobat is, in effect, a dialect of the PostScript language, designed to apply the concept of device-independence specifically to make electronic documents portable by avoiding problems with font compatibility and so on. A file is encoded as a **Portable Document Format (PDF) file** with the Acrobat Distiller and can then be decoded with the Acrobat Reader. The main differences between conventional PostScript and Acrobat are:

- Acrobat does not include the full set of PostScript operators.
- Acrobat page description can discard some of the high-resolution data in a page, producing a compressed and more compact file than one generated by a PostScript printer driver.
- No device-specific information can be contained in or referred to in the Acrobat file.

Acrobat 2.0 optionally retains all the information in a PostScript file when it is converted to a PDF file. It can then be turned back into PostScript code if necessary.

10 File Output

This chapter deals with the interface between the creation of color pages and their reproduction on a color printing device. Regardless of how many copies of a publication are needed, pages must be carefully prepared for output and transferred to an output device. At some point in the process, pages will be imposed, trapped, screened, rasterized, and finally imaged on to paper or on to light-sensitive film or plates.

Preparing Files for Output

When files are sent for output, there are a number of things that should be checked to make sure that the job will output correctly and will not tie up the output device for an excessive amount of time. The most important items to check, and the most common causes of output failures, are:

- Are all the links in place?
- Are all the fonts and other resources used in the file available to the output device?
- Are all the job parameters such as page size, screen rulings, and so on correct?
- Have all the colors been specified correctly?
- Are separated or composite images required?
- Have all items been correctly scaled and cropped?
- Will there be excessive demands on the output device from the way that blends and paths have been used?

File Links

A page-layout program establishes links to graphics and images when these items are placed on the page. When the page is output, the application makes sure that all the linked files are output as they are needed. However, if any of the files has been renamed or moved after placement, the links will be broken. The application may then fail to find the right files and be unable to output the page.

This situation often occurs when a publication is transferred to a different media or a different machine in preparation for output, and the hierarchy of folders or directories is altered. Similarly, a graphic may be placed but subsequently edited and resaved with a different file name.

Page-layout programs such as QuarkXPress and Aldus PageMaker allow you to review the status of all current links and modify them if necessary. As you re-open the publication, the program will also prompt you for the current locations of any needed graphics if they cannot be found.

Graphics that incorporate other linked elements create extended link paths. When the page is output, the RIP has to find and process each linked element before it can output the page.

Avoid problems with file links by:

- Reviewing links before a publication is sent for output.
- Avoiding renaming files after they have been placed.
- Avoiding extended links where possible by nesting no more than two levels of graphical elements (including fonts) on a page.
- Ensuring that all linked files are included with the job when it is sent for output.

Figure 10-1. Links dialog box in QuarkXPress.

Picture Usage

Name	Page	Type	Status	Print
Macintosh HD:...:FIGURE 3.EPS	3	EPS	OK	√
Macintosh HD:...:Figure 4.EPS.YELLOW 2	4	EPS	OK	√
Macintosh HD:...:Figure 4.EPS.MAGENTA 2	4	EPS	OK	√
Macintosh HD:...:FIGURE 8.EPS	5	EPS	OK	√
Macintosh HD:...:Figure 5.EPS.BLACK 2	5	EPS	OK	√
Macintosh HD:...: Digital Color 9:9.6 1 channel.pict	6	PICT	Missing	√
Macintosh HD:...:COLORUP 2 CMYK.TIFF	6	TIFF	OK	√
Macintosh HD:...: Digital Color 9:9.6 1 channel.tiff	6	TIFF	Missing	√
Macintosh HD:...:COLORUP 2.PICT	6	PICT	OK	√

Update Show Me

- Listing all the files used in the publication in a note that accompanies the job.
- Copying the page layout file to the same folder or directory as the linked files when transferring to a removable cartridge or MO disk.
- If the publication is too complex to copy the page layout file to the same folder or directory as the linked files on a removable cartridge or MO disk, make sure that the arrangement of files is clear to whoever will eventually output the job.

Figure 10-2. Many levels of files-within-files make the interpreter work hard. Here an EPS graphic contains another EPS as a logo, which, in turn, contains a font. To output the image, the interpreter must search for each one in turn.

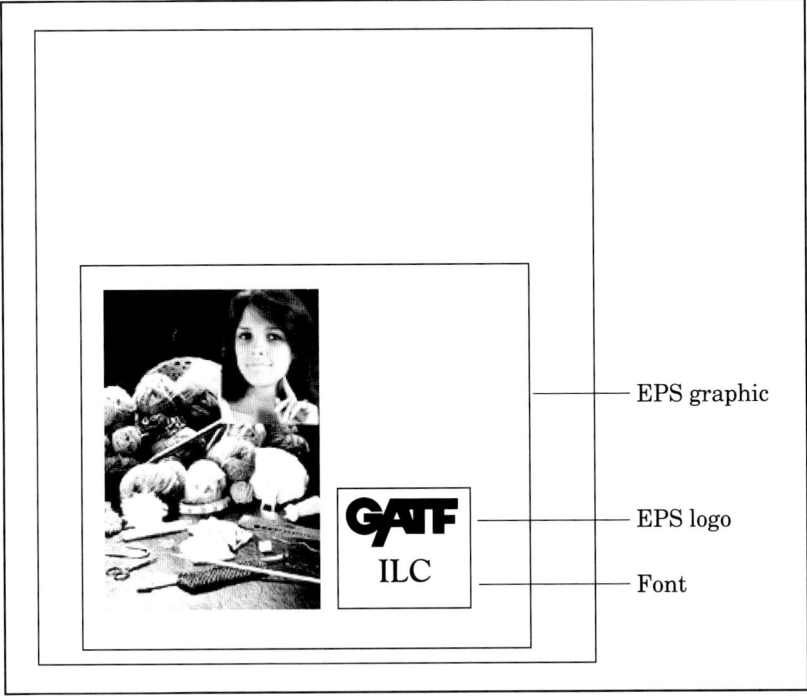

Fonts

If you have gone to the trouble to use a particular font in a publication, you will naturally want to make sure that the correct font is used on the output, not one that bears little resemblance to it. To achieve this, the output device must have the exact same font available to it as the one used in the creation of the publication.

Even fonts that have the same name but originate from different vendors can vary considerably in the cut of the letterforms, relative weight on the page, and the width of their characters. In most cases, the traditional font foundries, such as Monotype, supply the most authentic versions of classical typefaces, with complete character sets, a full range of styles and weights, and proper hinting. Obscure fonts from little-known vendors are the most likely to be unavailable at the output service or to cause output problems.

Fonts are copyrighted. In the U.S., it is considered acceptable to send a font to an output bureau for the purpose of running out a job, while in other countries, such as the UK, this would infringe upon the type vendor's copyright and it would be necessary for the bureau to acquire its own copy.

Avoid problems with fonts by:

- Checking that all fonts will be available to the output device.

- Listing all the fonts used in the publication with the exact font name, style, and vendor.
- Sending copies of any fonts that you have modified.

Job Parameters

Film orientation and polarity. Printing plants have different requirements for the presentation of film, according to the printing process and whether positive or negative plates are used. The usual requirements are shown in Table 10-1.

Table 10-1.
Film requirements for reproduction.

Process	Film emulsion[1]	Film polarity
Offset lithography	Down	Negative or positive
Gravure[2]	Down	Positive
Flexography	Up	Negative
Screen printing	Up	Positive

Notes:
1. The emulsion direction refers to the film as viewed from the right-reading side.
2. Most gravure printers accept film that has been generated for offset lithography.

Page size. Incorrect page size is a common cause of output problems. Check that the page size in the page layout is the actual trimmed size of the final job and confirm that the image width of the output device is wide enough to accommodate the page size.

Transfer functions. Transfer functions should only be applied to linearize the output from an uncalibrated output device.

Halftone parameters. Set the appropriate screen ruling, screen angle, and dot shape. The output device will substitute alternatives if the ones you specify cannot be achieved, or if more precise screening algorithms are available. If no halftone parameters are specified, the output device will use default settings. When sending files to a high-resolution PostScript Level 2 device, Accurate Screens should always be specified. If better screening technologies are available, they will be used and any PostScript parameters will be ignored.

Color

Color images and publications can be output either as **separations** or as **composite** color. Sending composite images means that less time is spent preparing files for output, but, for some devices, separated output is necessary.

Conventional printing processes need a plate for each color that is printed, and every plate requires a separate film. The output device will have to extract the separate colors from graphics and images, unless the information is sent separately. In the case of images, this can be done by saving separate files in EPS-DCS format, and, in the case of graphics and page-layout information, by sending files for output as separations.

Digital color printing devices do not require separate plates for each color, as they extract the values for each color from the files during output. Files sent to digital printers and proofing devices should always be sent as composites.

Imagesetters always generate separate films for each color. They may require files to be separated or composite, depending on how they process the color information. The bureau or trade shop will advise on whether to send separated or composite files.

Composite color objects (images or graphics) can be saved as either TIFF or EPS files, but the TIFF file format does not currently support separated colors. Separated objects must be saved as EPS files, using the DCS format.

Note that creating separated files does not mean converting them to CMYK, but simply extracting the separate color components so they can be processed individually. Conversion to CMYK must have already been carried out before a DCS file can be created.

A special color, which requires a fifth printing plate, has to be output to film separately. There are two things that must be avoided to prevent the special color from being converted into a process color. First, the option to convert colors to process in the page-layout application ("Process Separation" in QuarkXPress; "All to Process in Aldus Pagemaker") must **not** be checked. Secondly, the object containing the special must **not** be saved as a composite TIFF, but as an EPS file.

Avoid problems with color output by:

- Sending composite color to a digital color printer.
- Sending either separated or composite color to an imagesetter according to the requirements of the output service.
- Specifying separated color for objects containing any special colors.

Figure 10-3. Work Flow for Composite and Separated Output

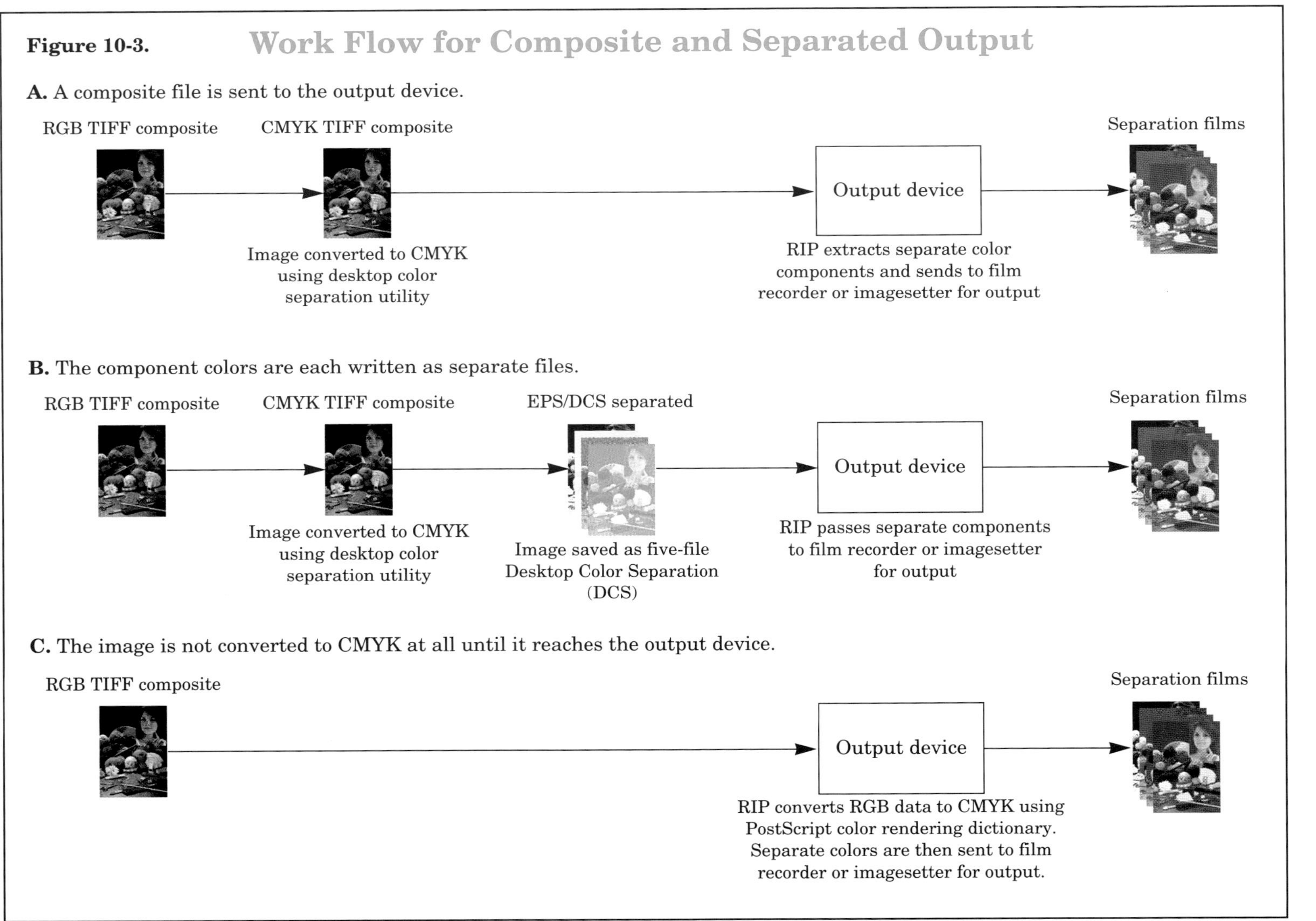
A. A composite file is sent to the output device.
RGB TIFF composite
CMYK TIFF composite
Image converted to CMYK using desktop color separation utility
Output device
RIP extracts separate color components and sends to film recorder or imagesetter for output
Separation films
B. The component colors are each written as separate files.
RGB TIFF composite
CMYK TIFF composite
EPS/DCS separated
Image converted to CMYK using desktop color separation utility
Image saved as five-file Desktop Color Separation (DCS)
Output device
RIP passes separate components to film recorder or imagesetter for output
Separation films
C. The image is not converted to CMYK at all until it reaches the output device.
RGB TIFF composite
Output device
RIP converts RGB data to CMYK using PostScript color rendering dictionary. Separate colors are then sent to film recorder or imagesetter for output.
Separation films

Other methods of avoiding problems with color output include: using an appropriate color separation utility or color management system to convert to CMYK, rather than the color separation facility of the page-makeup application or creating graphic elements in the CMYK mode when possible, instead of creating them in RGB and allowing the color values to be modified during conversion to CMYK.

Scaling

In an ideal world, original images and illustrations would always be created at the same size as the intended reproduction. In reality, it is often necessary to enlarge or reduce them. There are three ways of scaling an image: specifying a scaling ratio; specifying a percentage enlargement or reduction; or specifying the new dimensions.

To determine the scaling ratio, simply take one dimension of the final size of the image and divide it by the corresponding dimension on the original. The percentage enlargement or reduction is found by multiplying the scaling ratio by 100. For example, a 4×5-in. (102×127-mm) transparency is to be enlarged to fit a 6-in. (152-mm) column. Dividing the final size by the original size (6/4) gives a scaling ratio of 1.5, or an enlargement of 150%.

In many instances, it is only necessary to specify the new height or width, with the proportions locked to ensure that both dimensions are scaled together. Choose the most important dimension to specify, which is usually determined by the column width or design grid of the publication. Scaling vector objects, such as type and graphics, has no effect on image quality, as the output device will automatically use the best resolution possible.

If the file size is locked when images are scaled, the image will be resampled. This will alter the amount of data available for each scanned pixel, and the relationship between the size of the pixels on the original image and the screen frequency of the reproduction will be changed.

If a sampled image is enlarged significantly, the individual image pixels may become noticeable unless interpolation is applied by resampling the image. Scaling an image down will improve resolution, but unless it is resampled at the same time the resulting file will be larger than memory. Guidelines for choosing the correct scanning resolution for the output were described in Chapter 6.

The bounding box coordinates of the EPS file define the size at which the object will be output, regardless of whether it is

Figure 10-4.
Scaling.

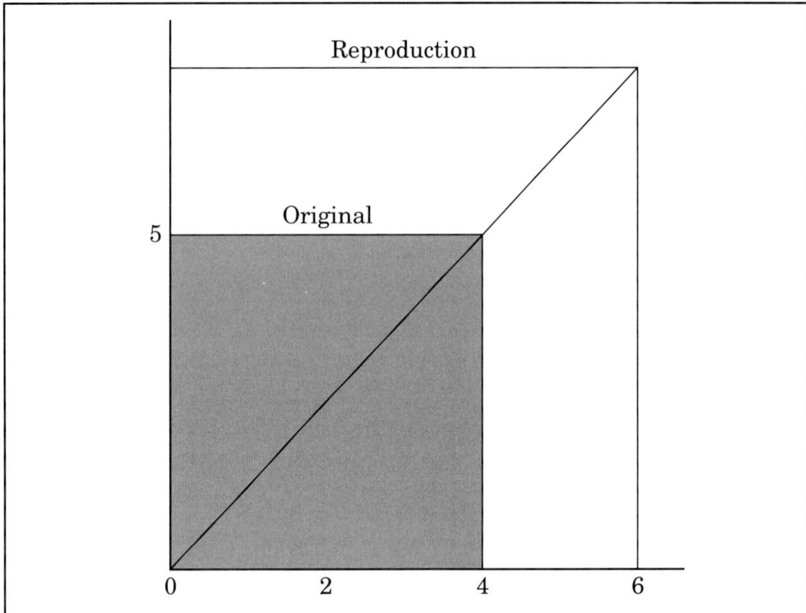

A graphic or picture is usually scaled by simply entering the new size. The scaling factor can be found by dividing the reproduction size by the original size, and, if necessary, this can be converted to a percentage by multiplying by 100.

a graphic or bitmap. The low-resolution preview of a bitmap image may look "jagged" on screen, but the resolution of the final reproduction will be defined by the high-resolution TIFF or PICT file to which the EPS is linked.

In PostScript output, scaling takes place prior to halftoning when the page is sent to the output device and rasterized. Scaling thus has no effect on the screen ruling of the printed image.

Avoid problems with scaling bitmaps by:

- Scaling and resampling them in an image-editing program to maintain the correct relationship between resolution and screen frequency.
- Whenever possible returning to the original so that it can be captured at the appropriate resolution, since scaling and resampling can cause some information to be lost from the image.

Cropping

If an EPS image is cropped, only the bounding box coordinates are altered and the actual sampled image itself remains unchanged. The file size will remain the same and the entire image will still be processed and rasterized. This can take a

Figure 10-5. Cropping an EPS image.

Cropping an image in a page layout program does not alter the image file, which must be processed by the interpreter before the unwanted areas are discarded. You can reduce file size and output faster if you crop in an image editing application.

large amount of extra time during output, as the RIP first processes the whole image and then executes the cropping instructions.

If a cutout around an image is required rather than a rectangular crop, it is defined with a cropping path. Everything beyond the cutout will then be discarded when the image is output (although like a rectangular crop, the cutout does not remove the unwanted data until the final stage in the output). The combination of complex paths and cropped images makes limit errors even more likely, and the flatness of the cropping path should be set as high as possible. If a large amount of the image is to be discarded it can also be worthwhile to make a rectangular crop in an image-editing program before creating the cutout.

Avoid problems with cropping sampled images by:

- Cropping in an image-editing program, unless the amount that is to be discarded is small.
- Avoiding complex cropping paths where possible.
- Increasing the flatness value of a cropping path.

Figure 10-6.
A cutout *(bottom)* is a crop with a nonrectangular cropping path. Making a rectangular crop first in an image-editing application *(center)* helps to minimize file sizes, especially on large images where the cutout is only a small part of the original image *(top)*.

Blends

Tint gradations and blends in graphics can give rise to two problems: processor overload and banding or shade-stepping.

A gradation is imaged as a series of lines of successively changing tonal values. Each line is effectively a separate object, and the PostScript interpreter has to render each one in turn. The more gradations there are in a graphic, the longer it will take to process. A complex graphic can take an unacceptably long time to output, or even cause the job to crash through a PostScript limit error. On some high-end recorders, there is a limit in the number of gradation steps that can be output, and again, processing will fail if this is exceeded.

Shade-stepping occurs when the transition between one tonal value and the next is visible. It can be seen when there are too few gray levels for a smooth, continuous gradation, and its effects are exaggerated by the sensitivity of the visual apparatus to edge definition. Shade-stepping can be minimized by using the maximum number of gray levels available, which in an eight-bit gray scale is 2.6 steps for each 1% change in dot size.

Figure 10-7. Adding a small amount of noise *(bottom)* can reduce or eliminate banding on blends and gradations *(top)*.

Avoid problems with blends by:

- Using the maximum number of steps possible in the gradation.
- Adding noise to a gradation in an image-editing application if shade-stepping is thought likely.
- Avoiding special color blends where possible.
- Converting complex graphics with multiple gradations and blends into sampled images.

To convert an EPS graphic to a sampled image or bitmap:

- Open the EPS file in an image-editing program.
- Set the resolution to twice the screen ruling at which the job will be printed.
- Turn off anti-aliasing.
- Save as a TIFF file.

The sampled version of the graphic will be the exact same on the final printed job as it was in the original object version, and, although the file size will be larger and will take longer to read into memory, it will be processed much faster. Note that if it subsequently becomes necessary to scale up the image by more than a small amount, the EPS-to-TIFF conversion of the original graphic should be repeated so that the image has the correct resolution.

Curves

Chapter 5 describes how PostScript outputs a curve as a series of points connected by straight lines. A smooth curve has many points and a low flatness value, but each connecting line is treated as a separate object that must be rendered

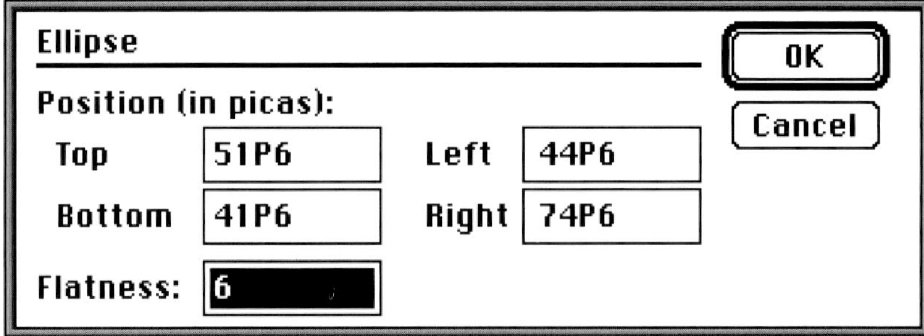

Figure 10-8. (A) Set curve flatness to 6–10 pixels when sending pages to a high-resolution device to minimize the time the interpreter spends processing paths.

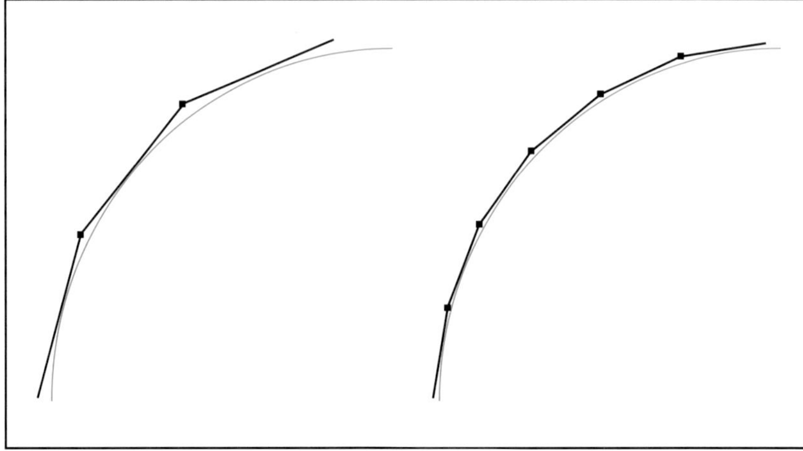

(B) The more points used to define a curve, the smoother it is, but the longer it will take to process and output. You can alter the number of points through the flatness property.

when the file is output. On a low-resolution device, such as a laser printer, this will not cause a problem, since the interpreter will rationalize the number of points to the resolution of the device. A high-resolution output device will be capable of inserting many more points, and, unless the curve flatness is set high enough, the output time may be extended.

In practice, curve flatness does not become visible until the setting reaches a value that is determined by the output-device resolution. It is usually possible to set a flatness value of six to ten pixels for output on a high-resolution device. Long and complex curves can cause PostScript limit errors, and sometimes it is necessary to split curves into two or more separate objects to avoid this problem.

File Checking

Having a job fail during output on an imagesetter can be a disruptive and costly occurrence. Potential output problems can be anticipated by running a **pre-flight check** that tests how the PostScript code will perform when it is run on a high-resolution device.

You can identify some potential problems prior to dispatching your job by making a low-resolution laser print. A successful laser print is not a complete guarantee that films will output successfully, as there are some possible problems (such as PostScript code errors) that will not necessarily be flagged. Naturally, if all the fonts needed to run a job are available to the laser printer because they are on the user's hard disk, but subsequently are not included when the job is sent for output on a high-resolution device, the job will not output successfully.

If the pages have been output as PostScript code, a higher level of assurance can be provided by the use of file-checking utilities such as Elseware's CheckList, Island Checker, and LaserCheck. Some of these utilities make a laser printer emulate an imagesetter, and thus pick up problems that might not be caught on an ordinary laser print. Others allow the user to proof a PostScript file on screen and display information, such as the presence of embedded files, most recent modification dates, and so on.

Another method of file checking is to use Adobe Acrobat to distill the pages into Acrobat PDF files. The distilling process involves executing the PostScript code, and during this process any errors tend to be flagged. Turning the Acrobat files back into PostScript results in more compact files and faster, more reliable execution when output.

Marking-up Files

If you are sending a job to a printer or an output service, you will have a much better chance of avoiding output problems if you send the following along with your files:

- A list of all the files used in the job, and details of file formats used.
- A list of the applications (and version numbers) used to prepare the files.
- A list of all the fonts used, with the exact font name, style, and the name of the manufacturer of each font.
- A specification for the job that identifies details such as the title, number of pages, output size, and any screening parameters.
- A low-resolution proof.

Even if the proof is only a black-and-white laser print, it will help the output service to resolve questions such as the correct placement, scaling, and cropping of graphics and images.

Many printers and trade shops have prepared information sheets and checklists for their customers to help reduce the possibility of files that will not run. The Scitex Graphic Arts Users Association has produced comprehensive guidelines (Computer-Ready Electronic Files, or CREF) on how to prepare and present files in digital form, and many output services use these guidelines as a basis for agreement with their clients. A clear understanding of what is expected avoids disputes over payment for work on client-supplied files. (The CREF guidelines appear in full on the CD.)

Making Alterations

Alterations are an inevitable feature of most printed publications, and it is essential that they are handled systematically to avoid spiralling costs. An approval cycle (as described in Chapter 11) should be devised and corrections made wherever possible at the most appropriate point.

Alterations to a job that is in production can be made by sending a new file, by having the output service edit the existing files, or by manually stripping in corrections to the films. The output service should be able to recommend which route to take, depending on the time and cost constraints of the job.

Alterations and edits to a job prior to output normally result in the application adding the changes to the file. By performing a ***Save as. . .*** with a new filename, instead of a ***Save,*** the application rewrites the file and produces a more economical description of the object. It is a good practice to do a "Save as" immediately prior to output, although it is essential to ensure that file links are not broken in the process.

Output Services

In terms of output services, you have these choices: sending your job directly to the printer for output; using the services of a trade shop or output bureau; or developing your own in-house output facility.

Going direct to the printer eliminates one link in the supplier chain and avoids a possible area of conflict. On the other hand, specialist output services can add value to your job and ensure that any problems are resolved before the films are received by the printer.

Many service bureaus began life as trade typesetters and tend to operate under different disciplines than color reproduction specialists do. One indicator is how often they calibrate the output from the imagesetter—a good operator will output and measure a test element once or twice a day to make sure that exposure and processing conditions are not causing a drift in the dot values that are being output on film.

In-house film output is appropriate for publishers with the resources to acquire and operate an imagesetter or film recorder and the associated processing. Imagesetters are usually the most expensive prepress equipment investment. Low-cost models are available but they are not as consistent or as productive as the more costly versions. Low-cost imagesetters are not normally equipped with register punches, and the possible additional stripping cost when the pages are imposed should also be considered.

When using outside services, some important questions to ask are:

- What are the estimated output costs per page?
- What rate is charged for alterations?
- What type of equipment is used and what is its technical capability (such as resolution)?
- What resident fonts, color rendering dictionaries, etc., are available?
- What are the maximum output dimensions?
- What kind of proofing is available?
- How far downstream can they take the job? For example, can they produce one-piece imposed and punched film ready for platemaking?

- What communication links are available for file transfer and what are the costs?
- How long will files be stored after output and in what form?

When an output service receives a job, they will normally check your list of files, fonts, graphics, and so on, and any proofs supplied with the job. Next, they will load the page-layout files and check that all EPS and TIFF files are in place and correctly named and linked. They may also check that any user-defined trapping has been done correctly; that colors have been defined as separate or composite as appropriate; that fonts and any other necessary resources are available; and that any other job parameters are correct. After making any necessary adjustments, the job will be processed and finally checked against your low-resolution proof and any specifications you have supplied.

If you have sent the job as PostScript code (using the "Print-to-Disk" option), the output service will only be able to examine the job with a preview or file checking utility.

Trapping

When a design calls for areas of color to abut, there is a risk that slight misregister during printing will cause a white line to appear between the two colors. Misregister of as little as 0.0005 in. (0.01 mm) can be visible to the eye if the colors are highly contrasting, and while register between printed colors is usually held to an accuracy between 0.001 in. and 0.004 in. (0.025 and 0.1 mm), other factors, such as paper

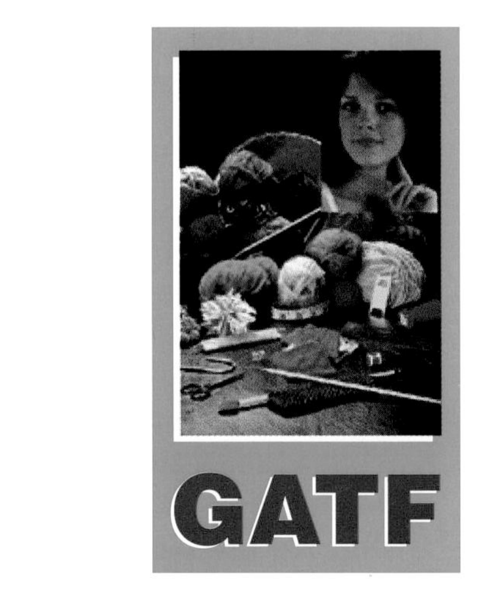

Figure 10-9. Misregister occurs when colors are not printed in the correct position or (in PostScript processing) when the imagesetter cannot image the films with sufficient accuracy.

stretch and variation in the dimensions of film output, also contribute to the perception of misregister.

Spreading the two colors into each other slightly prevents the white line from appearing. This process, known as **trapping,** can be completed by manual or by electronic methods.

The amount of misregister to allow for depends mainly on the size and dimensional stability of the paper. A multicolor press holds perfect register between colors once the plates have been positioned, and any misregister is caused by other factors, such as slight errors in fit between the films; the necessary tolerance in positioning the plates on the press; and paper stretch during printing. Printing on web presses and on sheetfed presses that do not have enough units to print all the colors in one pass will lead to much greater variations in register.

Figure 10-10. Trapping with conventional photographic methods is simply a case of spreading colors into each other slightly. This cannot be done in PostScript, so an extra trap object is created.

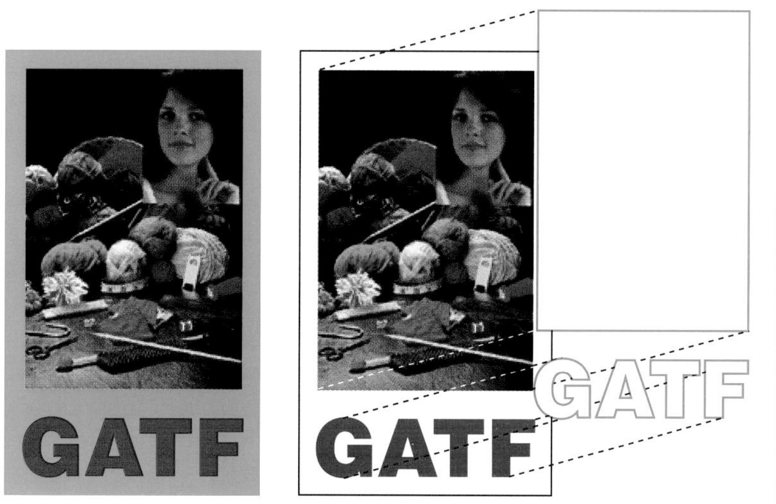

To provide trapping of the images in the illustration at the left, a 0.75-pt. cyan box was placed around the picture and set to overprint. Also, a 0.75-pt. cyan outline of the letters "GATF" was placed around the magenta letters and also set to overprint. (The background of the illustration at the right has been removed to make it easier to see the trap objects.)

Many printers are achieving very high standards of plate registration, aided by punch-register systems and computer-controlled cylinder movements. The inevitable spread that occurs on press when wet ink is transferred to the sheet is often enough to trap any remaining misregister, and, as a result, many printers do not require trapping at all. Nevertheless, trapping is an important consideration that should not be overlooked, and it is essential that the amount of trap is agreed to by the printer.

Creating the spreads (where an object is enlarged outward) and chokes (where the background of an object is enlarged inward) is a skilled and time-consuming process when traditional film-based methods are used. Many complex graphics are either difficult or impossible to trap manually, and there is inevitably a degree of variation depending on the individual stripper's interpretation of the job. Electronic trapping offers much greater control and precision, and offers the possibility of creating traps that could not be generated manually, such as color blends.

Trapping can take place on the desktop or at the output stage. On the desktop, it can be completed in illustration programs, such as Adobe Illustrator and Aldus Freehand, when an extra PostScript object is created by stroking the border between two objects. The stroke is then set to overprint the two objects. Since the stroke straddles the boundary, its width should be twice the trap width that you want to create.

It is also possible to specify output preferences in a desktop page-layout application. Trapping in QuarkXPress or PageMaker is more efficient than creating individual trap objects, as trap settings can be applied to a whole document as well as to individual graphics. The trap settings in Quark are application preferences, and thus are not included with the document when it is sent to an output service. They must be sent separately so that they can be inserted at output.

At the output stage, dedicated trapping utilities running on workstations, the trapping facilities in a high-end CEPS system, or RIP-based trapping programs are used. High-end CEPS systems and dedicated trapping programs analyze the page to locate regions of color that touch and then trapping is handled automatically. Trapping utilities such as Aldus TrapWise, Farrukh Trapper, and Island Trapper apply traps to EPS files, running largely unattended after the initial setup. The three methods of trapping are:

- **Vector trapping.** The graphic objects in the file are analyzed and new objects added to the file where necessary.
- **Raster trapping.** The file is rasterized and the individual pixels compared, with new pixels added.
- **Hybrid trapping.** The file is rasterized and examined pixel by pixel, with new trap objects added to the file.

Automatic trapping utilities are much more powerful than manual stripping methods or desktop trapping, but their relatively high cost makes them more suited to output services than to publishers. In many cases, trapping is best applied by the output service or printer. They will have more knowledge of the specific requirements of the press and the paper and will probably have more powerful trapping software at their disposal.

Trapping is a tedious and time-consuming process to perform on complex graphics and it is difficult to apply at all in cases where one of the objects is a blend, or where more than two colors touch. However, should you choose to carry out trapping yourself, these are the basic rules:

- Spread lighter colors into darker colors.
- Keep the trap width to a minimum to avoid an unwanted border or the appearance of a third color.
- If the two colors trapped are equally dark, spread the background color into a foreground object.
- Spread backgrounds into photographic images.
- Do not trap white knockouts.
- Do not trap within images.
- Do not trap type in small point sizes or with fine strokes or serifs.
- Use color combinations that allow you to overprint the type onto the background.
- Use common colors for an object and its background.
- Avoid traps greater than 0.004 in. (0.1 mm) for sheetfed work, since this is the limit of normal press misregister.
- Remember that most programs are only able to handle trapping information on separated files not composites.

Imposition

When a job is printed the number of pages on the printing plate will depend on the size of the finished job and the press format. There can be up to sixteen pages (or even more on small format jobs like pharmaceutical inserts) on each plate, and it is essential that all the pages are positioned accurately relative to each other so that when the job is folded the pages appear in the correct sequence. A single transposition can result in a large quantity of printing being scrapped, and even seemingly minor errors can create extra work in binding or unpleasant effects in the finished job.

The imposition process is accomplished by:

- Stripping page film together either manually or with automatic step-and-repeat equipment.

- Using high-end CEPS equipment and dedicated work-stations.
- Using desktop imposition programs.

In the past, designers and publishers have not needed to be concerned with the mechanics of how a job is imposed, although knowledge of the imposition scheme can help in optimizing the use of color in a publication. Desktop publishing systems are concerned mainly with the page as the unit of production, and extending this to page imposition may seem the next logical step, as it increases the publisher's control over production and allows them to deliver complete plate-ready output to the printer. However, it also means taking responsibility for a complex area of production that is usually the domain of the printer.

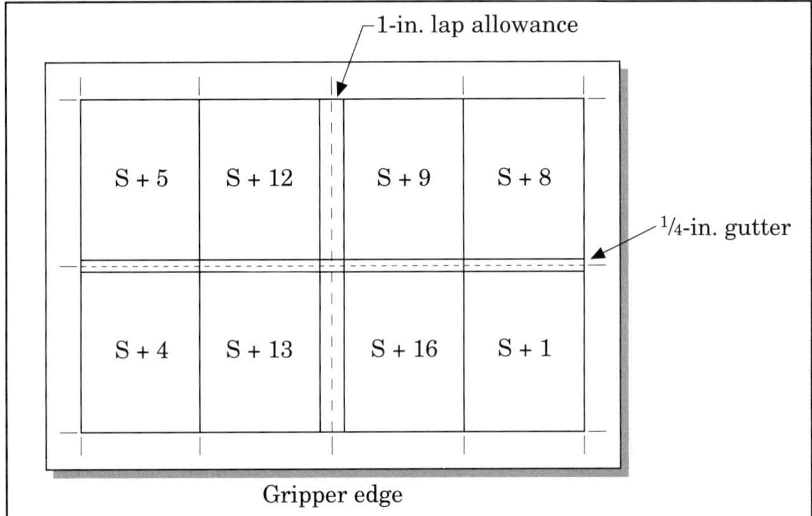

Figure 10-11. Imposition scheme for a stitched publication. S is the section number, with sections numbered from zero outward.

Moving from output of pages to output of imposed sections brings about some additional complexities and changes the production workflow. Some of the issues to consider are:

- The workflow will ideally be fully digital, and if color separated films are received from other sources, such as advertisers, they must be combined with the digital data after output.
- The maximum output width of the imagesetter determines the size of the film that can be output. The most common installations have an output width of 18–20 in. (450–500 mm), which allows four pages to be output on a single piece of film.

- Any alterations and corrections will require re-output of the entire film, unless they are to be stripped in manually.
- The larger the size of the piece of film, the greater the likelihood of slight inconsistencies in output size, which will lead to misregister.
- The time taken to "rip" for a full sheet with eight or more pages is considerable, and it is often more convenient to output smaller batches of pages depending on the overall workflow and other jobs in progress.
- Manually imposing page film is a relatively straightforward operation, and the amount of time that is saved by automating the process is not as much as the productivity gains that can be made elsewhere.
- Large amounts of storage are needed for rasterized image data, even if they are stored only temporarily until a job is completed.

Imposition programs, such as Aldus PressWise, Farrukh Systems Impostrip, and INPosition (a QuarkXPress extension), can be used to impose individual pages and incorporate gutters, trims, and so on, as long as the printer is in agreement about the actual folding method. Some imposition programs produce a scaled-down flat plan that can be checked before the job is output.

Factors that are taken into account when planning an imposition scheme include:

- The size of the finished job.
- The size of sheet or reel that is printed.
- The folding and binding equipment that will be used.
- The total number of pages.
- The number of pages in a section or signature.
- The paper grain direction.
- Any allowance for laps.
- Any allowance for shingling.

Laps are added to folded sections to allow the suckers on saddle-stitching machines to open the section up so that it can be dropped onto the saddle. The lap allowance is usually between 0.25 and 0.4 in. (6 and 10 mm).

Shingling of pages is necessary in saddle-stitched publications that are more than 0.1 in. (2.5 mm) thick (48 pages of 70-lb. [100-gsm] coated, book paper). The inner sections are pushed outwards as they are inserted into the other sections,

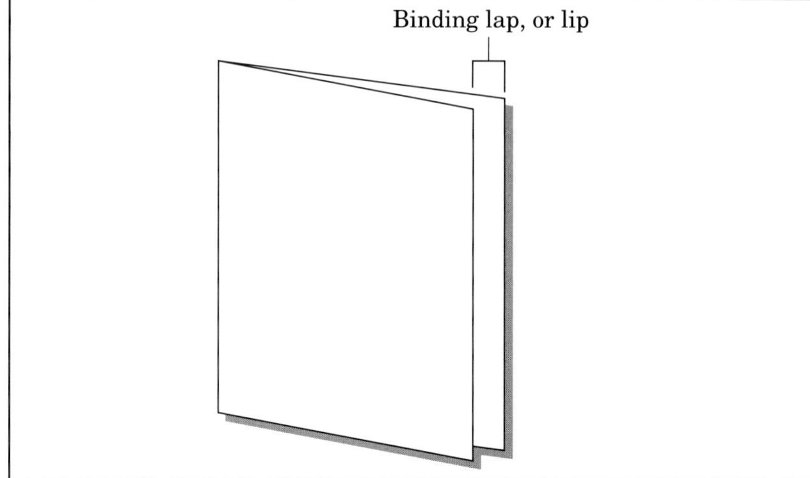

Figure 10-12.
A lap is created so that the binding equipment can open the folded section in preparation for inserting and stitching.

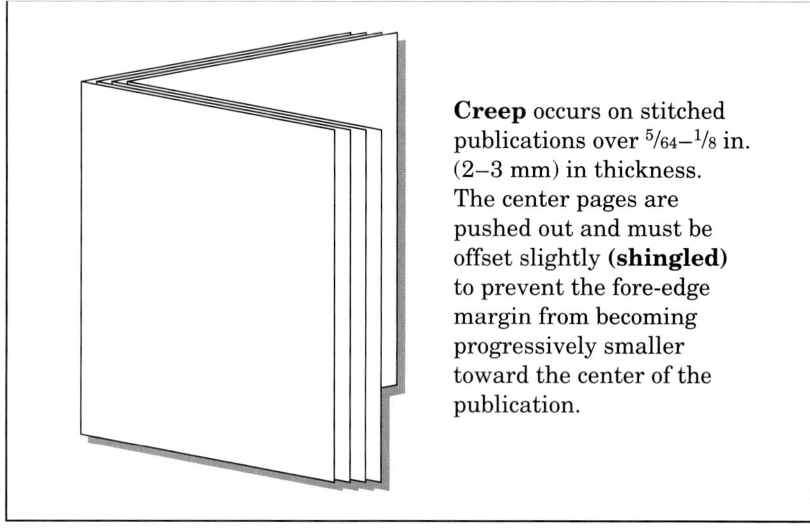

Creep occurs on stitched publications over 5/64–1/8 in. (2–3 mm) in thickness. The center pages are pushed out and must be offset slightly **(shingled)** to prevent the fore-edge margin from becoming progressively smaller toward the center of the publication.

Figure 10-13.
Shingling.

and fore-edge margins will be truncated unless the pages are offset slightly to compensate.

If the width of film that can be output by the imagesetter is less than the width of an imposed sheet, it is possible to output strips of film that can be joined together after output. Registration tables to facilitate this process are used by some printers.

If the imposition is being done by stripping films, it is almost always worth sending pages as **printer's pairs** instead of single pages. There is no gutter or lap to include between the two pages at the spine (except in certain kinds of glued bindings), and it is very easy to determine which pages make up the printer's pair:

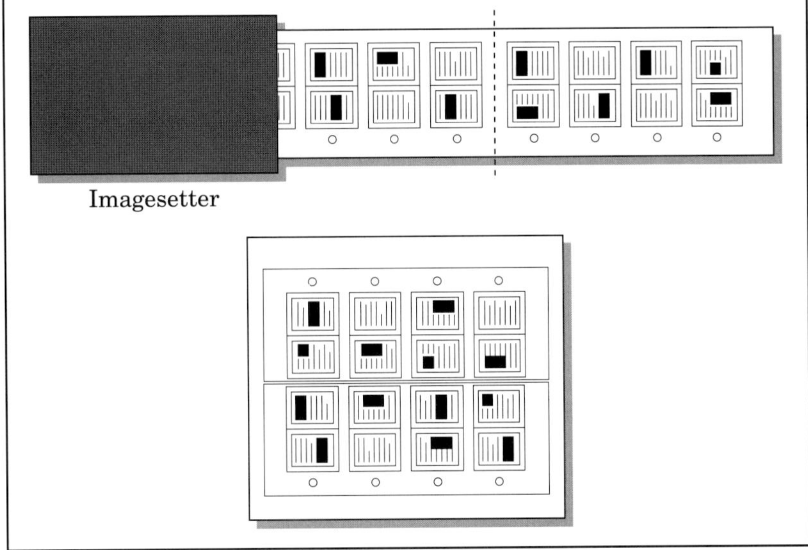

Figure 10-14. An imagesetter generates film strips when the width of the imposed sheet exceeds the maximum film width that the machine can output. These film strips are then combined.

- For saddle-stitched jobs, such as magazines, the page numbers of the printer's pair add up to one more than the number of pages in the publication.
- For gathered jobs, such as books, the page numbers of the printer's pair add up to one more than the number of pages in the section plus the number of pages in all the previous sections.
- The odd-numbered page always appears on the right of the printer's pair.

Register marks on the pages allow individual films to be imposed faster and more accurately, either manually or by automated step-and-repeat equipment.

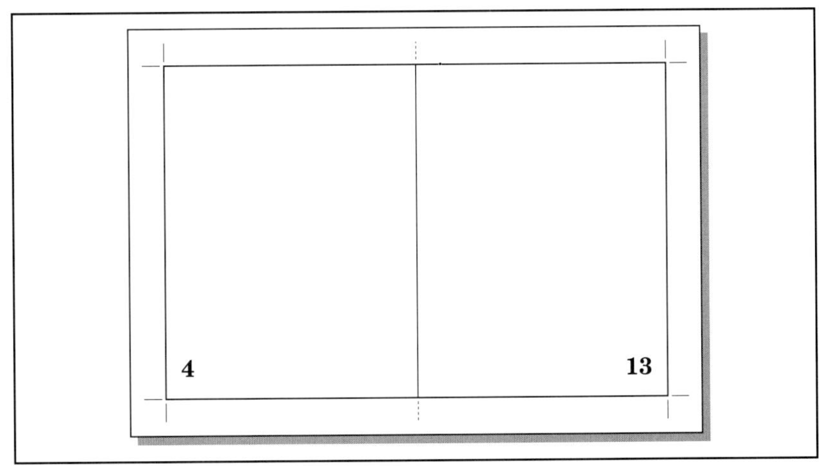

Figure 10-15. Not every job can benefit from being output in fully imposed form, but it is almost always worth preparing pages as **printer's pairs.**

The Output Device

A PostScript output device has two basic components: a PostScript interpreter that receives and processes PostScript data and a marking engine to image the material being output. Marking engines transfer colorant directly to paper (in the case of digital printers and proofers) or expose a light-sensitive medium (in the case of imagesetters and platesetters).

The marking engine needs to have the image in a form that it can transfer. It needs a binary or gray scale value for each device pixel, depending on whether the marking engine supports variable intensities of image through dye sublimation or other gray scale output.

The process of converting the received image data into a bitmap of device pixel values is known as **raster image processing.** It involves a series of steps:

- First, PostScript code is executed by the interpreter, which converts the user space coordinates into the coordinate system used by the output device and produces a **display list** of vector drawing instructions in an internal device-specific format.
- Next, transfer functions and halftoning are applied to images.
- Finally, the display list and the raster images are converted to device pixels in the address grid of the output device.

Although conceptually the interpreter is part of a PostScript output device, it does not have to physically reside within the device itself. It can be an independent system, capable of serving one or more marking engines, or it can be located within a standard platform host computer. An interpreter can also be either hardware-based (for fast execution) or software-based (for ease of upgrading).

Many high-end systems use Adobe's Configurable PostScript Interpreter (CPSI), which, as its name suggests, is a software interpreter that can be configured by the output device vendor to exploit device-specific features. Advantages of using a CPSI are:

- The system can enable the user to edit the PostScript data if necessary, altering features such as the page size, resolution, and the use of fonts.
- Screen previews can be incorporated in the system, displaying the publication on a monitor so that the user can see exactly how it will be output before downloading to the marking engine.

- The memory and processor resources of a workstation or powerful desktop system can be used.
- The interpreter can work in conjunction with Adobe's PixelBurst display list processor ASIC to accelerate output.
- Proprietary, device-specific features, such as screening technologies, can be integrated into the system.

Instead of rasterizing the display list directly to device pixels, it can be translated into an alternative proprietary format for output on high-end output devices. This is done either through proprietary high-end **gateway systems** or by CPSI systems. Once the data has been converted to a proprietary format it is possible to apply high-end features, such as screening techniques.

The amount of data created when a file is rasterized for high-resolution output is approximately 100 times greater than on a laser printer. Because of the much higher memory requirements, high-resolution devices do not output an entire page at once, but divide the output area into horizontal bands. The rasterized page is stored temporarily on a hard disk while each band is sent in turn to the marking engine. For this reason, high-resolution systems are known as **band devices** rather than **page devices.**

There are many benefits in using the RIP to carry out functions that are properly executed in device space, since it exploits the processing power available and also allows editing to take place right up until final output. Functions that can be carried out in the RIP include:

- Color conversion to CMYK.
- Separating composite images.
- Halftoning and dot-gain compensation.
- Trapping.
- Imposition.
- OPI image storage.

Conversion to CMYK, dot-gain compensation, and trapping are all highly device-dependent operations, requiring information about specific device characteristics and the final output media if they are to be carried out accurately. By using the RIP for these functions, page descriptions remain device-independent longer and are more portable. They can then be distributed to different output locations with every confidence that the results will be acceptable in each case.

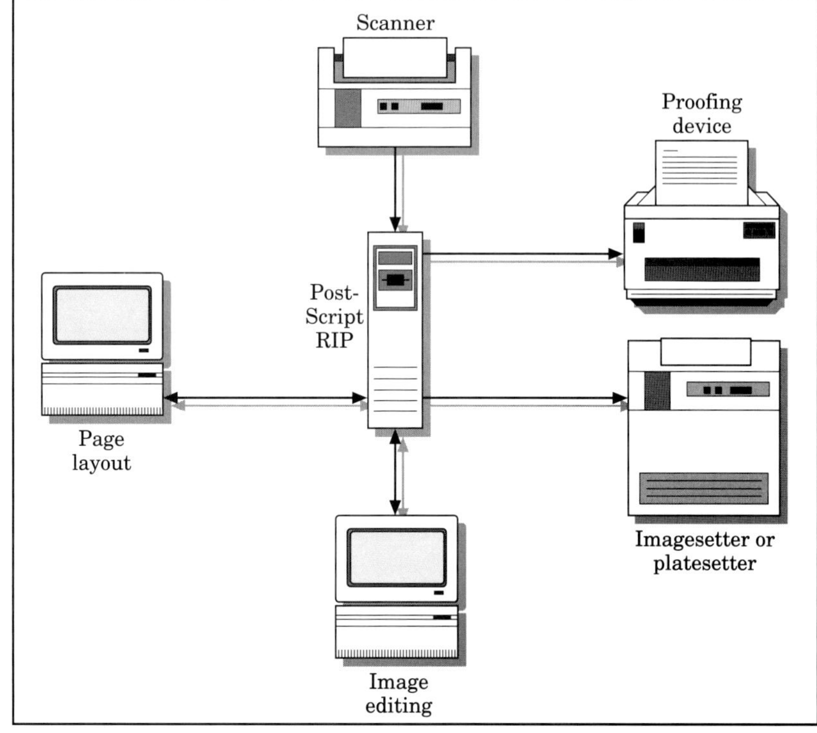

Figure 10-16. Increasingly powerful processors make it possible to turn the RIP into an all-purpose OPI server, a color conversion and trapping system that can support multiple output devices.

RIP technology is an area of rapid technological advances, with foreseeable developments including multiple processors, powerful hardware components like the PixelBurst coprocessor, and more intelligent software architectures.

Halftone Considerations

A halftone is built from individual device pixels, which in an imagesetter have only two possible values, black or white. The device pixels can be "switched on" (imaged by the marking engine) according to the requirements of the image to be halftoned in two principal ways: by a spot function or by a threshold array.

A **spot function** is a mathematical function that controls the sequence in which device pixels within a halftone cell will change from white to black as the tonal value specified for the cell increases. At the time that the spot function is specified the resolution of the target output device does not need to be known, as the function is resolution-independent.

A spot function is specified by the user application according to the dot shape chosen by the user. In applications that allow custom dot shapes it is possible to define the spot function by entering PostScript code.

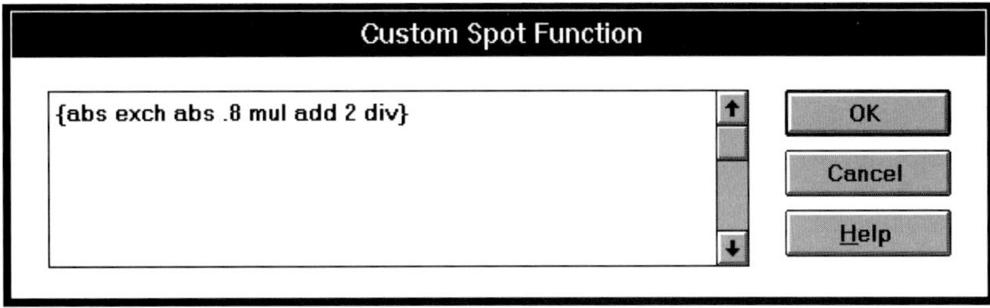

Figure 10-17. Halftone dot shapes can be user-defined with the custom-spot function found in many applications programs.

Figure 10-18. Threshold array.

A

63	60	52	40	44	48	56	64
55	35	32	20	24	28	36	57
47	27	15	8	12	16	29	49
43	23	11	4	1	5	17	37
39	19	7	3	2	9	21	41
51	31	14	10	6	13	25	45
59	34	26	22	18	30	33	53
62	54	46	42	38	50	58	61

B

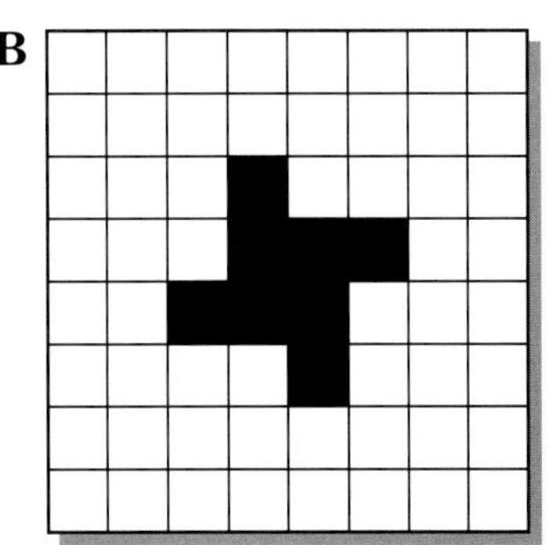

A threshold array defines the order in which device pixels are imaged as the gray scale value increases. In this example, a halftone cell consists of an 8×8 array of device pixels that are switched on from the center outward (A). A 12% dot, corresponding to a gray scale value of 8 in this threshold array is shown in B. A small threshold array can be constructed and tiled across the whole output device address grid. Small differences between cells permit more flexibility in the screening systems used.

A **threshold array** allocates a threshold value to each device pixel. When an image is sent to the interpreter, it compares the threshold value of each device pixel with the tonal value of the corresponding region of the image. All the device pixels with threshold values below the image tonal value will be switched on, while the remainder will remain off. The target output device must be known when the threshold array is calculated, as it operates in terms of individual device pixels.

If a user application specifies a threshold array in the halftoning parameters, these values are used directly by the output device interpreter. If a spot function is specified, the interpreter will use this to calculate its own threshold array internally. The end result is always a threshold array of device pixels based on the address grid of the output device.

A threshold array is defined for a single halftone cell in PostScript Level 1, but in Level 2 implementations it can be based on multiple cells to give a better chance of precisely matching the requested halftone parameters. Calculating the threshold array is a computationally intensive process, but once the calculation has been performed the halftoning of individual images goes very quickly. The threshold array can be held in a screen cache in the output device.

The interpreter's screening algorithm decides which device pixels will be included in a halftone cell, according to the halftoning parameters of screen angle and frequency.

The screening algorithm will determine how well the requested halftone parameters are matched. A simple Level 1 interpreter may only be able to achieve one set of screen parameters; while in a Level 2 interpreter using Accurate Screens or a similar algorithm, many thousands may be possible. The threshold arrays for the more complex Level 2 screening algorithms require much more processing than the simple Level 1 halftoning, and Accurate Screens can be disabled when printing to a low-resolution device.

Even with this degree of control, there can be problems with certain kinds of images. With the traditional screen angles (see Chapter 4), the yellow screen is angled at 15° to cyan and magenta. Ideally, a 30° angle is necessary to minimize moiré, but with four colors in the screen set it is not possible for each one to be angled at 30° to the others. Yellow is selected for the other angle because it produces the least objectionable moiré in most subjects. Midtones that are predominantly composed of yellow with cyan or magenta (such as grass and flesh tones) are the most prone to moiré as a result. If moiré is likely, it is possible to exchange the yellow screen angle with another color; alter the screen frequency of the yellow; or use a frequency-modulated (stochastic) screen.

The spot function default in most PostScript interpreters is the Euclidean dot, which is a composite shape built up from different spot functions. It simulates the traditional square dot obtained from a photographic halftone screen, with a distinctive checkerboard pattern in midtones and round dots elsewhere in the tone scale. The traditional square dot and the PostScript Euclidean dot show a jump in tonal value in midtones as the corners of the squares join up. This tone shift can be a problem in images that are dominated by midtones, and smoother transitions can be achieved by choosing an elliptical or rhomboid dot shape.

Figure 10-19.
(A) Square dots enhance the sharpness between tones.

(B) Elliptical dots create smoother tone transitions in midtone areas, such as flesh-tones.

A threshold array for frequency-modulated halftoning has two main differences from a conventional halftone screen:

- The threshold array is not cell-based, but instead a randomized array is built.
- Single device pixels would be too small for a high-resolution device to image consistently, so small groups of device pixels are used to form spots of the required size.

A truly random spot placing has a somewhat clustered appearance (rather like the spacing of the stars in the night sky) instead of being dispersed evenly through the address grid. Many frequency-modulated screening algorithms usually use a technique called **error dispersion** to prevent spots from clustering together, and thus give a less clumpy appearance. Error dispersion is computed on the fly during output, making it a processor-intensive operation.

Flat tints and gradations, where a very even appearance is expected, can look grainy when some frequency-modulated screening algorithms are used. It may be preferable to use conventional screening to avoid the graininess. Alternatively, a small amount of noise can be introduced. The smaller the spot size used, the less grainy the appearance of the tone will be.

Exposure Systems

Film and plate exposure systems use a high-intensity light source (usually a laser diode or LED) to carry out a raster scan of the light-sensitive material in a manner similar to the way an electron gun builds up the display image on a computer monitor. The address grid is based on the stepping increment in the vertical direction, and the frequency with which the laser can be switched in the horizontal dimension. Both horizontal and vertical addressability is constrained by the size of the smallest laser spot that can be imaged.

Several techniques are available to enhance the output resolution of low-resolution exposure systems, such as those used in laser printers and digital color printers:

- Modulating the point at which the laser is switched on and off to allow a variable imaging length along the raster scan line.
- Modulating the laser intensity and thus the spot size.
- Using spot-size modulation to vary the effective width of the raster scan line.
- Installing a controller in a host computer that bypasses the device's own controller.

- Using algorithms that analyze the characteristics of the image and modulate the spot size accordingly.
- Using algorithms that modulate the halftone dot shape and position and achieve a higher apparent resolution without actually changing the imagesetter spot size.

Figure 10-20. Address grid of an output device.

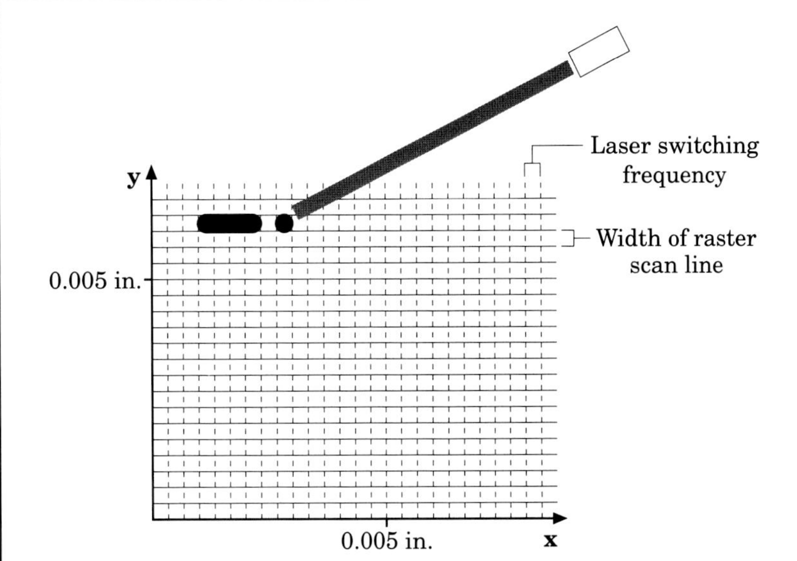

The address grid is a coordinate system of device pixels, the size of which controls the placement and resolution of halftone images. Pixel size is determined mainly by the stepping increment of the raster scan in the vertical dimension and the laser switching frequency in the horizontal dimension. Many devices support a range of different output resolutions, each one having its own logical address grid. Note that the address grid is considered to be a rectangular matrix of pixels, although the actual laser spot is round or elliptical. The practical minimum spot size is around 8–10 microns, as it becomes difficult to image consistently to film below this level.

HiLine Screening from TransCal offers a further alternative in which a single halftone cell is divided into four by a special PostScript spot function. The result is a doubling of the halftone frequency and a smoother appearance.

Frequency-modulated screens use very small dots constructed from single laser spots. These spots range from 14 to 20 microns in lithographic printing, although at the smaller sizes they are more prone to losses during plate exposure and processing and to wear during printing. In flexo printing, spot sizes are 40 microns and upward. Because of the small spot size in comparison with a conventional halftone dot, special care must be taken to calibrate plate exposures and avoid dusty working environments.

One of the most fundamental problems with film and plate output in the PostScript environment is a lack of imaging precision. Positional accuracy of a few microns across the film or plate is necessary to hold all the separate colors in register, but in reality many devices do not achieve anything like this level of accuracy. Output devices that are not able to hold and repeat a high degree of accuracy every time the films are output cannot be considered color-capable.

In flatbed exposure systems, the film or plate is advanced after each scan line by a roller or **capstan;** while in a drum system the material is moved into position and held securely as the laser rotates to image the plate or film. Drum systems hold register more consistently and can be fitted with register pins to hold the material in position while it is exposed. Some platesetters punch the plate after exposure, using register marks exposed on the plate.

Register punch holes also provide a means of accurately positioning films and plates after exposure. Imposed film assemblies (**flats**) are held in position on the plate in the contact frame with register pins, and the same punch holes are used to mount the plate on the press.

Different register systems are available, all of which make holes in different sizes and positions. The most widely used are the Stoesser system (most common in the U.S.), Billows/ Protocol (UK), and Bacher (continental Europe). A system made by Kodak is used for films only, and proprietary film and plate output devices may have their own register-system designs.

Emulsion density on film should no less than 4.0, in order to prevent any light from passing through the film when it is exposed to the plate. The density is controlled by the amount of exposure and by processing factors such as development time, temperature, and rate of replenishment of fresh developer. Film and plate emulsions need to be highly sensitive in order to minimize the imaging time, but on plates there is a resulting loss of image durability that can be a problem if long runs are required. A degree of latitude is built in to the emulsion to allow for small fluctuations in exposure and processing, but the more sensitive the emulsion, the less latitude there is.

The film or plate material is handled in light-proof cartridges, and after exposure it is transferred to a processor that develops, fixes, washes, and dries it. Some imagesetters and platesetters incorporate in-line processing.

Laser light sources used in imagesetters produce laser light at the red end of the spectrum. They are cheaper to manufacture than blue lasers, but their output is of lower intensity. They require film of relatively high sensitivity, in which there is more costly silver metal. Some devices use an array of lasers instead of a single one, allowing it to expose multiple raster scan lines simultaneously.

Laser exposure systems are evolving rapidly, and some high-resolution devices incorporate removable laser-array assemblies that can upgraded without having to replace the entire mechanism.

Computer-to-Plate Technology

Many printers are investing in computer-to-plate (CTP) systems that bypass film entirely. With electronic imposition of complete flats, it makes sense to go a stage further and expose plates instead of film, eliminating several prepress production stages.

Imaging directly to plate also does away with the distortions introduced in film-based platemaking. It is possible to resolve fine image detail more consistently, which is a special benefit with frequency-modulated screening where very small spots are being imaged.

Litho plates are quite thin, and if the base material is flexible enough they can be loaded in an imagesetter in roll form and exposed. Alternatively, dedicated plate exposure units (known as platesetters) can be used for metal plates, and these systems can incorporate automatic register punching.

In certain cases, CTP loses out to conventional film-based platemaking due to the speed and low capital costs of conventional platemaking equipment. For example, when duplicate plates or reprints are needed, a CTP system has to repeat the imaging process, while a conventional platemaking system has only to re-expose the film. Film is a convenient storage medium that is cheaper than archiving rasterized data on magnetic media. Proofing can also be a problem unless digital proofs are accepted as contract proofs.

In many instances, it is not possible for every element in a job to be supplied in digital form, and then it is necessary to combine film produced conventionally with the digital data. In hybrid workflow environments, automatic step-and-repeat

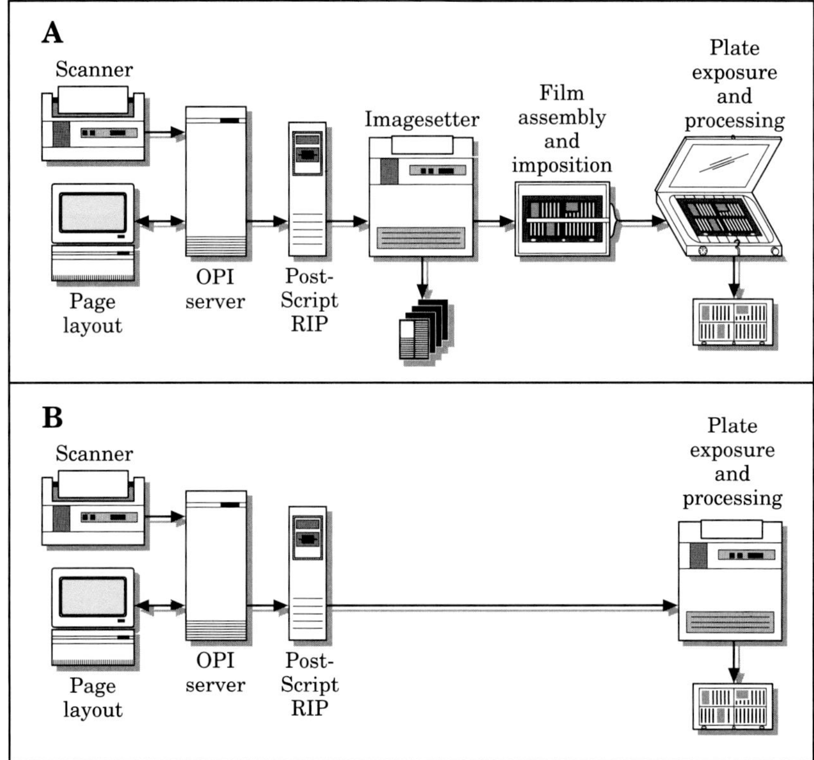

Figure 10-21. Computer-to-plate technology (B) eliminates the film output and stripping stages (A) in the production workflow.

machines may be used to add the film-based material. The platesetter receives the imposition instructions and exposes the digital information, masking the areas that are missing. The device then uses the register marks as a guide to position the films and expose them conventionally.

Alternatively, film or artwork can be scanned and converted into digital form. Very high resolution scanners are used to avoid image quality loss on line artwork, such as type with fine strokes, and to avoid the need to descreen halftones, which risks changing color values. One type of scanner designed for this purpose converts the scanned data directly into PostScript code, which can then be inserted into a PostScript CTP workflow.

Film is a convenient storage medium that is cheaper than archiving rasterized data on tapes or optical discs. When alterations are required the new matter is either stripped in manually or the films are re-output. It is more or less impossible to edit rasterized CTP data. Changes must be made to the customer files and new plates produced whenever alterations are required.

Platesetters are usually very large as they must be able to handle the full plate size for a given job (plates cannot be assembled from strips like films). Some models incorporate automatic plate-handling mechanisms and can accept plates up to 48×66 in. (1,200×1,650 mm). They may incorporate workflow management (including queuing and preparing files while the previous job is being exposed), automatic compensation for shingling, and placement of color bars, register marks, and fold and trim marks. These systems at the very end of the prepress production workflow are installed at printers or occasionally at larger trade shops.

In contrast to conventional photographic methods in which the whole plate is exposed from film simultaneously, in direct-to-plate systems only the area under the laser is exposed at any one time. Consequently, the plate coatings for direct-to-plate systems must be more sensitive, responding to the very brief exposures that they receive. Such coatings are too sensitive to handle in daylight, and, unlike conventional plates, they must always be handled and loaded in the dark. By using high-sensitivity plates and multiple blue laser exposure heads, exposures at 4,000 dpi can be similar to those for conventional diazo and photopolymer plates.

11 Proofing

Proofing is a key element of the production process. Without it, errors would not be corrected and costly reworking or a loss of value in the finished product would result. Good management of proofing tools enables you match the final job closely to the client's expectations at the lowest possible cost.

When looking at proofing systems, it is important to consider both the role of the proof in the approval cycle and the proofing technology used. This chapter will help you to understand the different proofing systems on the market and the context in which they are used.

The main reasons for making a proof are:

- To approve or, if necessary, correct a job before it is printed.
- To show how design decisions will be realized when the job is printed.
- To form a basis for agreement on what will be produced by the printer and paid for by the customer.

To fulfill these functions, the proof should be a good simulation of how the job will look when it is printed, and it should be fast and economical to produce so that it does not consume too much of the time or resources available. The accuracy of the simulation of the final print is of critical importance. Producing an uncalibrated proof that bears no relation to how the press will print the same dot values is at best a waste of time and potentially a recipe for disaster. The key point is that the proof should always match the characteristics of the printing process, not the other way around.

Proofing Stages

Proofs can be made at any stage in the production process, from initial concept to printing and binding. There is a point, however, where the role of the proof changes from a client-designer communication to a client-printer communication. Up to this time most proofs will be generated as part of the design process and will include thumbnails and roughs to show the initial design concept, followed by visuals and laser proofs of the layout and typography.

Figure 11-1.
Typical approval cycle.

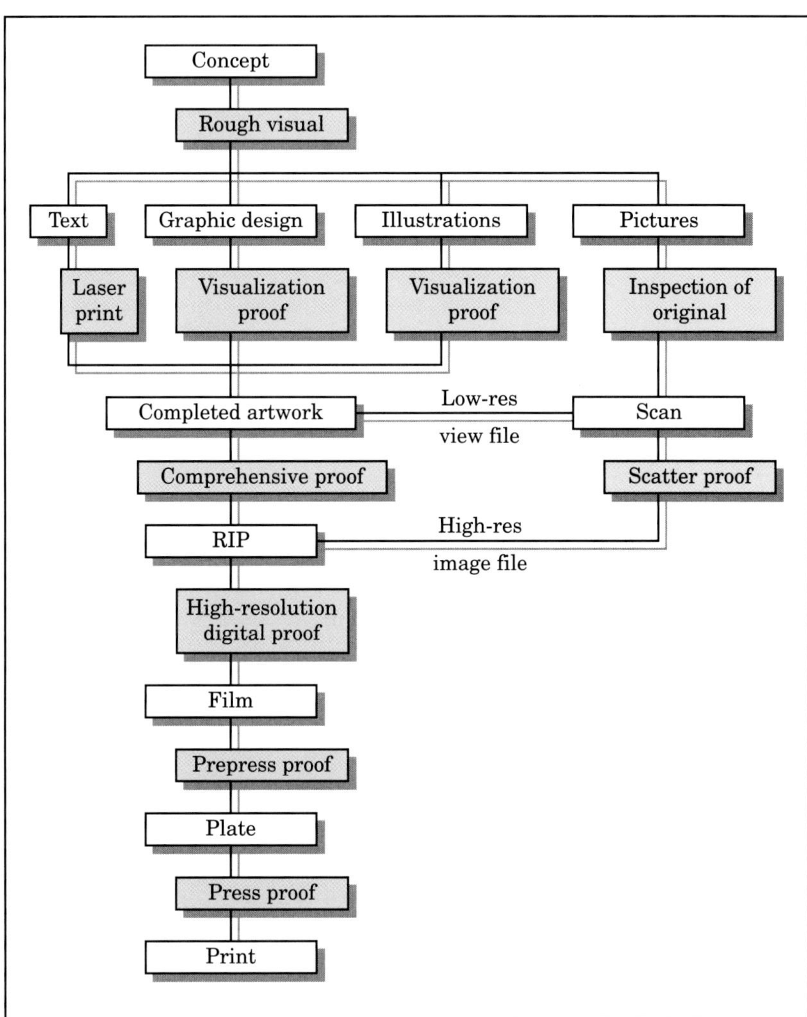

From the point when the job is sent to production and film and plates are output, the purpose of the proof is no longer to support the exploration of different design possibilities, but to demonstrate that the production process has correctly implemented the specification and design. In both cases, the emphasis is on approval, and, in a well-managed job, approval of each stage in production is reached as quickly and efficiently as possible.

The key proofing stages are:

1. **A visual or rough.** This allow s approval of the designer's concept of the job before complete page layouts are produced.
2. **A design proof.** The layout proof or "comprehensive" shows the finished design, with all the text and image elements in place. (At this stage, it may not be possible to show exactly how illustrations will appear on the final job, in which case they are approximated.) It can also be used as a reading proof for the text if the copy has not already been finalized.
3. **An intermediate proof.** Proofs made from the color separations before they are assembled with the other page elements (sometimes called scatter proofs) can be used to show how color separations have been carried out and how the images appear at the size and crop chosen and with the selected halftone parameters of screen ruling and dot shape. Fully composed pages, incorporating text and graphics elements of the page in position can be proofed as page proofs.
4. **A final color proof or contract proof.** This closely simulates the finished job and may be produced on separate sheets or made up as a "book proof" to look like the finished job. The printer will use this proof as a guide for the production run and will match it as closely as possible.

The comprehensive proof allows the customer to approve the design of the job, while the contract proof is approved as a more or less accurate simulation of the final printed job.

Requirements of Proofing Systems

These different proofing stages pose different demands on both the technologies used and on the interpretative skills of the user. Choosing the right proofing system involves an appreciation of the requirements of each proofing stage and the capabilities of the proofing systems currently on the market. The actual requirements of each stage will depend on the job and working practices of those involved, but will typically include the following:

Visuals. Accessibility, economy, and speed are the most important requirements for the designer, who may wish to produce a series of options for a client and make modifications quickly and with a minimum of cost and effort. The ability to produce color visuals from digital data is useful, but at an early stage in the design process, rough sketches and thumbnails may be generated manually using colored markers or other media.

Design proofs. The ability to show an accurate representation of all the textual and graphical elements in the finished design is vital. This means that the page must be interpreted in the same way by the RIP in the proofing system as it is in the imagesetter—a common problem is that the fonts used in the design are not available to the proofing device and, as a result, the output looks different.

Design proofs are usually made on laser printers with much lower output resolutions than imagesetters. Design proofs generated in this way will not show the precise weight or sharpness of the text, and tints are printed at a screen ruling much coarser than the final print. Tints also tend to look darker than on the final print.

Color is usually an important element in the design proof, although it is often impossible to match the exact color appearance of the final output or show the effect of color editing.

Intermediate proofs and final color proofs. Proofs that are used to assess production quality need to be accurate, flexible, consistent, fast, and economic. Accuracy is probably the most important requirement of final color proofs as the client will want to see a realistic simulation of the final printed result. This implies that the colors and the densities used should be the same as those used by the printing process; the tonal rendering should be accurate; and the paper should be the same as the one used for the job itself. The distortions created in the printing process (such as dot gain) should be mirrored accurately in the proof, and thus the flexibility of adjusting the proofing system to simulate the printing characteristics of dot gain and density accurately is important.

Final color proofs have traditionally been produced by the trade shop or printer making the color separations, and they are responsible for ensuring that the proof matches the characteristics of the printing process. The use of digital prepress systems gives designers and publishers the possibility of creating proofs before files are sent for output to film or plate. If electronic proofs created in this way are to be used as final color proofs, it is essential that care is taken to calibrate the proofing device to closely match the printing characteristics.

Consistency between proofs made from the same color separations is also important, since otherwise it would not be possible to use a proof as a guide to the corrections needed. If a particular proofing system produces a slight error in its output, it can still be interpreted successfully as long as the variation is consistent. Color proofs should ideally be cheap and quick to make, and multiple copies should be available at a low unit cost.

Proofing Technologies

There are now scores of different proofing techniques available, each one of which meets a specific range of needs. Proofing system technologies can be divided into electronic proofs, photomechanical prepress proofs, and press proofs. Digital proofs are output from the electronic page-makeup data, while photomechanical prepress proofs are made directly from the final films, and press proofs are printed with the printing plates.

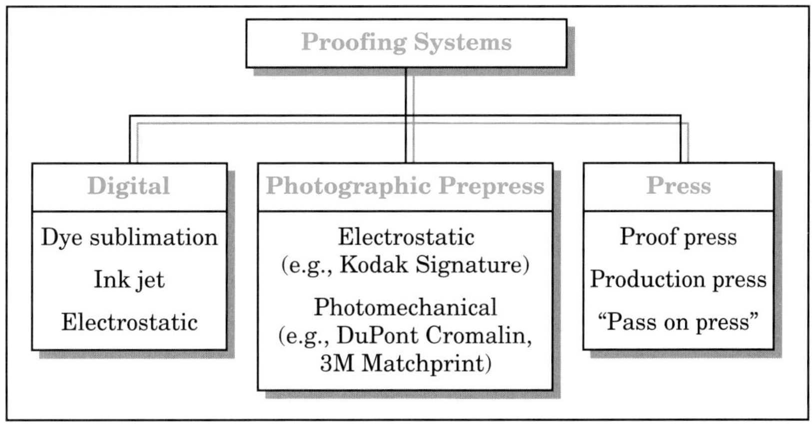

Figure 11-2. Various proofing systems.

Digital Proofs

Digital proofs, such as laser prints, have been used by designers for many years as visuals and for approval of finished layouts and typography. The move toward desktop color publishing has created a need for a digital proof that shows how color will reproduce and that can also be used as a final color proof. Vendors have developed a number of systems to meet this need, and digital color proofing is now a real possibility, although complete simulation of every aspect of print on paper is probably not a realistic goal.

Electronic color proofing opens the door to revolutionary changes in prepress methods. It is a key enabler of digital color prepress, as it allows client approval of all page makeup and color separations and editing before the files are sent to the printer or to a bureau for output to film.

Electronic proofs are made directly from digital page and image data, at a relatively early stage in production in comparison with other proofing methods. As might be expected, they tend to give a less-accurate prediction of what the finished job will look like. Most digital systems do not produce a conventional halftone dot, relying instead on dithering or continuous-tone printing to reproduce tonal values.

As with scanners, there are high-end, mid-range, and low-end proofing systems. Only the more costly high-end devices, such as 3M Digital Matchprint, DuPont Digital Cromalin, and Kodak Approval, will give a result in any way comparable to a conventional prepress proof. If one accepts the need for a degree of interpretation, mid-range systems are capable of producing usable results. Low-end systems are strictly visualization tools; trying to simulate the effect of print on paper is out of the question.

The speed of digital proofing is dependent on the speed of data transfer and rasterization, as well as the speed of the imaging device. In some systems, the raster image is kept in the memory of the output device, and multiple copies can then be made at a lower unit cost than the cost of a single proof.

Digital proofing systems give the user a great deal of control over printing characteristics, with complete freedom to adjust tonal reproduction curves as necessary. However, because the colorants are very different from printing inks, color values are not precisely simulated. Special colors are not available in electronic proofing systems and must be simulated with the closest CMYK combination. If the customer

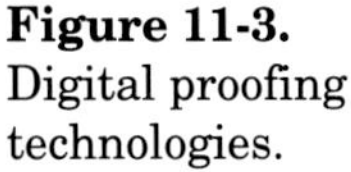

Figure 11-3. Digital proofing technologies.

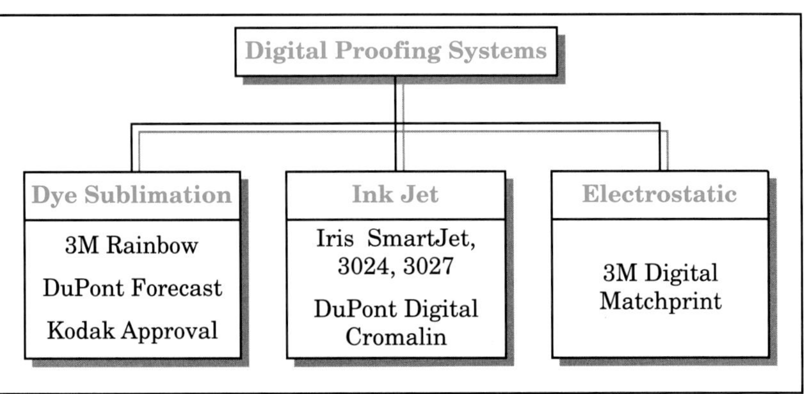

requires a highly accurate final color proof, digital systems cannot be used as a substitute for a photographic or press proof.

The three types of digital proofing technologies used are electrostatic, ink jet, and thermal systems.

Electrostatic systems. Laser printers are regularly used for proofing elements of page design and typography. Color laser printers have proved to be an invaluable method of visualization proofing, and, when used in conjunction with an appropriate RIP and interface, provide quite reasonable results. One major advantage of the color laser printer is that once the data has been "ripped," pages can be printed at the speed of the marking engine. The color laser printer is

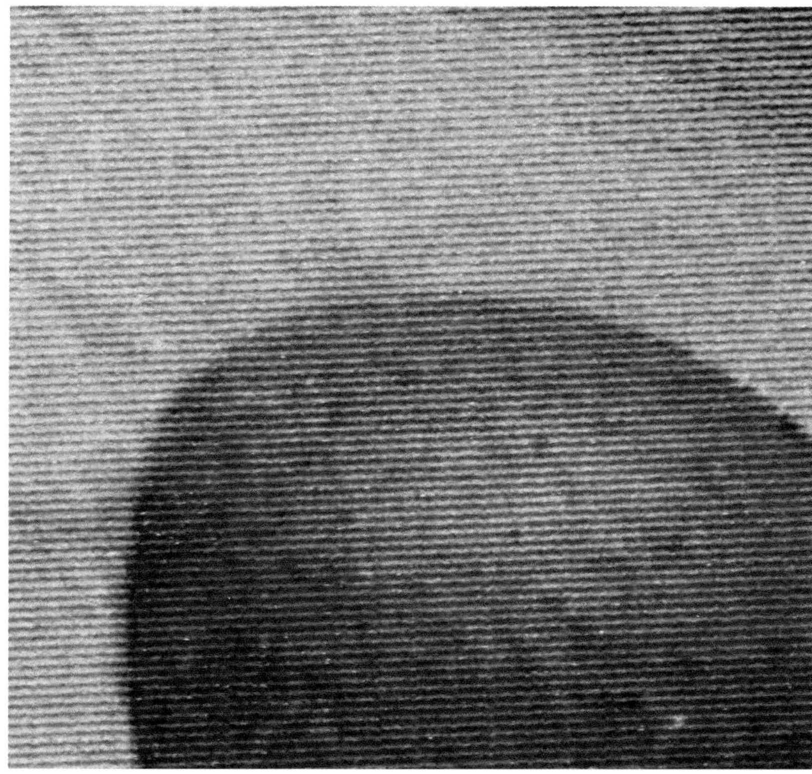

Figure 11-4. Visualization proof produced by a color laser printer with a Fiery RIP. (Detail enlarged 10×.)

at present the only digital proofing system that can produce multiple copies of proofs economically.

One high-end system uses liquid toner to produce high-resolution electrophotographic proofs, and this has the advantage of working at a much higher resolution than a dry toner system.

Ink jet. Ink jets used for color proofing are different from low-end page printers. High-end ink jet proofing devices use Hertz technology to produce variable-size ink droplets, giving an approximate simulation of halftoning. Ink jet printers can use many different types of paper as long as they have the right level of absorbency.

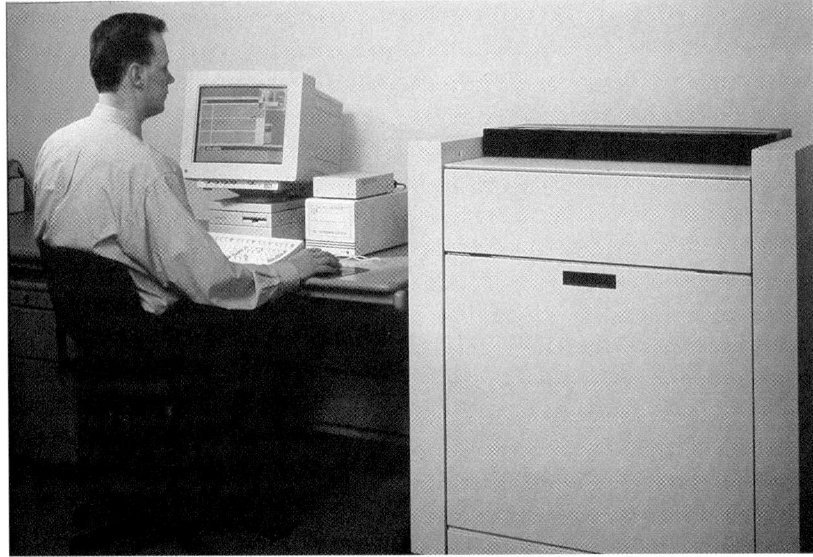

Figure 11-5. DuPont digital proofing system, an ink jet proofing device. *Courtesy E. I. du Pont de Nemours & Co., Inc.*

An example of the output produced by the Iris ink jet device can be seen in Figure 13-2.

Dye sublimation. In a dye sublimation proofing device, tiny resistors are heated and vaporize a colored wax onto the proofing substrate. Like most digital proofing systems, thermal printers do not simulate the halftone screen, but by varying the voltage that is applied to the resistors, the data controls how much colorant is vaporized and the resultant density of color on the proof. The result is similar to a continuous-tone photographic print.

Substrates are usually restricted to papers with a special finish to accept the colorant. Consumable costs for dye sublimation printers are higher than for other systems, but the capital costs tend to be lower.

Dye sublimation has been the most successful digital proofing technology. Dye sublimation devices, such as the 3M Rainbow, are gaining acceptance as intermediate proofs and even as final color proofs.

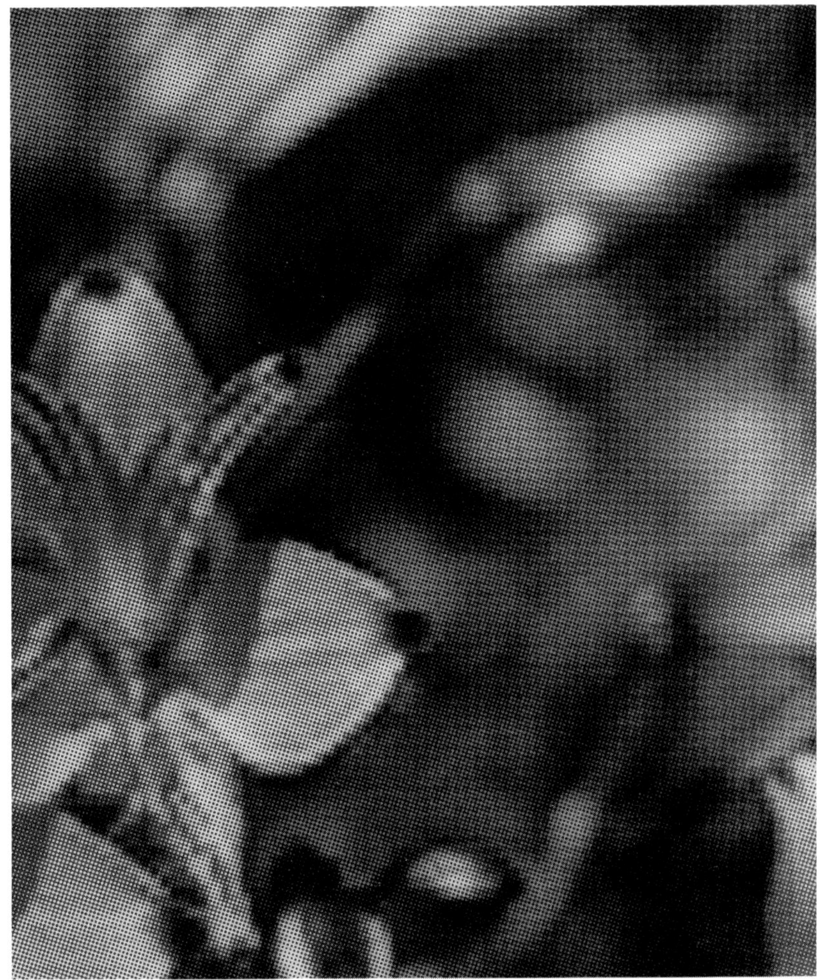

Figure 11-6. Dye sublimation Photo CD thumbnail proof produced by Kodak's PCD printer. (Detail enlarged 10×.)

Selecting a digital proofing system. The following factors are important to examine when considering electronic proofing systems:

- **Output size.** Press proofs can be as large as the final printed sheet, while prepress proofs can be made in sizes up to approximately 36×25 in. (914×635 mm) with room for bleeds, trim marks, and so on. Digital proofing systems tend to have more restricted formats and are often unable to print beyond the page area. The proof's image area must exceed the size of the image by around 0.5 in. (12.7 mm). In other words, an image area of 9½×12 in. (241×305 mm) is the minimum for proofing a single page with room for bleeds, etc. It is often necessary to proof two pages to show the effect of a double-page spread, and output sizes of 18×12 in. (457×305 mm) are required.

Figure 11-7. Kodak Approval Digital Color Imager. *Courtesy Eastman Kodak Co.*

- **Substrates.** Some systems require special papers to be used, or restrict the range of weights or finishes. This may not be too important for visualization proofs, but it makes it impossible to show how the job will appear when it is ultimately printed.
- **Data format.** Most systems will accept files in PostScript format, but some systems are designed to work only with high-end color electronic prepress systems in proprietary formats. PostScript interpreters are available as options on some systems.
- **Halftoning capability.** Very few digital proofing systems replicate the halftone screen with any accuracy. Alternative approaches include dithered dots, contone output, and a combination of the two.

The most widely used high-end digital proofing system is the Scitex Iris ink jet, available in a range of sizes up to 33×44-in. (838×1,118 mm). For many clients, it creates an acceptable contract proof, and by using the Brunner digital control element and calibration system, it can deliver highly consistent color proofs.

3M Digital Matchprint and Kodak Approval are currently thought to produce proofs that come closest to simulating printed color and the halftone dot, although the number of installations so far has been small. Other systems are likely to emerge in the near future from both traditional graphics suppliers and also from color printer specialists, such as Tektronix and Mitsubishi.

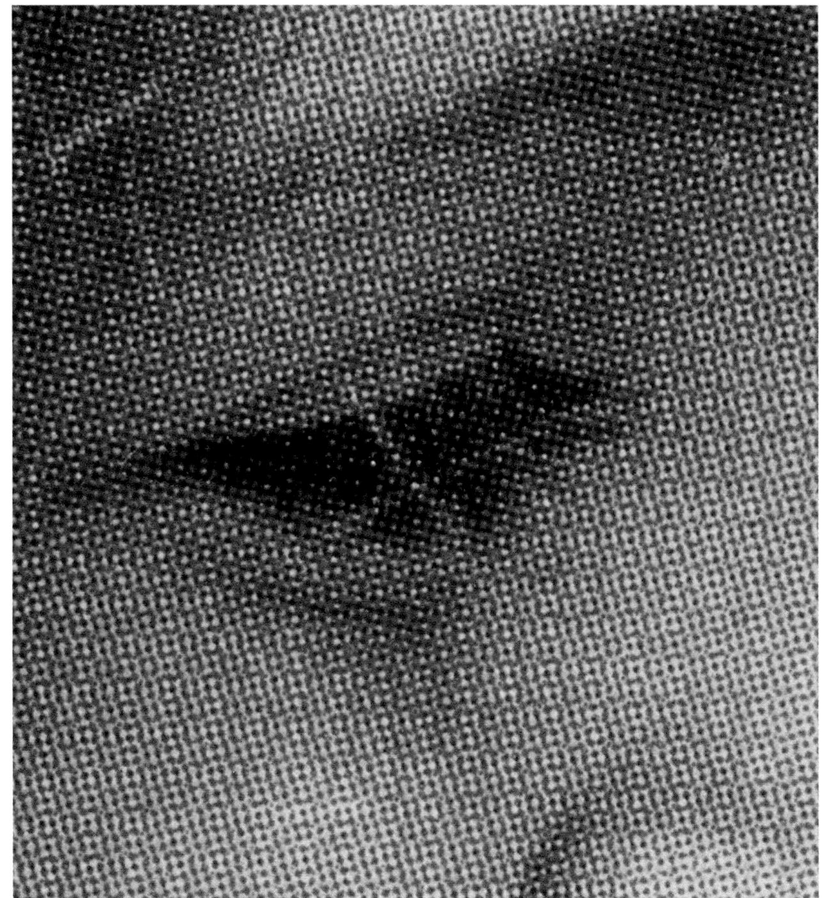

Figure 11-8.
Kodak Approval Proof.
(Detail enlarged 10×.)

Kodak's Approval is a dye sublimation system that uses a laser to transfer colorant from donor sheets to an intermediate, which is then laminated to the proofing substrate. The resolution is 1,800 dpi, and the maximum output size is 13×19 in. (323×489 mm).

The Rainbow desktop color proofer from 3M is a mid-range 300-dpi dye sublimation system that offers a good compromise between accuracy and cost. The output size is large enough for two pages with bleeds.

Digital proofs are made directly from digital data and cannot be calibrated using standard film test elements like the control strips used on press proofs and photomechanical

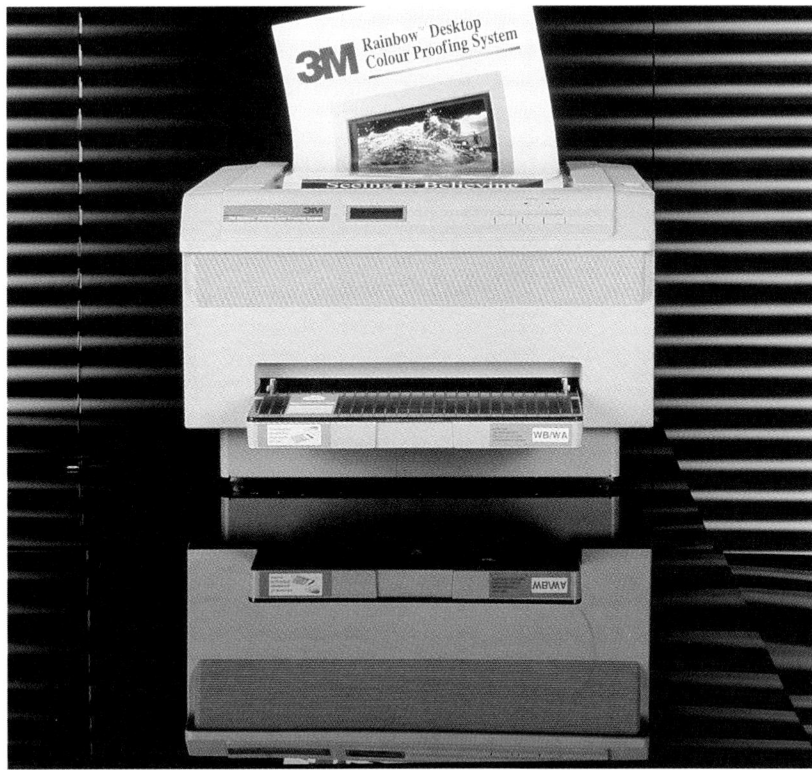

Figure 11-9. 3M Rainbow dye sublimation proofing device. *Courtesy 3M.*

proofs. To provide a means of checking the output from digital proofing devices, it is a good practice to include a digital test element on every page as it is output, as described in Chapter 14.

Soft Proofing

If an image or a page is being approved in digital form and a hard copy record is not required, proofing may be done on a color monitor. This gives an opportunity for repeated editing and correction to be carried out interactively during the design phase, without the need to transfer files to another output device. Soft proofing is currently used as an element in electronic page composition systems and in ad agencies that have on-line links to repro houses so they can view the effect of image editing and correction in real time. The need for standard viewing conditions must be taken into account in soft proofing, and users should understand the limitations involved. Accurate monitor calibration minimizes the difference in color appearance between the screen display and the printed output.

Soft proofs cannot be used as final color proofs in most situations for two basic reasons: firstly, the screen image cannot match the printed image with complete accuracy, since it is made up of the light emitted by RGB colored phosphors, rather than the light absorbed by CMYK printing inks; and secondly, there is no physical record that can be submitted to the printer or kept by the client.

Using a color monitor for approval is nonetheless likely to play an increasingly important role, as it situates the proofing element of the color reproduction process firmly on the designer's desktop. If done intelligently, with color interpretation carried out with the aid of color sample books and tint charts, and with appropriate allowance for the difference between transmitted and reflected color, it is possible for an experienced designer to shorten the production cycle considerably.

Monitor proofing of high-resolution image files can be a problem due to the need to access very large files. It is also only possible if both the creator and the approver are using the same application and computer platform, and if all the fonts used are available on both platforms.

Such problems can be overcome by using portable digital document systems. These systems convey the appearance of a publication without including the actual page layout and image files.

Adobe Acrobat has the most functionality of the portable document systems and also has the greatest ability to convey the color appearance of a document accurately. By using Acrobat Distiller, the creator of a publication can compress a digital document to a size appropriate for the approval version (i.e., at a resolution suitable for viewing on screen or making a laser-printed proof). The resulting Portable Document Format (PDF) file can be sent on disk or transmitted electronically via modem or ISDN link.

The approver only requires a copy of the Acrobat Reader in order to view or print a PDF file (regardless of the fonts, applications, or computer platform used in its creation). With Acrobat Exchange it is also possible to attach alterations and comments to the document before returning it to its creator for amendment.

Soft proofing and digital document systems enable publishers to save on the time and costs involved with the traditional hard-copy based approval cycle. They also make possible different methods of reaching final approval, including interactive alteration (with immediate display of the effect of changes) and pre-publication review by a larger number of people.

Prepress Proofs

Most color printing is proofed with photomechanical prepress methods. Photomechanical prepress proofs are made by exposing the films to a light-sensitive medium and applying a colorant. Color proofs require the exposure and coloring processes to be repeated for each printing color.

Figure 11-10. Eurosprint: a compact DuPont Cromalin prepress proofing system. *Courtesy E. I. du Pont de Nemours & Co., Inc.*

Photomechanical proofs are faster to make than press proofs, taking typically around twenty minutes to expose and process the four colors. Unfortunately, where more than one proof is needed, the entire production cycle must be repeated, and photomechanical proofs become relatively expensive when multiple copies are wanted.

Consistency is usually a strong point with photomechanical proofs, but variation is certainly possible if operating conditions are not completely standardized. The systems that have gained widespread acceptance, DuPont Cromalin, Kodak Signature, and 3M Matchprint, all give a good approximation of the finished result, with good control over dot gain and density.

Table 11-1. Advantages and uses of various proofing methods.

Digital Proofs

Advantages of digital proofs:
- Approval can be reached at an earlier stage.
- Eliminates expense of correcting final films.
- Can be produced by designer or publisher.

Use digital proofs when:
- Accuracy of simulation of final result is not critical.
- Substantial alterations are likely.
- Film is not being used (in direct-to-plate systems or in digital color printing).

Soft Proofs

Advantage of soft proofs:
- Eliminates time and cost of hard-copy proofs.

Use soft proofs when:
- Interactive correction is desirable.
- Hard-copy proof is not required.

Photomechanical Proofs

Advantages of photomechanical proofs:
- Cheaper than press proofs.
- Allow approval at an earlier stage than press proofs.
- Eliminates the cost of correcting plates.
- Accurately shows detail, such as halftone dot structure.

Use photomechanical proofs when:
- A single copy of the proof is adequate.
- Simulation of ghosting, printing inks, and so on is not critical.

Press Proofs

Advantages of press proofs:
- Multiple copies can be produced economically.
- Inking variables, such as ghosting, that will occur on the final job are simulated.
- Press proofs can be printed on the job paper.
- They use printing inks with the same hues and overprinting characteristics as those used on the production press.
- They can be printed on both sides and made up as book proofs, if necessary.

Use press proofs when:
- Clients have difficulty in interpreting other types of proofs.
- A very accurate simulation of the final job is required.
- Multiple copies of the proof are needed.

AgfaProof and Konica Konsensus have been introduced more recently and are popular with many printers and their clients. Cromalin and Signature proofs can be made on virtually any paper.

Multilayer laminates used in prepress proofs can give a deceptively high level of gloss, which leads to disappointment with the finished job unless the client makes an allowance for the additional gloss. Matte finishes are available for most systems and should be used unless the finished job itself is going to be laminated or UV varnished.

Colorants have an appearance very similar to printing inks, although the hues are slightly different and tend to appear a little warmer in most systems. The Cromalin, Matchprint, and Signature proofing systems all have ways of simulating press dot gain, although in most cases they achieve it with optical effects instead of by mechanically increasing the size of the dot. There are some limitations inherent in this approach, such as an inability to convey the effect that different screen rulings have on dot gain or to match the very high levels of dot gain experienced on materials like newsprint, but on the whole they are reasonably accurate when made correctly.

Press Proofs

In the past, when a proof was needed, the printer had to print copies from the type, blocks, or plates that would later be used to print the job. Prepress proofing systems have to a large extent replaced the press proof, although there are still circumstances when press proofs are the best method of proofing. They are made, as their name suggests, on a printing press using the printing plate that will be used in the production run. They are usually produced on specially designed presses that are very fast to prepare for printing, but print much more slowly than a production press, making them economic for the very small quantities needed for proofing.

From the point of view of image quality, there are two important differences between proof presses and production presses: firstly, because the impression force is much lighter, a proof press prints with much less dot gain; and secondly, because of the way sheets of paper are fed, there is no danger of wet ink marking parts of the machine or setting off against the back of other sheets in a pile. As a consequence, a proof press can print a sharper dot and a heavier ink weight than a production press. The operator needs to take care to simulate the density and dot gain of the press that the job will be printed on, or the result will be a proof that looks great but cannot be printed.

In practice, there tends to be considerable variation between press proofs. The nature of the process makes it impossible to guarantee that the inking will be the same each time, so when a proof is remade there can be a color difference. A job with very exacting requirements may proofed on a production press that is the same or very similar to the one that will run the job. This is inevitably more expensive, as the preparation time will be greater and will be charged at a much higher hourly rate.

Another form of press proof is the pass-on-press. The client goes to the printer and sees printed sheets (or sections on a web press) at the beginning of the run, while the operator is adjusting the position of the image and the ink weights. This is an effective way of controlling a job right up to the point when it is on the press, but it should not be used as a substitute for approval at an earlier stage. Only the overall ink weights can be adjusted at this stage, and any alterations that require changes to the color separations will involve rescheduling the job for printing later, after the films have been corrected and new plates made.

Press proofs are usually made on the same paper as that specified for the finished job and can be printed on both sides if necessary and made up into a "book proof." They can also be given the same finish as the final job, by varnishing, laminating, foil blocking, or whatever else is called for by the design.

Choosing a Proofing System

A well-implemented approval cycle allows the client to get the finished job that they want without incurring additional expenses and delays, and the proofing system that is used should assist in achieving that goal. It should aid the designer in communicating and controlling the important aspects of each job and monitoring their reproduction throughout the process. With this in mind, the main factors that will affect the choice of proofing system are:

- The cost of producing the number of proofs required.
- Whether manual or electronic prepress techniques are used.
- The importance of color accuracy.
- The ease of making changes.
- The degree of interpretation necessary.

Questions to ask about a proofing system include:

- What types of colorants are used and how well do they simulate the inks used in printing?
- What size of paper is accepted by the proofing device and what is the maximum page size that can be output with bleeds, trim marks, and register marks?
- Can proofs be made on the job paper, or are special papers required?
- What is the surface finish of the proof?
- Can the proofing device accept PostScript data?
- Can it simulate the printed halftone, including the halftoning parameters of screen angle, screen ruling, and dot shape?
- What kind of calibration facilities are available with the system?
- What is the speed of output and the size of the memory and page buffer?
- Is a special working environment, such as controlled operating temperature and humidity, required?

When considering the purchase of a proofing system, compare proofs with the finished printed work that has been output from the same data. If they cannot achieve approximately a close match, the proofing system may only be suitable for visualization purposes.

Many publications use more than one proofing system. One common practice is to make final color proofs only for advertising, where accuracy and approval are more critical, and to use a cheaper system for the proofing of editorial illustrations.

Whatever type of proofing system is used, some form of control elements should be incorporated so that ink weight and dot gain can be checked. If proofs are produced by a trade shop or printer, they should be asked to include a control strip on the proof. For electronic proofs, a small test element should be included in the output file.

Evaluating Proofs

Two key objectives in color reproduction are realized by an effective approval cycle. The first is to achieve the best reproduction possible, consistent with the inevitable constraints of time and budget, and the second is to make the production process as smooth, efficient, and painless as possible. Proof evaluation plays an important role in this.

Getting the best reproduction possible naturally means that errors should be identified for correction and any serious flaws in the design should be rectified. Most problems arise from either failing to correct a significant error at the right time, leading to extra costs or the loss of product value; or from effecting minor changes that make little or no difference in the finished job, but add to its production time and costs. Occasionally, these are two sides of the same problem, one that has been referred to elsewhere as losing the "significant few" among the "trivial many."

The way to avoid these problems is to set up an approval cycle for each job, identifying the elements that must be approved and specifying the point at which approval should take place and who will be responsible for it. The simplest way of ensuring that everything is checked at some stage or other is by producing a checklist. This helps to make sure that everyone involved is following the same plan. Overlooking something altogether is nearly always the most disastrous kind of mistake that can be made. Correcting something at the wrong stage tends to be the next most costly problem, followed by making errors in marking up corrections.

Attention also needs to be directed at identifying as early as possible the most important elements in the job. This will guide not only the people doing the work, but also those who are responsible for approving it. People need to know what the priorities are: whether the chairman's tan is more important than the boardroom wallpaper, for example.

Proof evaluation is assisted by the use of various tools, most of which are quite inexpensive.

- Linen tester.
- Set of printed color samples, including tint charts and Pantone swatch books.
- Transparent grid to check squareness of type and images.
- Transparent screen ruling and screen angle testers.
- Illuminated transparency viewer with 5,000 K light source.

Companies that commission a large enough volume of print may also find it useful to install:

- A proof viewing cabinet with a 5,000 K light source for consistent and accurate color appraisal.
- A densitometer for evaluating ink weight and tonal values.
- A spectrophotometer for measurement and comparison of color values.

The terms "corrections" and "alterations" have quite distinct meanings. Corrections are changes that are necessary to fix errors made by the printer, whether made during color separation, page makeup, or some other stage. If these errors are identified at the appropriate stage they will be corrected at no cost, but the client may be charged if the errors are not noticed and corrected until later.

Alterations are changes made at the client's request. A new picture or text item is an alteration; as is changing the color balance of a reproduction to make it different from that of the original illustration. The printer is entitled to charge for all alterations, although actual practice varies widely, with some printers absorbing the cost of minor alterations in the quoted price and others expecting to make a proportion of their revenue from alteration charges.

Version Control

Make sure that proofs are clearly marked "first proof," "second proof," and so on to avoid possible confusion. Copies of proofs should be kept as well as a record of any corrections specified (perhaps by photocopying the marked-up proof). If possible, file all proofs or copies of them centrally so that you can easily resolve conflicts about who is responsible for errors or "audit" the approval cycle to improve working methods. It should be possible to trace through a set of proofs for a job to discover where an error appeared and what corrections, if any, were specified.

If there is a chance that proofs will get mixed up, add the title of the job and the number of the section or signature in a waste area on each proof. Many applications are able to add the current date to a file when it is output, and this "electronic date stamping" can be used to monitor which version is the latest. When circulating proofs make sure that people know when they are to be returned and which version they are viewing.

Marking up Corrections

There are no widely recognized symbols for correcting images that communicate information as well as the standard correction marks for text. The Hamlyn correction symbols (known as BS 4785 in the UK) are sometimes used, but are unfamiliar to many designers and printers, and, in any case, do not facilitate marking up color alterations. The absence of a set of correction symbols means that changes other than text corrections must be indicated by writing clearly on the proof.

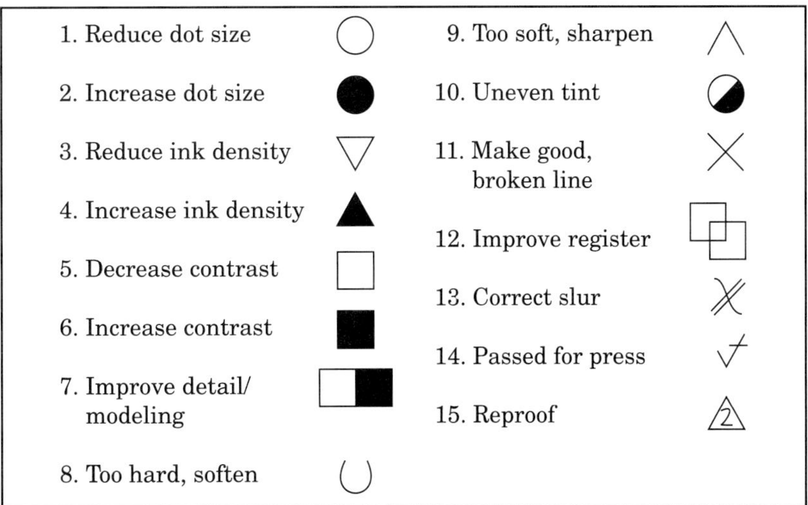

Figure 11-11. Hamlyn proof correction symbols.

The intentions of publishers and designers sometimes remain unclear to the trade shop or printer owing to differences of terminology or interpretation. The objective should be to write clear, precise, and unambiguous instructions that cannot be misunderstood.

Corrections and alterations should always be in writing. Where they are communicated verbally, written confirmation should also be sent by fax or by mail to avoid any possible ambiguity.

Getting to "Yes"

The proof should not be seen as a battlefield for ritualized combat between opposing forces, but as a tool to enable everyone involved to work together to achieve a result that pleases the client. If a proof is returned free of corrections, it does not necessarily imply that the designer has failed to locate an error, but more likely that everyone involved has succeeded in getting the job right the first time.

Reproofing

It is sometimes necessary to make a second proof. This is likely to occur because the first proof revealed a substantial error on the part of the trade shop or printer or because the subject matter is considered to be of such importance that the effect of even slight corrections must be seen before the job can be passed for printing.

In the first case, the client should not pay for the cost of reproofing. If, however, the proof was a "reasonable" rendering of the design, which followed the designer's instructions faithfully and included acceptable reproductions of any original illustrations, the reproof becomes necessary because the client has requested author's alterations or minor corrections. This means that he or she may be asked to pay for the second proof.

When reproofing for a minor alteration, it may be possible to save time and costs by making a proof of just the corrected item. A laser proof of a type correction, for example, or a scatter proof of a color separation will be much cheaper than remaking a large-format final color proof.

Why Proof at All?

Proofing has always been an integral part of print production, but its essential function—allowing inspection and approval of work done—has been called into question by contemporary quality management thinking. From a quality assurance perspective, proofing is a tool for getting a job right eventually, when what we should be looking for is a way of getting it right the first time—every time.

Increasing standardization of the printing process, combined with the trend towards carrying out prepress work at the design stage, point to the possibility of eliminating the distinction between the design proof and the final color proof. It is becoming technically and economically possible to produce a finished prototype of a job for customer approval, and for this prototype to act as both an iterative design proof and, following approval by the client, as a final color proof.

This approach requires:

- Rigorous standardization and calibration of every element of the production process.
- More accurate digital proofing tools.
- An ability by the designer, the client, and the printer to interpret the digital proof.

Many printers already apply basic quality assurance methods, and the Quality Assurance Standard ISO 9000 has been adopted in many industrialized countries. In principle, if we are confident that the production process used is technically capable of producing the right result, and the inputs into the process (the design, specifications, original illustrations, and the materials used) are all acceptable, then there is no real reason why the finished job should be significantly different than what the client wanted.

The main obstacles to this happening are the variations that occur within the process, including such things as fluctuations in ink weights, and the difficulty of ensuring that all the inputs are absolutely right and will not need subsequent alterations. Process variation can be reduced through better process control and standardization, but the production tolerances permit a degree of variation from the specified target values for characteristics like density and dot gain. Finalizing design elements and specifications at an early stage is also to some extent counter-intuitive, in that it does not correspond to the way that we naturally work—we tend to find out what we really meant to do after we have done it!

Nonetheless, electronic prepress could play a part in bringing about a change to more quality-conscious methods of working. Digital proofing tools have the potential to be used to produce a full prototype or visualization of a job at the design stage and support interactive alterations until it can be finally approved. If the job could then be passed into a well-controlled production process working to known standards, no further proofing would be necessary.

12 The Conventional Printing Processes

The changing market for printed products, with a greater demand for color and a greater emphasis on quality assurance, has brought about radical changes in the technology and management of the printing industry. Desktop imaging and publishing have significantly reduced prepress costs, shortened lead times, and made possible new products that could not have existed before. They have also brought significant savings in preparation costs, and publishers can now expect better quality, faster turnaround times, lower prices, and a much more flexible approach toward meeting their specific needs.

The conventional printing processes are mature technologies, based on simple physical or chemical principles that have developed and evolved over many years. Electronic methods of generating color reproduction have had less of an impact on the technology of putting ink on paper than in the prepress arena, although major changes are taking place in direct imaging to plates and presses. The main changes in press development have been threefold: reducing the time taken to prepare and run each job; automating press functions; and adding interfaces to sophisticated quality and production management systems.

Radical changes in the ways in which printing plates are created have taken place in recent years. Digital methods have been used to reduce or eliminate the intermediate image transfer steps in all the conventional printing processes and are even being used to output the finished job. These technologies are still emerging, but they will become increasingly important in the future as their commercial value is proven.

The cost, in real terms, of color printing has fallen dramatically in each of the last two decades, making color a real option for every printed product. The production costs per copy of a typical mass-market color magazine, from origination through to delivery of finished copies, are now on a par with the toner costs for a single color laser print. Continuing advances in plate imaging methods and pressroom automation will deliver further reductions in real costs to publishers, although these reductions are likely to be of an incremental nature.

The only way of bringing production costs down by a further order of magnitude would be to pass them on to the user, perhaps by distributing the information content of the publication in electronic form for viewing on screen or for output by the user on-demand using a local printing device. While this approach is commercially viable for specialist products, for the mass market the conventional printing processes remain the most cost-effective means of publishing text and images.

Many publishers and other print buyers are strengthening their supplier/customer links through improved communications. Most large and medium-sized printers have a management information system (MIS) that documents and controls production and have high-bandwidth data transfer links, such as ISDN. Electronic data interchange (EDI) systems allow a printer's customers access to estimating and job tracking routines in order to obtain pricing and current production status information on work in progress. Further development of such links, in conjunction with press control systems such as Heidelberg's CPC-Data that provides an interface between the press and the MIS, offers the ultimate prospect of direct access to the press for both direct-to-press imaging and control of press operations, such as job queuing and run length.

The major conventional printing processes are offset lithography, flexography, gravure, and screen printing. These are all established technologies capable of producing commercially acceptable color on a range of materials. Lithography has by far the largest market share, but technological advances in other processes, especially in flexography, render its continued dominance uncertain. Letterpress is still used in certain niches, such as label printing, but it cannot compete with the other processes for cost-effective color printing.

Modern printing presses are designed to achieve economies of scale. A single printing plate may carry up to thirty-two pages, and there will be as many printing units on the press as is necessary for economic production. Many presses are fitted with ancillary equipment that will dry or cure the ink and then cut and fold the paper into a finished periodical or book. Numbering, perforating, and gluing may also be performed in-line on the printing press.

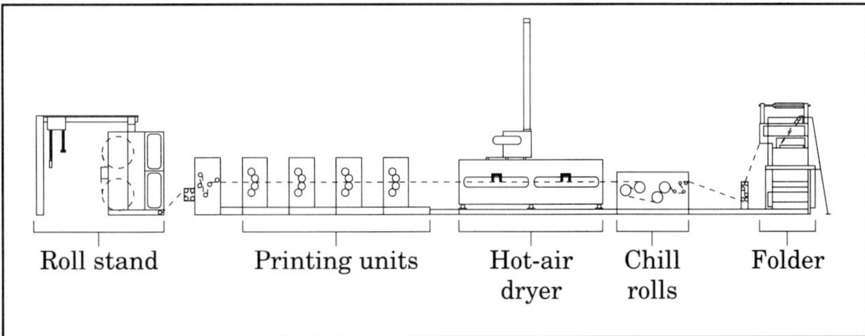

Figure 12-1. Schematic of a heatset web offset lithographic press.

The largest sector of the market is occupied by general commercial printers, producing anything from small leaflets and CD inserts to reports, brochures, and short-run magazines. Other major sectors of the printing industry specialize in books, periodicals, newspapers, direct mail, point-of-sale, security printing, and the various forms of packaging and product decoration.

Price is nearly always the most important consideration when print buyers place a contract, and the printer with the equipment best adapted to produce the job efficiently, at an acceptable level of quality, will be most likely to win the contract. Printers face continuing pressure to invest in equipment and technology that improves their ability to meet market demands. A prime example of this is the long-term trend toward installing multicolor presses capable of printing four or more colors in one pass, in response to the growing demand for color. Another is the investment in press technology that speeds up makeready (through devices such as automated plate-changing equipment, paper stack handling, and remote-controlled ink adjustments), as a response to the publishing trend to shorter run lengths and greater diversity of titles.

Print faces increasing competition from electronic media. Where a publication consists mainly of large volumes of text, CD-ROM can be a far cheaper method of distribution. When users want sound, moving images, or interaction, multimedia may be the most appropriate format. However, the cost of distributing large files in many applications and the convenience of accessing a hard copy weighed against the limitations of viewing information on a screen often makes print the most suitable and cost-effective media. On-demand printing of publisher-supplied electronic information on small color printers remains a possible threat to traditional print in the long term as the technology of digital color printing continues to develop. The most likely projection is that the overall consumption of information will continue to rise, and print will continue to coexist with other media.

The major printing processes have their own characteristic features that differentiate them. The most important of these are:

- The way in which the image is formed on the image carrier.
- The method of inking the image carrier and transferring the ink from it to the substrate.
- The ways in which the ink is dried.
- Whether the material is printed in reel (roll) or sheet form.
- The particular constraints of each process.

Note that all the characteristics listed above are strongly influenced by the type of paper used. Smoother, coated papers allow high ink densities, minimum dot gain, long tonal ranges, and fine screen rulings, while more absorbent papers with rougher surfaces affect these variables adversely.

Other factors that determine the suitability of a process for a particular product include:

Paper infeed. Paper (and other substrates such as board, plastics, and metals) can either be fed into the press in a continuous reel or web or in single sheets. Web presses run faster than sheetfed machines and can print on cheaper and lighter materials that are not rigid enough for sheet feeding, including lightweight coated stocks, plastics for packaging, and metallic foils. Web presses are equipped with folding units that deliver a complete magazine or book section, instead of just a printed sheet.

Ancillary equipment. To enhance the continuous production flow, many presses are equipped with numbering, scoring, gluing, perforating, or coating devices positioned in-line after the last printing unit. Where a job requires these operations, presses fitted with the appropriate ancillary equipment will be much more economical than completing this work off-press.

Number of in-line printing units. Printing presses commonly have one, two, four, or more printing units, each one printing a single color. Printers in certain specialty markets like greetings cards often have presses with six or more units. Unless the print run is very short, it is most efficient to print on a press that has the same number of units as there are colors in the job. Four-color work, for example, should normally be printed on a four-unit press.

Versatility. Many presses can be reconfigured to produce different products. Multicolor sheetfed presses may be able to turn the sheet during printing, so that both sides can be printed in a single pass. Web presses can produce different products by reconfiguring the path of the web through the press and the folder unit.

Size. Printing presses are built in all sizes, taking sheets or rolls from 8 to 78 in. (210 to 2,000 mm) wide. Even larger sizes can be printed by the screen printing process.

Image carrier. Different processes require different printing surfaces or image carriers (printing plates, cylinders, screens, and so on), and they are a significant element in the cost of a job. Most output bureaus assume that a job is to be printed by sheetfed lithography unless otherwise instructed; for other processes, or for printing by web offset, the films may have to be made differently. Lithographic plates require positive or negative film that has the emulsion on the wrong-reading side, for example; while for flexography, right-reading negatives are required.

Range of substrates. The nature of the printing surface, the inks used, and the transport mechanism of the press all limit the range of substrates that can be printed. Only the screen printing process and ink jet (and one or two minor specialty processes, such as tampo printing) can print on items that cannot be fed through a press, such as fully formed cartons, other assembled products, and so on.

Ease of image change. Press manufacturers have invested a great deal in reducing the preparation time (known as makeready) associated with mounting and positioning each new printing plate, preparing the paper feed, and adjusting the ink flow. Fragmentation of publishing markets and the growing number of small, specialty titles has led to greater demands for shorter run lengths. Makeready reduction is a major goal in maintaining competitiveness. Automatic plate-changing equipment is becoming popular on multicolor presses, but printing a completely variable image in a run of one and changing to another image while the press is operating at full production speed is only possible in nonimpact processes.

Drying systems. Several methods of converting liquid ink films to dry films are used on printing presses. Some rely on the evaporation of ink solvents and others on a chemical change possibly assisted by some form of energy. The latter allow higher ink weights to be printed without setoff or marking.

The characteristics to consider at the prepress stage are:

- **Inking.** The typical ink weights printed and the nature of the colorants used.
- **Dot gain.** The change in dot values from film to print, which will require compensation on the films produced.
- **Tonal range.** The highest and lowest percent dot values that can be printed.
- **Resolution.** The highest screen ruling that can be printed.

Specific parameters to adjust or to compensate for during color separation or film output include:

- The maximum overprint possible.
- The spectral characteristics of the inks used.
- The smallest and the largest printable dot.
- The amount of dot gain.
- The type of halftone screens to be used.

If you are responsible for sending files for output straight to film, you may have to ensure that the relevant adjustments have been made.

By far the great majority of printing surfaces (or image carriers) are produced photographically. This is done by exposing a film positive or negative onto a light-sensitive coating and then processing the printing surface to create the image and nonimage areas. Methods of creating the image by exposing direct from digital data are now available for most processes, but have not yet been widely adopted by printers.

Lithography

Offset lithography is the dominant printing process, owing to its high print quality and the relatively low costs of plate preparation and press makeready. A lithographic plate has a water-receptive surface (or, in the case of waterless lithography, an ink-repellent surface) of aluminum or plastic in the nonimage areas and an ink-receptive, light-sensitive coating in the image areas.

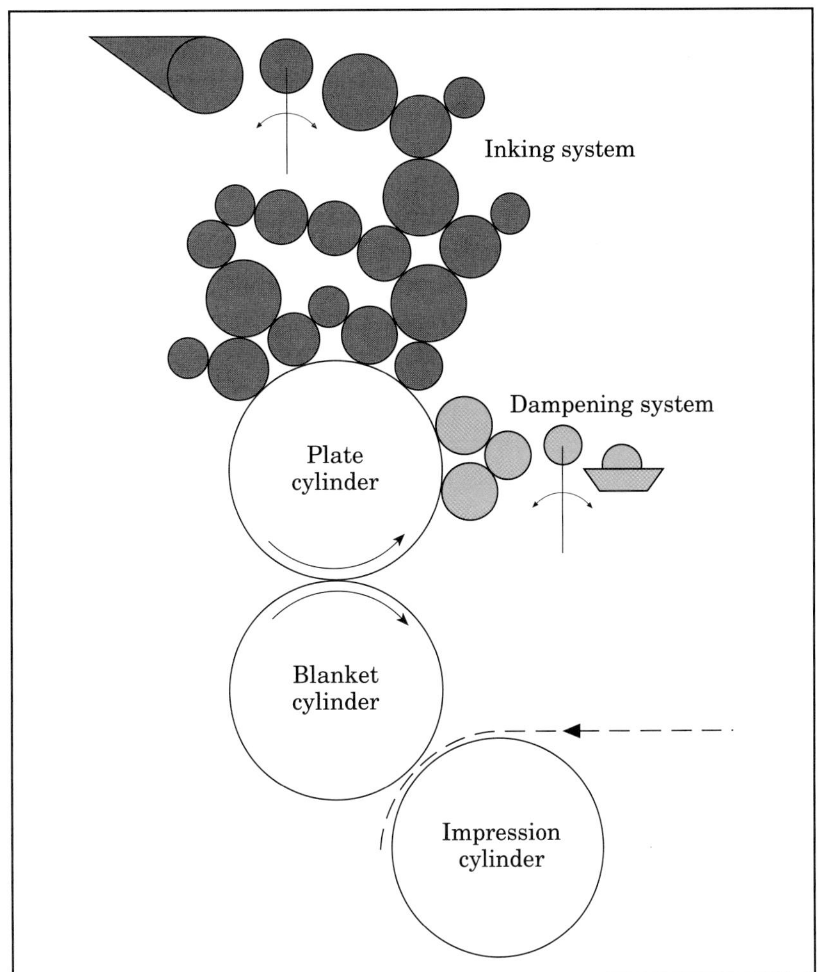

Figure 12-2. The lithographic process.

During printing, inking and dampening rollers are in contact with the plate. The nonimage areas are wetted with dampening solution and repel ink, so that it only adheres to the image areas. This condition continues as long as the ink/water balance is correctly maintained.

Ink transfers from the plate to a rubber blanket, which then transfers the image to the substrate. The blanket's resilience allows it to mold to the paper surface, producing a clean, even impression even on textured papers.

As with other processes, the maximum ink weight that can be printed is determined by the need to avoid setoff (the transfer of wet ink from the face of one sheet on to the reverse of another in the delivery pile) and marking (the smearing of wet ink on parts of the press), as well as the filling-in of halftones and tints.

Lithographic plates are relatively cheap to make, demanding little skill to achieve consistent results. They are very thin (0.006–0.020 in. or 0.15–0.5 mm) and can be stored for several years if preserved with a coating of gum. An aluminum lithographic plate will hold image detail down to around 5 microns, enabling it to print with the finest resolution and detail of all the processes

Screen rulings can, as a result, be extremely high. Rulings of 600 lpi and above have been achieved using waterless plates, although 150–200 lpi is more usual in commercial printing on coated papers and 100–133 lpi on uncoated stock and newsprint.

Presses are built in configurations from single-color sheetfed machines up to very large web units that are coupled together to print publications with multiple pages. The paste inks used in lithography contain catalytic drying agents that cause the ink to dry slowly in normal room conditions. UV-curing systems are widely used to give instant drying and high gloss levels. Infrared systems are the main alternative method of accelerating the drying process. On web offset presses, coated papers are printed with inks that set hard after being heated and then chilled. Web presses fitted with this equipment are referred to as **heatset,** and other web presses are called **coldset.** Heatset presses are necessary for web printing on coated papers.

Lithographic presses will print on papers and boards up to 0.04 in. (1 mm) thick (depending on press design), and both smooth and textured surfaces can be printed. Metals and plastics are more difficult to print by lithography due to their inability to absorb the printing ink. Only specialty printers handle these materials.

The main limitations of lithography are inherent in the use of water as part of the process. The balance between the water and the ink is very sensitive and easily upset. Ink may appear in nonimage areas if there is too little water, or alternatively, the ink will fade and water marks will appear in image areas if there is too much water present. Other effects can include inking inconsistencies, such as roller marks in solids and tints. The inking system also requires careful setting and monitoring, and most waste occurs at the beginning of a run as the printer adjusts the color registration and ink levels.

Attempts have been made to eliminate these problems. One approach, known as waterless lithography, uses plates with a silicone layer to form the ink-repellent nonimage area. It has not yet been widely adopted, partly because of a reluctance to innovate and partly because a new set of problems is caused by the absence of water. Waterless lithography has been used successfully in Japan for some time, and it is likely that it will become more widespread in the future. One advantage of waterless lithography is that it makes very fine screen rulings possible.

Anilox inking, derived from flexographic inking systems, is being used successfully in some markets, such as newspaper printing. A simple inking system with a large transfer roller engraved with tiny cells ensures that the same ink film thickness is transferred to every part of the image.

Modern multicolor presses invariably have computer controls that accelerate functions like ink setting and register control. Some press manufacturers have developed systems that offer fully automated control of quality by on-line measurement of the sheet or web as it is printed and automatic follow-up adjustment. The high capital cost of these systems and the difficulty in controlling all the relevant variables have limited the number of printers who have installed them.

For very long runs of color printing, lithography competes with the gravure process, especially in the production of color periodicals and catalogs. Perhaps more important from the printer's point of view has been the replacement of a significant amount of small offset capacity by copiers and laser printers, although the high per-copy costs for color copying mean that small offset presses remain competitive on longer runs, while delivering higher quality.

Lithographic plate preparation. Lithographic plates are coated with a light-sensitive material. A film positive or negative is secured against the plate and exposed to a high-intensity light source that leaves the nonimage areas soluble in a developer. Since lithographic plates are very thin, it is also possible to expose them in an imagesetter if the plate material is sufficiently flexible. Plastic plate material in roll form, which is cut to the correct length for the press after imaging, is used in plate or imagesetters. Preparing plates in this way is known as direct-to-plate or computer-to-plate.

Flexography

Flexographic presses print from a flexible relief plate using liquid inks. A simple inking system makes the flexographic press relatively easy to set up and run. An anilox transfer roller ensures even plate inking without the need for careful adjustment. Inks can be either solvent-based (mainly for printing on nonabsorbent materials such as plastics and glass) or water-based (especially for absorbent materials like paper and board). The main solvent used is alcohol, although a small proportion of more hazardous hydrocarbons is also used. Most flexographic printing is now done with water-based inks.

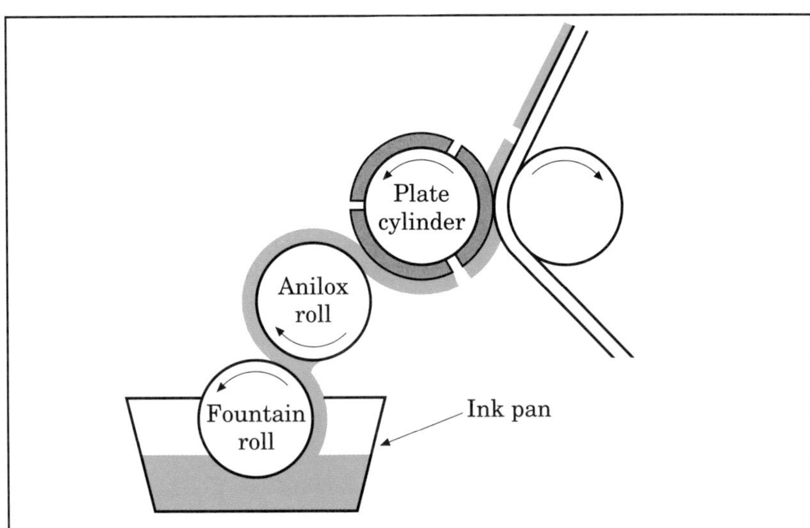

Figure 12-3. The flexographic process.

The main drawback of flexography is the distortion of the image as it undergoes pressure during image transfer. Solid areas are not seriously affected, although when printing on nonabsorbent materials there is usually an unprinted line (or "halo") around the edge of the solid. Small type tends to be squashed, however, and halftone dots are badly deformed. The result is that the tonal range that can be printed may be as little as 25–50% on an absorbent substrate like newsprint. It is also difficult to print finer screen rulings, with 150 lpi being the usual upper limit that is only achieved on very smooth materials like plastics.

Flexography as a process has come from being something of a "poor relation" of other processes, fit only for the lowest-grade work and for substrates that could not easily be printed by lithography, to a position where it has been talked about as a challenger to lithography as the dominant printing process. It is unlikely that flexography will ever match the resolution and tonal range of good-quality lithographic color, although improvements in quality through developments in inks, press design, and platemaking continue to be made. For example, plates have been developed that are thinner and harder than previously. By using these plates with lighter printing pressures and appropriate inks, sharper images can be printed with less distortion and dot gain. Printers have also employed laser-engraved ceramic anilox rollers to control the precise volume of ink that is transferred and replaced conventional heat drying ovens with UV-curing units to achieve lower dot gain.

Flexographic plate preparation. Plates for flexography were originally made by molding rubber to a relief (letterpress) image. This method has been superseded in many plants by photographic methods and electronic engraving. Photopolymer flexo plates are made by exposing a thin (0.04–0.10 in. or 1.0–2.5 mm) plastic material that has a light-sensitive coating to a photographic negative of the image that is to be printed. Exposure hardens the image area, and the nonimage area is then "washed out" by solvent to leave the image in relief.

The thickness and resilience of the plate material results in image distortion when the plate is mounted on the press and subjected to the pressure of printing. The image lengthens slightly in one direction, which can cause problems in some products like packaging where a precise image length is required. A slight anamorphic distortion, known as **disproportioning,** is applied during preparation, or alternatively, the plate can be exposed in position on a cylinder. The complications of flexographic platemaking require specialized prepress systems, and it is not feasible to use film that has been prepared for lithographic printing.

Direct-digital methods of plate preparation are rapidly increasing in importance in flexography, since they eliminate intermediate production steps, shorten lead times, and integrate with electronic copy preparation methods. They also offer the only route to achieving quality levels comparable with the other printing processes, through improved color registration and better control of final dot sizes.

Figure 12-4.
DuPont photopolymer flexographic plate.
Courtesy E. I. du Pont de Nemours & Co., Inc.

Laser-engraved rubber plates are made by mounting the rubber plate material on a cylinder and vaporizing the non-image areas with a CO_2 laser. The image data can be fed either from an analyze cylinder on which the artwork is mounted, or from digital data prepared in a DAR (Digital Artwork and Reproduction) electronic prepress system. Flexographic print quality is markedly improved by the use of frequency-modulated screening and high levels of gray component replacement.

Gravure

The strength of gravure has always been in long-run quality color in the periodical, mail-order catalog, and packaging fields, together with advertising color pre-prints for newspapers, but current changes in publishing practices and markets (including growing regionalization in periodicals; the shift to flexography for carton printing; and the elimination of pre-prints in newspaper production in favor of run-of-press color) have tended to lead the move away from gravure.

The potential for gravure printing in other markets such as color books remains unrealized because run lengths are falling as publishers adopt strategies that call for smaller inventories, shorter run lengths, and more frequent updating of titles.

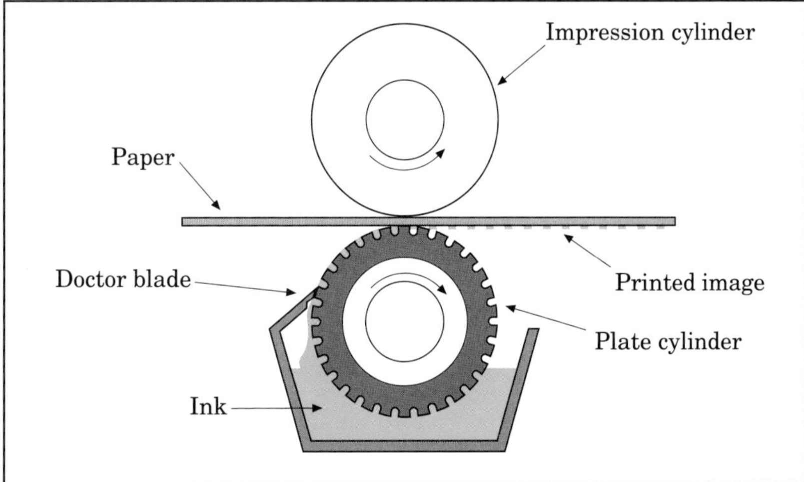

Figure 12-5.
The gravure process.

In gravure printing, the image area on the printing cylinder is recessed so that it is slightly lower than the nonimage areas. The whole printing cylinder rotates in an ink trough, and a steel blade scrapes the ink off of the cylinder's surface so that it remains only in the recessed image areas. Ink transfer from cylinder recess to paper is often electrostatically assisted, with the ink and the impression cylinder given opposite charges. Because the depth of the image recess is variable, it is possible for a gravure press to print ink films of variable thickness, unlike other processes. This produces a continuous-tone image with no halftone screen, and, as a result, gravure printing can exhibit excellent tonal qualities.

If the steel doctor blade is not supported in solid areas of the image, it will remove ink from the recesses. For this reason the image is created from small individual cells, each cell having a depth that corresponds to the tonal value required. The cell structure is not noticeable in images, but can be quite objectionable in text which has a ragged appearance not unlike 200-dpi laser printing.

Cylinder preparation is time-consuming and costly, making gravure competitive only on longer runs. The image on a gravure cylinder lasts for many millions of impressions without wear. Color variation is virtually eliminated by the design of the inking system, making the process highly suitable for printing packaging where consistent color is very important.

There are two main types of gravure presses: large publication presses, producing multi-page jobs like catalogs and periodicals; and smaller presses printing flexible packaging, wallpaper, gift wrapping, and so on. Gravure presses are normally reel-fed, with the exception of a small number of sheetfed presses designed for proofing and the printing of cartons and short-run, high-value products.

The hazardous nature of solvent-based gravure inks have caused some problems for gravure printers. Aromatic hydrocarbons, employed for their ability to promote the efficient transfer of ink from cell to paper and to evaporate quickly from the paper after printing, give rise to high rates of VOC (volatile organic compound) emissions, which are known to cause environmental and health problems. Ink manufacturers have developed water-based alternatives, but there are problems in formulating them so that ink transfers consistently to the paper without leaving residues on the cylinder. Further work needs to be done in developing alternative inks and papers.

Apart from the ability to produce long print runs economically, the main strengths of gravure are consistency of color and its ability to print good quality color on very cheap uncoated papers. Once the cylinder has been imaged, the ink weight that is printed cannot be altered, which is a great advantage in applications, such as packaging and consumer catalogs, where color consistency can be of critical importance. As long as the paper surface is smooth (and preferably supercalendered), even the lowest grade mechanical papers give good results. Very cheap papers with supercalendered surfaces can be printed, and this is often a factor in choosing gravure over lithography for the production of periodicals and catalogs. The heavy ink films possible with gravure enhance the brilliance of special colors and metallic inks. Plastics and other nonabsorbent materials can also be printed without difficulty.

Gravure cylinder preparation. The gravure cylinder is normally solid steel plated with a skin of copper, and the image is formed by etching or engraving a pattern of cells with a variable depth. After proofing, the copper may be plated with chromium to harden the surface and extend its life.

Cylinders can be imaged either photographically or electronically. Photographic imaging involves exposing a film positive to a tissue with acid-resistant properties. The tissue is attached to the surface of the cylinder and chemically etched, the "resist" controlling the depth of etching.

Photographic cylinder etching is still in widespread use in plants specializing in packaging, but has been superseded in most publication gravure plants by electronic engraving. This process is similar to analog scanning: a positive is prepared and mounted on an analyze scanner, which sends image data to an engraving device on which the cylinder is mounted. A stylus scans the cylinder, "pecking" cells to the required depth. There can be up to twelve scanning heads on the analyze drum and a corresponding number of engraving heads on the cylinder.

Figure 12-6. Gravure cylinder engraving on a Helio-Klischograph. *Courtesy Linotype-Hell Co.*

Gravure positives have in the past been continuous-tone film or bromides prepared photographically from mechanical artwork and transparencies. Publishers now prefer to supply halftone film positives prepared in the same way as positives for offset lithography, and an "offset gravure conversion" (OG) method is used to convert the halftone positive to a continuous-tone image.

Electromechanical engraving lends itself naturally to digital prepress, by simply replacing the analyze scanning of the positive with image data from a page-makeup system. This considerably shortens cylinder production times, since there is no need to convert the original artwork to continuous-tone positives and mount them on the analyze cylinder. Quality is also improved by direct cylinder engraving. Interfaces between the engraving system and PostScript front-ends are being developed and are having a major impact on both periodical and packaging markets, enabling gravure to compete with flexography and lithography in shorter run lengths.

Attempts to replace electromechanical-stylus engraving with laser or electron-beam engraving have not been successful thus far. It has proven difficult to develop materials that can be easily vaporized by a laser while also remaining sufficiently durable to resist abrasion by the doctor blade and the printing substrate. Electron-beam engraving systems also remain too costly for widespread commercial use, and development work in this area has ceased. Photopolymer plates (produced in the same way as flexographic plates) have also met with little success.

Screen Printing

Screen printing is a stencil printing technique, in which ink is forced through the open areas of the stencil, through a mesh screen, and onto the substrate.

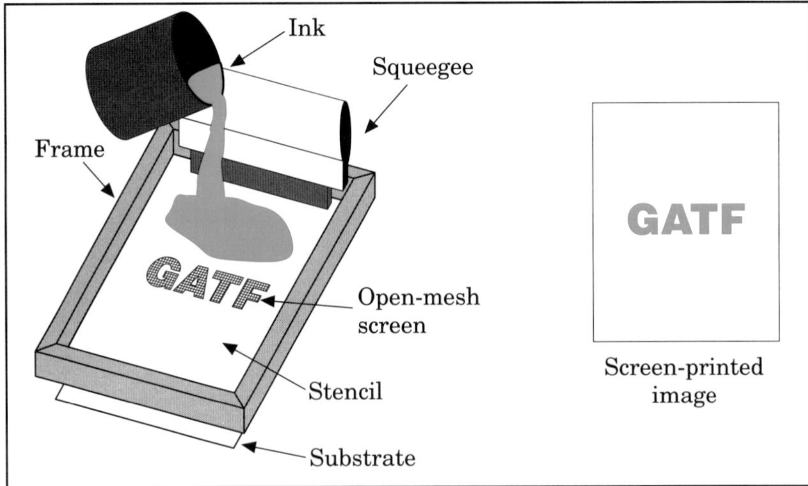

Figure 12-7. The screen printing process.

Like the other conventional processes, the fundamental principle is extremely simple, and equipment for screen printing can consist of no more than a frame, a bed, and a squeegee. More complex equipment may be used for high-speed multicolor printing, or for dedicated machines printing directly onto products or packs. The ability of the screen printing process to print on any substrate makes it very versatile. It is the only process capable of printing items on mirrors, ceramics, bottles, plastic pots, and road signs.

In screen printing, as in flexography, small highlight dots cannot be held easily on the stencil. The halftone screen ruling and the tonal range are limited by the size of the openings in the screen mesh and the ability of the ink to flow through without clogging. Inks and meshes are selected with the application in mind; nylon and polyester meshes with a mesh count from 50–500 openings per inch are available together with very fine stainless-steel and phosphor-bronze meshes for high-resolution work such as printed circuit boards.

Hazardous solvent-based screen inks are being phased out in favor of water-based inks for most applications. High-speed and multicolor presses are normally fitted with UV curing to prevent the wet ink from marking.

Screen printing is an extremely versatile process with continuing improvements in quality. Because very heavy ink weights are possible, it is the first choice for display items, such as point-of-sale materials, signs, and other items where strong, eye-catching colors are required. One interesting application is in printing solid areas on prestige brochures and book jackets that have color and text printed by lithography, taking advantage of the much heavier and more consistent ink weights possible in screen printing. However, some of the traditional screen printing market for very short run posters is likely to be lost to ink jet printing in the future.

Screen printing stencil preparation. Stencils for commercial screen printing are made by exposing a light-sensitive stencil material through a film positive. Nonimage areas are hardened during the exposure, and the image areas can then be washed away with water. The stencil is attached to the mesh screen before wash-out. Direct-exposure systems for the production of screen stencils from digital data are used only in specialized product areas.

Hybrid Presses

Printing presses that print by more than one process are becoming increasingly common. Printers can use the relative advantages of each process to optimize the quality and production efficiency of the end product. A flexography/gravure hybrid, for example, offers the tonal quality and long-run efficiency of gravure, combined with the ease of preparation associated with flexography, to create effective promotional literature or other targeted information. Similarly, a web offset press fitted with ink jet heads can overprint variable customer information during the run of the press.

Standardizing Printing Characteristics

Before films or plates can be made, it is essential that the exact characteristics of the printed output are known in order to set gray balance and tone compression correctly and compensate for any distortions, such as dot gain. For the majority of jobs, it is not realistic to adjust the color separations for each printing press, since, in many cases, this information is not known at the time the films are output.

Rather than expect the film supplier to attempt to calibrate the films to the individual press, many lithographic printers work to established industry-wide standards. These standards specify printing characteristics that most printers are capable of matching. The publisher needs only to know which standard applies to automatically generate correctly adjusted films. The most common standards are incorporated into applications like Adobe Photoshop, making it unnecessary to specify details such as the precise dot gain compensation for each color, since they are included in the way the program builds up its color separation tables.

Table 12-1. Standards for color printing.

Standard	Published by
Specifications for Web Offset Printing (SWOP)	SWOP, Inc.
Eurostandard Offset	System Brunner
Specifications for European Offset Printing of Periodicals (FIPP)	International Federation of the Periodical Press
Specifications for Non-heatset Advertising Printing (SNAP)	Printing Industries of America
UK Offset Newspaper Specifications (UKONS)	Newspaper Society (UK) and Pira International

In the U.S., SWOP (Specifications for Web Offset Printing) is widely used by lithographic printers. In Europe, Eurostandard is probably the most widely used of a number of different standards available. Separate standards for newspapers are available, including SNAP (U.S.) and UKONS (UK).

The alternative to generating films to known standards is to calibrate the films to the individual press, once its specific characteristics have been established. Where standards do not exist, publishers must obtain a specification for press characteristics from the printer. Otherwise, they must supply originals and allow the printer to generate the files.

Research is continuing into ways of establishing some elements of standardization in flexography and screen printing. The Flexographic Technical Association's research committee is working on defining and controlling variables in flexography and preparing guidelines for printers. The Screen Printing Association International is analyzing screen printing variables in order to achieve a degree of standardization, while in the UK the Screen Printers Association is developing a British Standard for screen printing.

Printing Problems

The main problems that occur with the printing processes can be briefly summarized as follows:

- **Substrate deformities,** including excessive moisture absorption that leads to misregister or curl and the rupture of the paper's surface, bringing about blistering, picking, and other defects.
- **Breakdown of the image/nonimage separation.** Image areas can wear or break up (flexography and lithography) or get dirty and fill in (gravure and screen printing), causing a loss of detail, especially in highlights. Similarly, nonimage areas can become worn (gravure and screen), fill in (flexography), or fail to repel ink (lithography). As a result, ink—usually in the form of streaks, spots, or a light overall tint—appears in the nonimage areas. Damage to the printing surface shows up as scratches or dents, and dirt can appear as printed or unprinted spots.
- **Inconsistencies in inking.** Lithography is especially prone to inking irregularities. These may be caused by a failure to set and maintain the ink and dampening levels accurately across the sheet or by a weaknesses in press design and maintenance. On the printed sheet, uneven inking appears in the form of bands in larger tint areas or ghosts (repeat images) in areas of solid color.
- **Incompatibility of one or more materials** with each other or with the printing process. Unexpected and sometimes unpredictable effects can occasionally occur and it difficult to pinpoint the exact cause of the problem. Most problems can be avoided by employing a combination of good design and specifications; by proofing at the appropriate stages in production; and by using reliable printing facilities.

13 Digital Color Printing

Digital color printing is a rapidly expanding sector. The conventional printing processes, while highly cost-effective on longer print runs, are unable to produce short runs of color print economically. As run lengths for all types of products continue to fall, the market for short-run digital color printing will undoubtedly increase. It has been suggested by Seybold that close to 50% of the entire print market in the U.S. is made up of runs of 10,000 or less, and that the availability of economic production methods could lead to 50% of the U.S. market consisting of runs of 1,000 copies or less.

Nonimpact printing is not, as some people have speculated, about to overtake the conventional printing processes. Conventional printing processes are faster and cheaper for medium to long runs and produce better quality. Digital systems cannot achieve quality comparable to conventional printing without a heavy penalty on output times. The cost of the toner alone for a single color laser print is around the same as the entire production costs, per copy, of a sixty-four-page color magazine printed by heatset web offset litho in a commercial run of 100,000 copies. Moreover, nonimpact systems that produce a quality equivalent to commercial offset would take up to twenty-four hours to print a single copy of all sixty-four pages, compared with a production speed of around 40,000 fully printed and bound copies per hour on a heatset web.

A more likely outcome is that the spectrum of price/performance, with gravure at the long-run end and screen printing at the opposite end, will be transformed to make room for a range of new systems producing an increasing amount of relatively short-run work. Shorter runs will continue to comprise an increasing share of the total printing market, making digital color systems probably the fastest growing sector of printing.

The newer printing technologies are also ideal partners and enabling technologies for electronic publishing, producing all kinds of printed output that would otherwise be technically or economically impossible. Nonimpact printers designed for higher production volumes are being developed, and inevitably the length of run at which it becomes cheaper to move from conventional to digital printing will continue to fall.

While conventional printing processes are mature technologies, in which developments in press design, inking systems, and materials are largely evolutionary and incremental, digital color printing is the focus of intensive research and innovation. Unlike the conventional processes, digital printing systems are falling in price and are also improving in quality of output, speed of production, and workflow management.

Digital color printing supports just-in-time production, individualized output, in-house production, distributed information, visualization and prototyping, compilations and offprints, and short-run printing.

Just-in-time production. In many areas of manufacturing, purchasers have reduced their inventory costs by buying goods as they are needed instead of ordering them for stock. Most printed items have an unpredictable demand, and purchasers are tempted to try to reduce per-copy costs by ordering large quantities. The risk of the items no longer being required or becoming out of date is balanced against the setup costs for reprints and the problems associated with running out of a product because of the long lead times printers require. By making short runs possible on demand without a cost penalty, digital color printing allows the purchaser to buy smaller lots more frequently. Short lead times and more frequent output also make it possible to ensure that the latest information is always included.

Individualized output. A key difference between conventional printing and digital printing is that the latter is not restricted to printing the same image on copy after copy. No tangible image carrier is produced because the image is formed by data that is rasterized and sent to the marking engine or print head. Thus the image is created anew for each sheet that is printed, and it is possible to vary it each time, depending on the ability of the RIP to process the new data at the same speed as the marking engine transfers it to paper. This possibility is of great interest to publishers and advertisers wishing to tailor a communication to what is known about the intended reader. Typical items produced in this fashion include documents with a proportion of boilerplate text but with some information relevant only to the client; direct mail targeted to the preferences of the individual consumer; and individualized instruction packages designed to accommodate a particular student's abilities. Other uses of variable-image printing include the overprinting customer information on newspapers and periodicals and product coding on cans and packaging.

In-house production. Purchasers can achieve cost and time savings upstream of the production process by eliminating elements associated with external purchasing, such as supplier liaisons, transportation of files and artwork, and arranging payment. This is already widely exploited in simple document production through in-house reprographics and facilities management units, but for quality color work most organizations use external printers.

Distributed information. Many reference items such as dictionaries, encyclopedias, manuals, catalogs, and so on are distributed most efficiently in electronic form, allowing the end user to view the information on screen or download to a local printing device only those items that are needed. The costs of distributing hard copies to multiple locations can also be eliminated by distributed printing.

Visualization and prototyping. Digital color printing makes it feasible to produce single copies or very short runs to test and approve visual concepts for new products, including both traditional items like cartons and new products like multimedia screen designs. Distributing a small quantity to potential users also makes it possible to test-market the product and draw users into an approval cycle traditionally limited to the designer and client.

Compilations and offprints. Some customers require specific journal articles or book chapters. If the original publications have been produced conventionally, the publisher will either have to send the client the entire book or periodical, or prepare an "offprint" by photocopying or by cutting up the printed copies. If the items are held in a database, producing digital output of individual articles and book chapters is no problem. They can even be bound together as a unique, customized publication.

Short-run printing. Items such as reports, manuals, maps, posters, and specialty books and magazines with pressruns that would have made their production completely unfeasible due to the setup costs of conventional printing processes are good candidates for short-run printing.

The Technologies

There are countless methods of actually transferring a rasterized image to paper. The contending technologies can be broadly grouped into nonimpact systems and conventional presses that have been modified to accept direct digital imaging of the printing surface. (The term "nonimpact" was originally coined to describe computer printers that did not employ printing heads that marked sheets by impact against a ribbon, as do teletype, dot matrix, and daisy-wheel printers.) For convenience, we have divided the nonimpact systems into ink jet (where a liquid ink is propelled onto the paper); electrostatic (where a toner is transferred by an electrical charge); and thermal (where a wax or dye colorant is transferred to the paper by heat). This classification is something of a simplification, and many devices do not fit neatly into one or other of the categories proposed.

Colorants and image transfer methods are unlike those used by conventional printing processes, and so color gamut, resolution, and tonal characteristics tend to be different. Screen rulings tend to be lower than in conventional printing. Dye-sublimation printers tend to produce the best quality results—with 300-lpi continuous-tone images that have the same amount of information as a high-resolution litho print. Electrostatic systems are capable of addressable resolutions up to 2,400 dpi, which enables a 150-lpi gray scale image to be printed. In all systems, there is a trade-off between imaging speed and resolution, so that, for example, ink jet heads mounted on web offset presses print very coarse images at full web speeds, while, at the other end of the scale, higher resolutions can be achieved on proofing systems that operate at slow speeds.

All nonimpact systems have three basic components: a raster image processor to convert the image into a bitmap suitable for the printer; a buffer that holds the rasterized image in memory ready for printing; and a **marking engine** that transfers colorant to the substrate. The RIP may be located within the printing device itself, or externally in a separate hardware or software RIP or in the host computer. In some cases, the printing speed of the marking engine can be as high as that of a small conventional printing press, but, in practice, the speed may be limited by the capabilities of the RIP and the page buffer.

Ink Jet

Ink jet printers generate ink droplets, either by forcing a continuous stream of ink through a nozzle (with the unwanted droplets deflected electrostatically to a waste gutter) or by propelling droplets on demand according to the image requirements. Drop-on-demand desktop ink jet printers propel ink by thermal or piezoelectric methods. **Thermal ink jets** (or

Figure 13-1.
Ink jet printing.

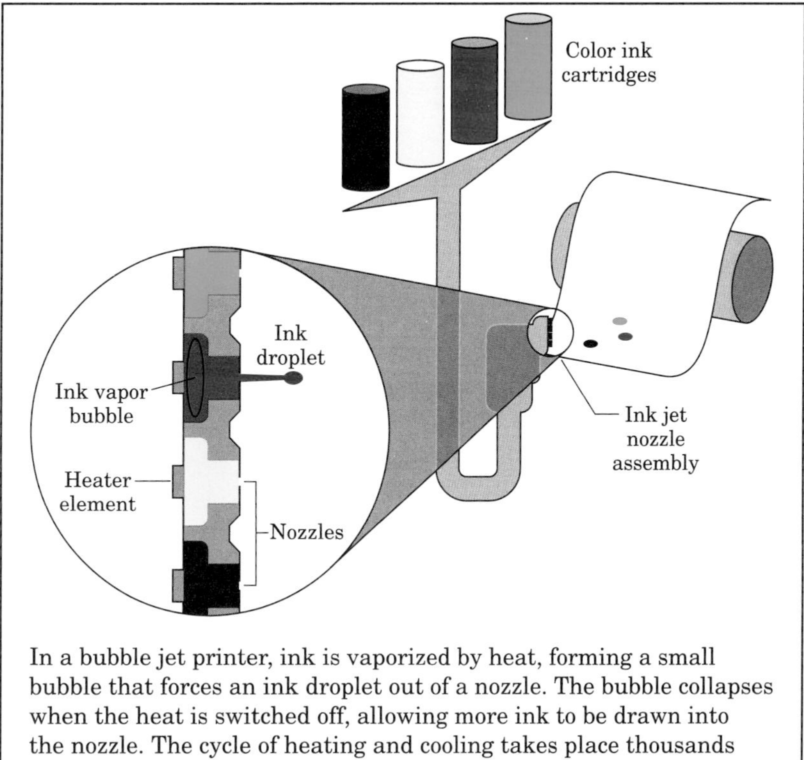

In a bubble jet printer, ink is vaporized by heat, forming a small bubble that forces an ink droplet out of a nozzle. The bubble collapses when the heat is switched off, allowing more ink to be drawn into the nozzle. The cycle of heating and cooling takes place thousands of times each second.

bubble jets) heat a tiny amount of ink until it vaporizes, its expansion forcing liquid ink through an aperture at a high speed, while **piezoelectric** (or phase-change) systems rely on the properties of quartz and ceramic materials to change

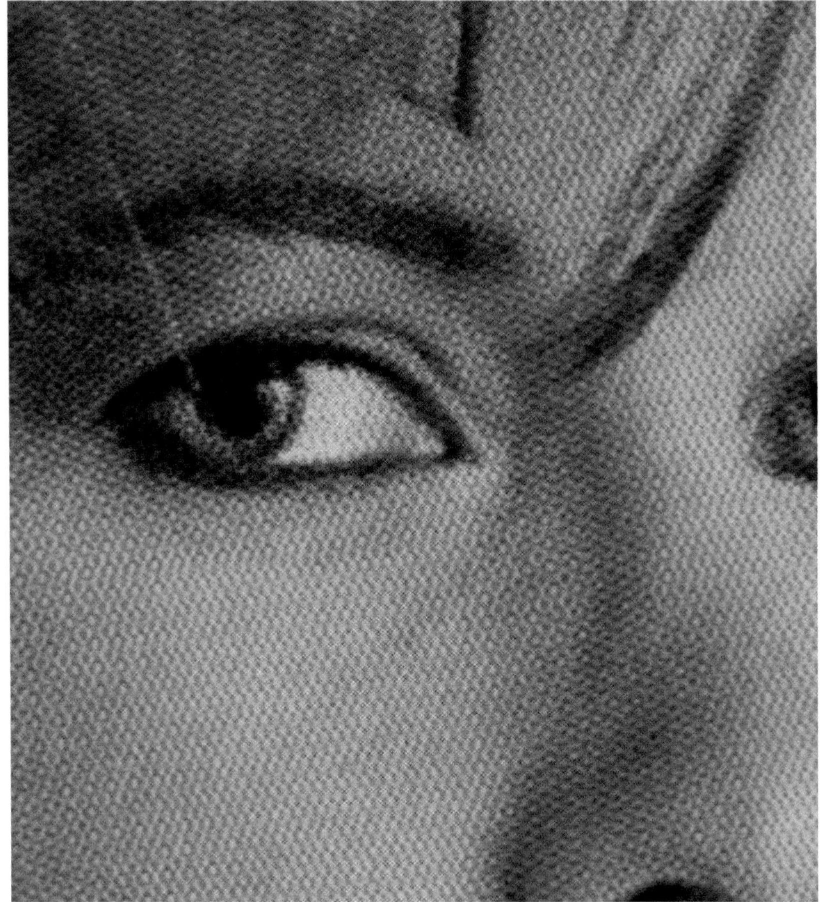

Figure 13-2. Sample of high-resolution ink jet output. (Detail enlarged 10×.)

shape when a charge is applied, mechanically forcing ink out through an opening. Continuous ink jets are used on web offset presses or in binding lines to add customer- or batch-specific information. Most systems are effectively binary—droplets cannot vary in size—but some continuous ink jet printers have the ability to send several droplets to the same location on the paper, resulting in the droplets merging and spreading as they arrive at the paper surface. The number of droplets that can be sent to the same spot determines the number of gray levels that the process can achieve.

Most desktop ink jet printers can produce resolutions comparable to low-end laser printers, at around 300 dpi. At this resolution, working at up to 20,000 cycles per second, a twelve-jet array takes a minute or so to print a single page. The lower resolutions and faster droplet generation of press-mounted continuous ink jets allow them to print at the full production speed of the press, which may be as much as 70,000 copies per hour.

Ink jet devices can print on most papers, although drying is slow on stocks with low absorbency, and wicking (ink spreading into the paper fibers) can occur on highly absorbent materials like newsprint.

Desktop color ink jet printers produce color documents and visualization proofs, but higher resolutions are needed for approval proofs, and even these cannot reproduce the halftone screen exactly as it will appear in the final printed job. With some color ink jet devices, the ink used is solid at room temperature and briefly liquefies as it is heated prior to printing. It then resolidifies immediately upon reaching the paper, providing a sharper image and stronger colors since the paper does not absorb this ink as it would any normal liquid ink.

Electrostatic Printing

Electrostatic printing covers photocopiers, laser printers, and other printing devices that employ the xerographic principle of using an electrical charge to attract toner to image areas. A pattern of charged areas corresponding to the image that is to be printed is created on a dielectric drum. Toner with an opposite charge is brushed over the drum, where it adheres only to the image areas and is then transferred to the paper.

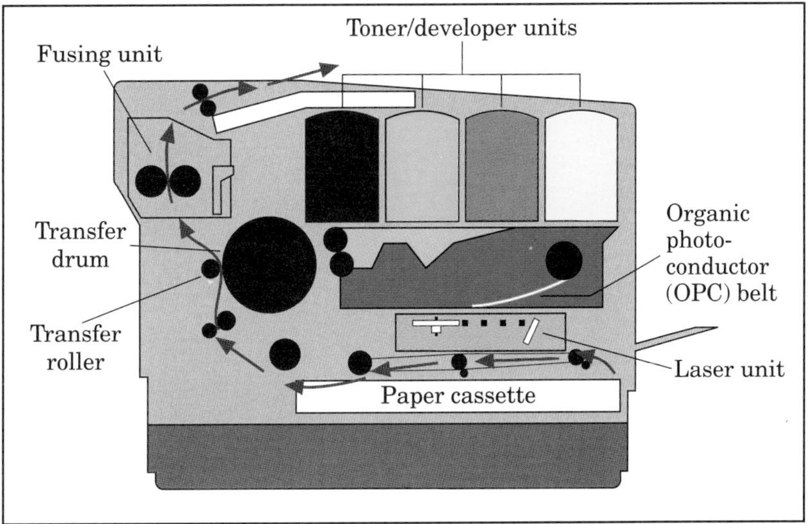

Figure 13-3. Schematic of color laser printer.

The image is formed on the drum by first applying a charge to the whole drum. A high-intensity light source scans across the surface, switching on and off according to the image

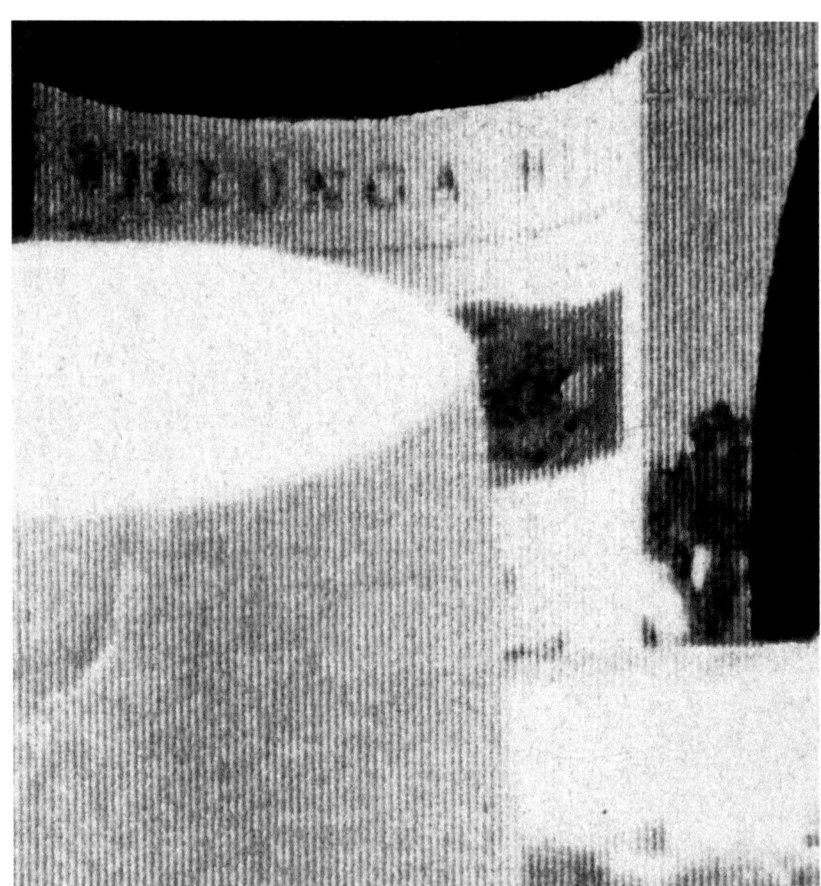

Figure 13-4.
Color laser prints. (A) The laser scan lines are visible in a conventional print. (Detail enlarged 10×.)

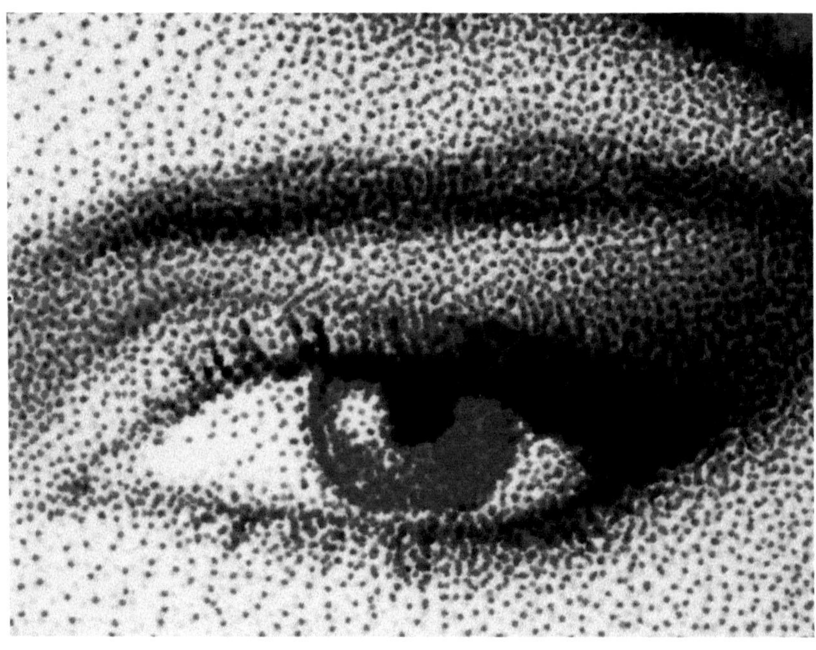

(B) Here frequency-modulated screening is used, although at a much lower resolution than would be found in litho printing. (Detail enlarged 10×.)

requirements, and the charge is dissipated wherever light falls on it. In a photocopier, the light is reflected from an original resting against a platen through a lens on to the drum, while, in a laser printer, the light sources are laser or LED devices driven by digital image data.

High-speed copiers like the Xerox DocuTech scan originals instead of employing a lens system and can accept both digital data and hard copy originals.

A similar type of printer, called electron beam or ion deposition, generates a stream of negative ions to form a charged image directly on the drum. These devices do not have the resolution capability of laser printers, but are much faster and are widely used for document printing.

Laser printers usually have resolutions of 300–600 dpi, although 2,400 dpi is technically feasible and users can expect new products that take advantage of the possibilities of higher resolutions. Toner particle size (around 10 microns) and the resolving power of the transfer drum set the ultimate upper limits on the possible resolution.

High-resolution electrostatic systems using liquid toners (instead of solid particles) produce high-quality color prints, but they are more expensive than solid-toner systems. Toner particle size (around 2 microns) is smaller than solid toners.

The toners available for color laser printers tend to have purer colors than printing inks, and are thus able to print a wider gamut than the conventional printing processes. This is especially noticeable in the blue-purple-mauve region. Color laser printers can produce reasonable low-end color proofs, at much faster speeds than ink jet printers.

Thermal Printers

Although the term "thermal printer" covers a very wide variety of different techniques, two are of particular importance: thermal transfer and dye sublimation. Both types use semiconductor resistors to heat the colorant so that it can be transferred to the paper. In thermal transfer, the colorant is effectively melted onto the paper, like a miniature version of wax sealing and, in dye-sublimation printing, the colorant is vaporized before transfer to the paper.

Thermal systems that produce binary images do not have adequate resolution to form halftone screens and instead use coarse dither patterns to reproduce continuous-tone images.

By applying a variable voltage to the resistors in a dye-sublimation printer, different densities of colorant can be transferred to give a gray scale instead of a binary image.

Figure 13-5.
Thermal printing.

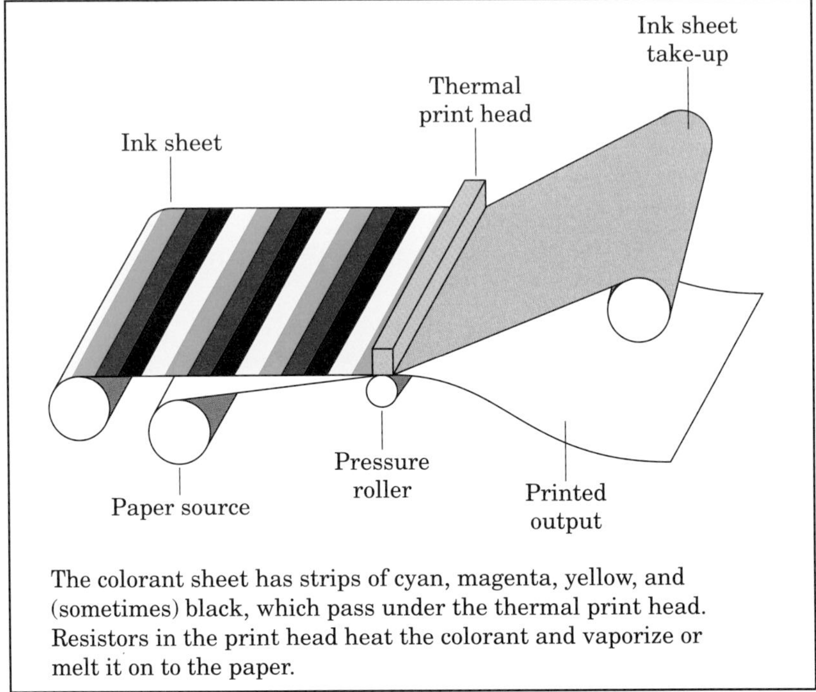

The colorant sheet has strips of cyan, magenta, yellow, and (sometimes) black, which pass under the thermal print head. Resistors in the print head heat the colorant and vaporize or melt it on to the paper.

Figure 13-6.
Thermal dye sublimation print. (Detail enlarged 10×.)

The dyes of the three primary colors (black is often unnecessary due to the high density of the CMY solid overprint) combine, resulting in a continuous-tone image very similar to a photographic print. Dye-sublimation systems of this sort do not simulate a halftone dot when used for proofing, and because a continuous-tone image is produced a resolution of around 300 dpi is adequate.

Dye-sublimation printers produce brilliant, saturated colors. The slow speed of output makes them suitable mainly for one-off prints such as color proofs, prints from digital cameras, and presentation materials. Special papers are required for most systems.

Volume Printing using Digital Color Presses

For longer runs, electrostatic systems are currently the most successful technologies, with speeds that approach those of conventional lithographic printing. In the future, it is possible that ink jet may emerge as the most viable digital printing technology, but at present the difficulty in achieving acceptable resolution at high production speeds excludes ink jet from color printing at speed.

In order to compete with conventional printing presses, digital color printers combine some features of conventional press configuration with innovative imaging methods in a hybrid design that resembles neither the small-scale office printer nor the conventional production press.

Since high production volumes are essential to recover the relatively high capital costs of digital presses, it is important for users to consider workflow management, including the preparation and rasterization of pages, as well as the physical speed of the marking engine. Most systems have some form of buffer to hold “ripped” pages prior to actual transfer to the imaging device and may employ workflow management routines, including imposition, job queuing, color management, and OPI file replacement to ensure the smooth handling of color pages and images. In some cases, the press may be unable to handle the amount of data needed to change the whole image on each impression, and only a part of the page can be variable on each copy.

Digital color presses are faster to set up than conventional presses since there is no need to adjust position or inking levels. Proofing is done by printing a single copy of the job for approval on the digital press itself, prior to output of the remainder of the print run. The proof, an exact facsimile of the production run, is in effect a production press proof.

Current electrostatic printing technologies include dry electrophotography (with pigmented toner powder as the printing medium); liquid electrophotography (with pigment particles suspended in a liquid); and phase-change electrophotography (with pigment suspended in a waxy solid that is briefly liquefied during image transfer).

The drum technology used in electrostatic digital printers is essentially the same as that used in laser printers and photocopiers, and it must be replaced regularly. On a high-volume multicolor printing system, annual maintenance costs can be very high.

Xeikon DCP-1

The Xeikon DCP-1, developed by Xeikon of Belgium, uses dry electrophotography and employs a multi-processor approach to enable fully variable data to be processed. It is reel-fed, printing up to 2,100 pages per hour. The maximum sheet size is 12×17 in. (307×438 mm).

Figure 13-7. Color laser print produced by an Agfa Chromapress. (Detail enlarged 10×.)

Eight separate printing units print cyan, magenta, yellow, and black on each side of the paper. The imaging heads operate at a resolution of 600 dpi, but are able to vary the amount of charge imparted to the drum by the LED spot. The greater the charge, the more toner is transferred, and thus a variable spot density can be achieved. Up to sixty density levels can be imaged, giving a printed result that is roughly equivalent to offset litho at 133 lpi.

Barco and Agfa have developed front ends for the Xeikon engine. The Agfa Chromapress incorporates sophisticated workflow planning functions, together with automatic imposition, OPI file swapping, and Fotoflow color management. An Agfa-developed RIP takes PostScript data from a high-speed SCSI interface and carries out RGB-CMYK conversion. After "ripping," the rasterized data is stored in page buffers in the individual printing units, ready to transfer to the imaging engines.

Indigo E-Print

The Indigo E-Print has only one printing unit, but by feeding the sheet back through after each consecutive pass, it can print up to six colors on each side. Liquid electrophotography allows the E-Print to use pigment particles of 1–2 microns in size, giving improved resolution with smoother solids and better highlight detail in comparison with dry electrophotography. The liquid ink polymerizes instantly on contact with the paper, printing a very sharp image with no physical dot gain (although optical dot gain is still present).

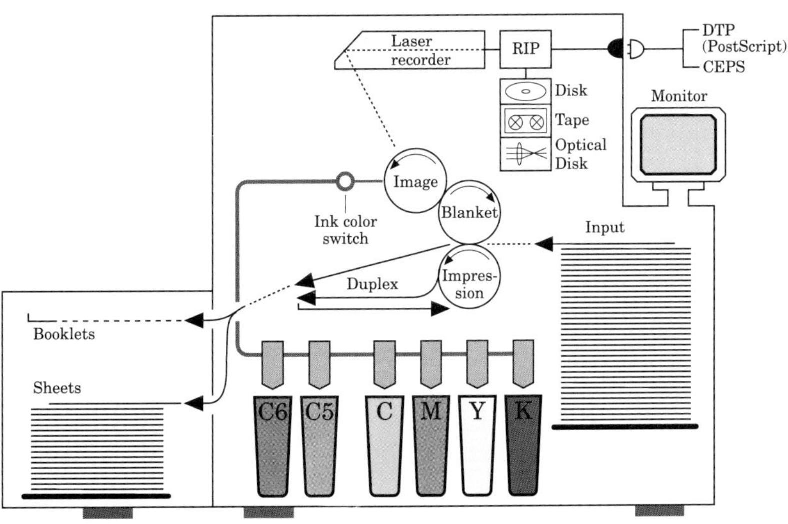

Figure 13-8. Schematic of Indigo E-Print 1000 printing device.

Printing speed is 8,000 pages per hour for one color, but every subsequent color halves the output speed. A four-color duplex job is output at a speed of 500 copies per hour. Print resolution is 800 dpi, and the resolution enhancement technology used makes the print appearance similar to conventional offset litho at a 150-lpi screen ruling.

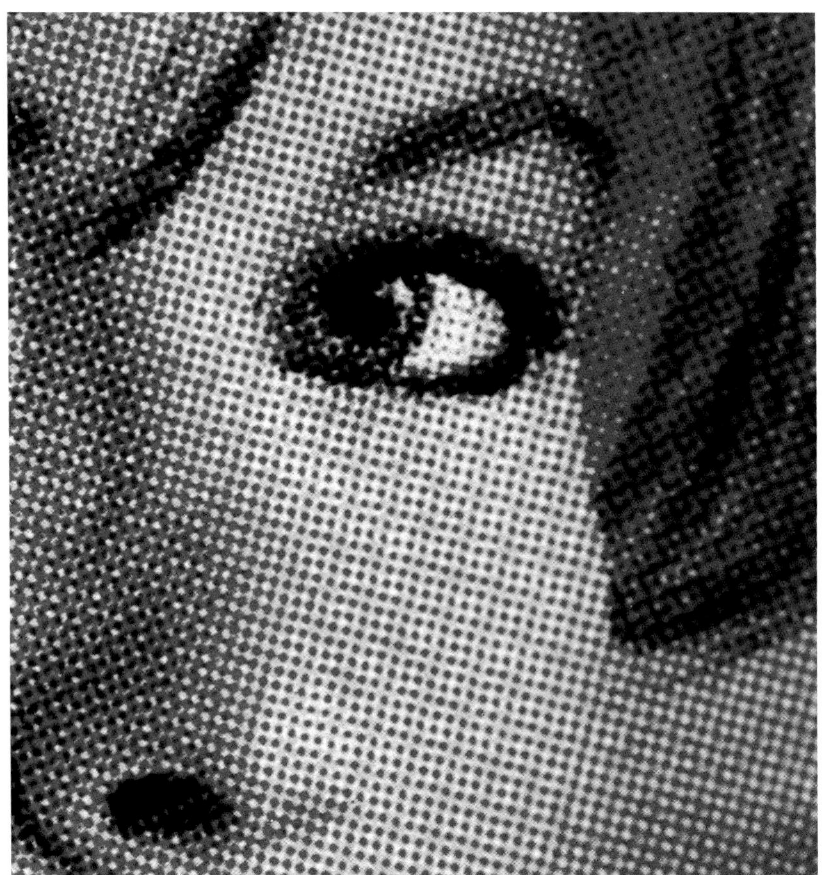

Figure 13-9. Sample output from the Indigo E-Print 1000. (Detail enlarged 10×.)

A 640-MB buffer stores up to 100 compressed and rasterized pages at a time. For longer runs, the press can only rasterize and transfer part of the page fast enough to vary it for each copy. However, it can rasterize the variable data and combine it with the constant page elements at the full production speed.

The single-unit design calls for the ink to be removed from the printing blanket after each revolution. To achieve this, the ink has to be formulated with relatively low adhesion, which also means that, as a result, it can be rubbed off some printing papers.

Other Digital Color Printing Systems

Digital color printing technologies will continue to develop. Some will represent radical departures; some will be evolutionary changes to current systems; and others will be novel hybrids of existing and new technologies. Color printing systems under development at the time of this writing include a digital gravure press from Sony and the Gutenberg electrostatic press.

Imaging on the Gutenberg press uses a phase-change ink—a solid mix of pigment and polymer—that briefly liquefies during transfer and resolidifies on contact with the paper. Like the Xeikon, it can apply a variable charge to the dielectric drum, thus print a variable ink density.

The high development costs of the volume digital presses actually makes the per-copy costs higher than that of smaller office-type color printers. Color laser printers, such as those marketed by Canon and Xerox, can achieve surprisingly good results if driven by a good RIP and color management software, while ink jet printers, from Hewlett Packard and Canon among others, are slower and give poorer quality results, but at a lower capital cost.

Modified Conventional Presses

Adapting conventional printing presses to direct-digital imaging is another route to achieving digital color printing, and one that the manufacturers of conventional presses can be expected to follow. The Heidelberg GTO-DI press, for example, is an adaptation of the small offset GTO with a direct-imaged waterless plate in place of the conventional dampened printing plate. Imaged on or off press by a sixteen-beam laser diode array, the plate consists of a layer of ink-repellent silicone bonded to a sheet of polyester. The laser beam destroys the silicone-polymer bond, enabling the silicone to be wiped from the image areas, revealing the ink-receptive polyester layer beneath. Each laser diode is connected to an optical fiber, which transfers the laser light to lenses distributed across the plate cylinder.

Imaging resolution is variable up to 2,540 dpi, comparable to many imagesetters and allowing normal screen rulings to be used. The plates take twelve minutes to image, and the process is commercially viable on runs of 500 to 5,000, somewhat better than the run lengths of nonimpact digital color presses. A conventional press, using plates imaged by computer-to-plate methods and mounted automatically or semiautomatically, can be plated in less time than it takes to image the GTO-DI, but the DI has advantages in reduced in prepress operations and in register and color adjustments during makeready.

The GTO-DI is available as a four-color or a five-color press. Proofing cannot realistically be carried out on press, and digital proofs are the only method of producing hard copy for approval. However, a preview system allows the printer to check rasterized data for elements such as trapping, halftone appearance, and font substitutions.

An advantage that direct imaging has over conventional platemaking is that there is no degradation of the image on transfer from film to plate. This factor is particularly useful in images using stochastic screening, where small variations in the transfer of the small pixels that make up the image can cause large shifts in tone or color.

Figure 13-10. Heidelberg's GTO-DI press with direct imaging. *Courtesy Heidelberg UK.*

MAN Roland takes a different approach with its "electropolymer" system that consists of a dielectric printing cylinder with a plastic surface layer and a layer of electrodes immediately below. The printing surface is imaged when the electrodes are charged and attract a toner material, which then acts as an ink-receptive image layer.

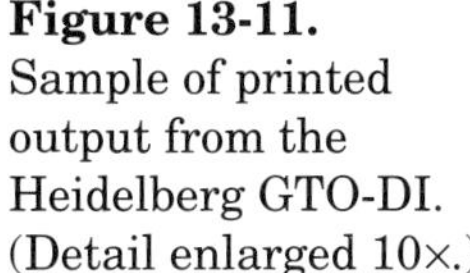

Figure 13-11. Sample of printed output from the Heidelberg GTO-DI. (Detail enlarged 10×.)

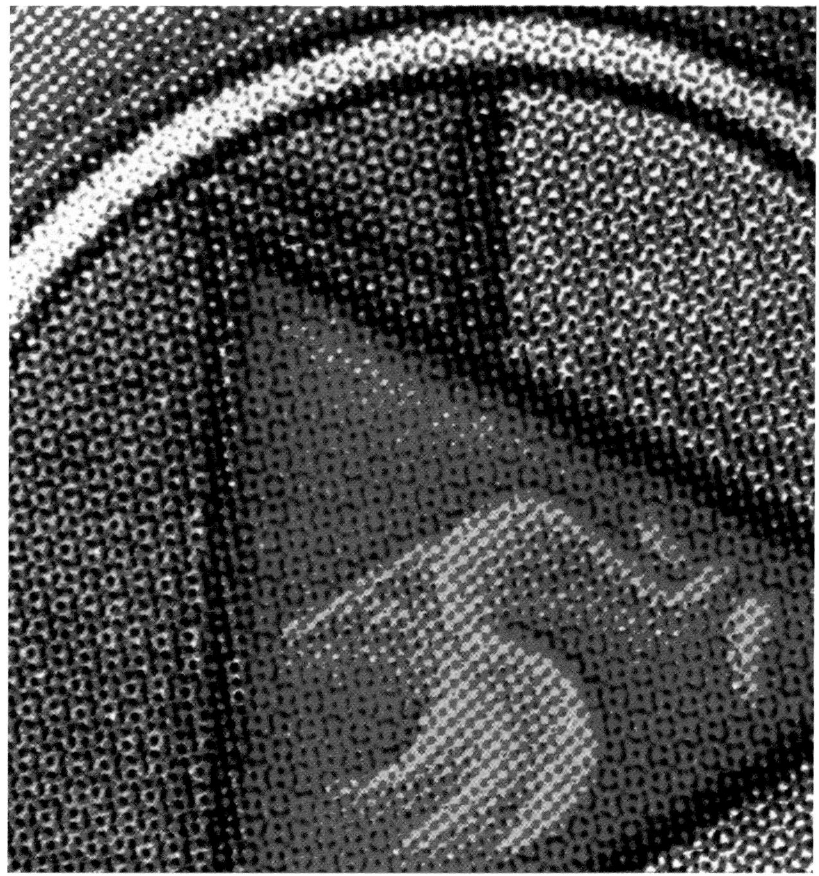

Modified conventional press designs must be able to image the printing cylinders very quickly, as the printing press has the highest capital cost of all the production equipment and unproductive time is extremely expensive. The potential advantages for a printer to use direct-to-press imaging are:

- The automatic registration of colors without adjustment during makeready.
- The ability to use image data to set inking levels across the sheet automatically.
- The possibility of directly interfacing with management information systems.
- Accepting jobs in electronic form for direct transfer to the press eliminates the need for prepress operations.

14 Color Management

In traditional color reproduction, the workflow is relatively straightforward. Images are scanned directly into CMYK following a basic set of output parameters embedded within the scanner, with occasional variations to accommodate the requirements of different processes, paper types, and any customer preferences. A single operator, who is responsible for every stage of the process from analysis of the color original to the output of color-separated films, is likely to have considerable experience and expertise in getting the best results from the system. The operator will be familiar with the requirements of proofing and printing and will regularly see the results of different scanner settings on different jobs. The scanner operator will also be working with CMYK data at every stage because no additional conversions between different color spaces take place after the scanner initially separates each image into CMYK.

Desktop color reproduction requires a very different workflow. There are likely to be many different sources of color images, such as Photo CD and digital cameras as well as a wide range of scanners, all with different characteristics. Color images may also be output to many different devices, including digital color printers, digital proofing devices, and conventional presses. Increasingly, the printing press is geographically remote from the point at which the image is captured or edited. Images may also go through one or more transformations between different color spaces, such as scanner RGB, monitor RGB, CIE-based independent color space, and CMYK proofing device, before reaching the destination CMYK values of the final output device. Some images will be intended for output on more than one device, such as documents that are published in both electronic and printed format and advertisements scheduled for reproduction in different publications. Different individuals may well be involved in the capture, editing, and output of an image. Rarely will one single person be responsible for every stage between input and final output. Even if this is true, he or she will not be familiar with the characteristics of all of the devices that may be used.

Many desktop users have been confounded by the question of who should be responsible for color quality in digital prepress. Service bureaus supply printers with films that have been generated from user files, and if the color separations and the films are produced without taking into account the requirements of the particular printing process, the result is inevitably unsatisfactory. One solution to this problem is to use a **color management system (CMS)** during both creation and output.

Figure 14-1. Color management architecture.

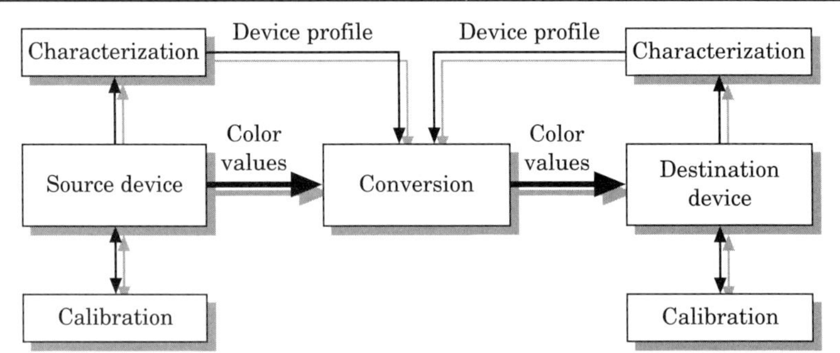

Profiles are generated for both input and output devices to define the way that they capture or reproduce color. These profiles tell the conversion routine how to create a lookup table to convert from the color values of one device to another. Devices are maintained in a stable condition, producing consistent color values through periodic calibration. The conversion "engine" of the CMS is a set of routines used to convert between source and destination color values.

Color management systems embed information about specific devices into software routines that control all aspects of color transformations. They attempt to ensure the consistent and predictable reproduction of color by optimizing the performance of different devices without involving the user in the detail level of the process.

The basic architecture of a color management system is shown in Figure 14-1. The devices used for the input and output of color are characterized by defining exactly how they capture or reproduce color information. They are calibrated to maintain stable performance, and the color values are transformed from one device or color space into another by a conversion routine.

Color management is an evolving methodology, but one that is already giving excellent results and holds the promise of giving the user the best available color match between originals, monitor displays, and printed output. It allows the user to focus on creation and reproduction without having to be concerned with the complex mechanics of device behavior and separation setup. It also gives users a basis for greater control over the reproduction process by configuring the color management system to suit their needs.

Characterization

A **device characterization** defines exactly how the CMS captures or outputs color (often by reference to a standard, such as device-independent color space), and creates a **device profile** that can be communicated to the conversion routine. **Source profiles** define input devices, and **destination profiles** define output devices.

Profiles can be generic (defining a class of output devices); device-specific (created to define the characteristics of a particular device); or custom (created or edited to meet a specific user's requirements). Profiles can be obtained in several ways:

- Basic, generic profiles are available within color management systems.
- Additional profiles are available from color management system vendors and from third-party suppliers.
- Specific device profiles are sold with some color devices.
- Users can create or adjust profiles by using a profile editor.

Where possible, it is better to calibrate a device so that it conforms to a generic profile than to create a custom profile for each device. Generic profiles make it possible to produce output that can be used by a range of devices without repeating the characterization process. For example, if all the color printing presses in a plant are set up so that density and dot gain match the SWOP standard, it is not necessary to conduct a "fingerprinting" exercise for each press in order to characterize it, and a job can be output to film before it has been scheduled for any specific machine.

Source devices capture device-specific RGB data. They are effectively colorimetric devices, using filters with a similar response to the human retinal photoreceptors, and, if the device is calibrated with standard color targets, it is relatively easy to convert the device-specific RGB into normalized RGB or into device-independent color.

Creating profiles for output devices is more complicated since different devices reproduce color in widely different ways, depending on variables such as density, dot gain, halftoning, and the type of colorants and papers used. In addition, conversion into CMYK is more complex than conversion into color spaces, since nonlinear conversions must be used.

Creating or adjusting a profile for a color device involves the following steps:

1. Capture (input devices) or print (output devices) a reference image containing color patches with known values.
2. Record the color values that are produced by the device.
3. Create profile data.

For an input device, it is sufficient to record the RGB values produced when the reference image is captured. Determining the color values produced by an output device involves measuring the reference image color patches that are produced by the device. For reflective colors, a spectrophotometer or colorimeter is required, while for monitors, either a spectroradiometer or a spectrophotometer adapted for transmissive sources must be used.

To create a profile for a new device, it is easier to start with a generic profile for a similar device and edit it, rather than create a profile from scratch.

Profile editors are available from several vendors, including Kodak's PICC (Precision Input Color Characterization) for source profiles; EFI's EFICOLOR for both source and destination profiles; and Agfa's FOTOTUNE for source and destination profiles.

Note that an imagesetter, although classed as an output device, does not require characterization because imagesetting is actually an intermediate stage before final output to a CMYK printing device, using the profile of the destination output device (the printing press). The imagesetter needs only to be correctly calibrated by the operator so that it produces consistent output.

Calibration

Devices should be calibrated periodically so that they consistently produce the same color values and continue to perform in the way defined in the device profile. The frequency with which calibration should be performed depends on the type of variables that occur. CCD-based scanners, for example, usually need little or no adjustment once the initial calibration has taken place. At the other extreme, film output devices, which are subject to factors such as exposure intensity, emulsion sensitivity, and processing variables, need to be checked as often as twice daily.

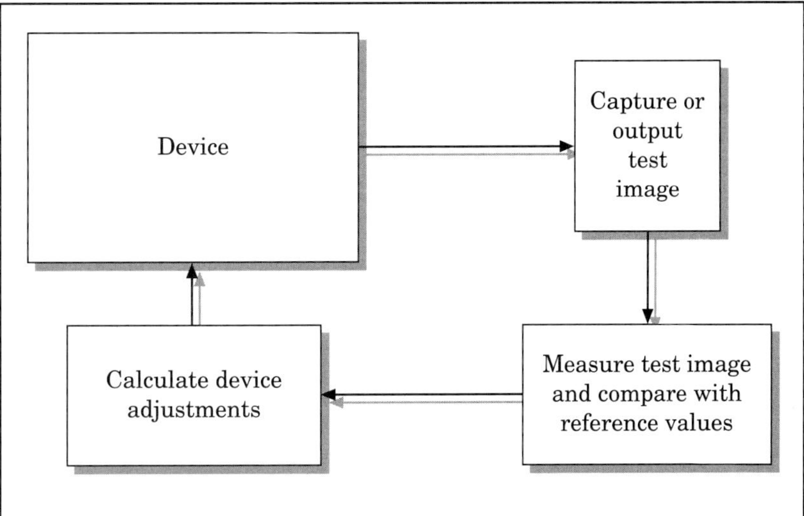

Figure 14-2. Device calibration.

The calibration procedure depends on the device in question, but the general steps are:

1. Establish the variables to be calibrated.
2. Capture or output a test image.
3. Evaluate the results.
4. Adjust the device accordingly.

To evaluate the output produced, some form of measurement is usually necessary. For accurate color measurements, the use of a colorimeter or spectrophotometer may be necessary, although many devices can be calibrated with densitometers or even by visual appearance. Calibration utilities eliminate some of the trial and error of adjusting devices to produce the correct output. They are supplied with some output devices, or they may be purchased from the device manufacturer or third-party vendors.

The calibration of different devices is discussed in the following sections.

Scanners. The tonal response and gray balance (or color balance) must be calibrated. A standard test image such as the IT8.7/1 or IT8.7/2 is scanned, and the resulting RGB values are compared with reference values. The resulting adjustment may be carried out on hardware controls on the scanner itself or, more often, in the controlling software.

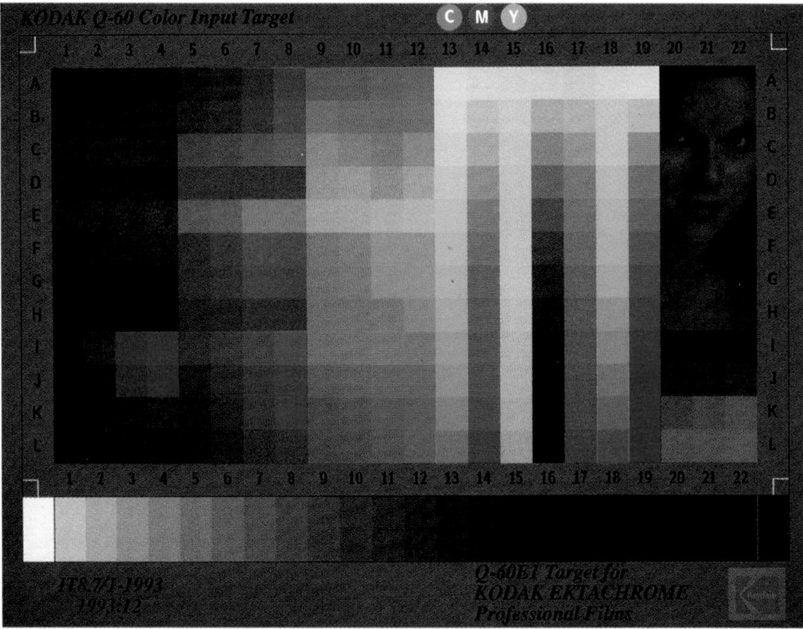

Figure 14-3.
IT8 standard reference image used to test and calibrate color devices.

The concept of auto calibration in which the test element is output to a color printer, the resulting print is rescanned, and the calibration adjustment is performed automatically by software has not proven successful. The routine described above is the method of adjustment currently preferred.

All types of input device, including Photo CD scanners and digital cameras, should be calibrated with the same basic procedure. Digital cameras need to be calibrated with a reflective test image and controlled illumination levels and subject distance.

Monitors. The monitor factors that should be calibrated are its white point, its brightness, and its contrast or gamma. Monitor calibration routines are incorporated into many applications, usually requiring a standard white point and gamma setting and sometimes additionally requiring the user to visually match the display of test elements.

Monitor calibration is particularly problematic because the ambient light frequently changes during the day, resulting in variations in the apparent display contrast. Furthermore, the calibration routines found in different applications can cause the monitor settings to change, leading to confusion since the appearance of a color image varies in different applications.

The effect of natural daylight should be minimized by using blinds and by arranging the room layout so that color monitors are sited away from windows. Subdued lighting conditions are better than brightly lit environments in areas where color judgments will be made from monitors.

Most working environments are lit partly by natural daylight, and, in this situation, it can be impossible to completely control ambient levels of illumination. The eye will adapt to the overall level of illumination that it perceives, causing the apparent brightness of the screen to change, even though the actual display intensity does not. The monitor's brightness and contrast settings should not be altered once calibration has been performed, as this would lead to uncontrolled fluctuations in display intensity. Instead, you can address changes in ambient illumination by creating a group of different monitor calibration settings for bright sunlight, overcast daylight, twilight, and night and then using the appropriate setting whenever critical color judgments are made. Placing a photographic light meter next to the monitor will tell you how much the ambient illumination changes during the day.

If the monitor is being used for color judgments, it is essential that care is taken to calibrate it accurately. Once done, the display in different applications should be handled by a color management system. It may be necessary to restrict the number of different applications in which color judgments are made to avoid potential conflicts in color appearance between them.

A general method for calibrating color monitors is as follows:

1. Convert an IT8 reference image to CMYK and print it.
2. Set the monitor white point to 5,000 K.
3. Ensure that the ambient illumination conforms to the standard viewing conditions.
4. Compare the display image with the printed IT8.
5. Adjust the monitor gamma to achieve the closest possible match between the printed test image and the display, paying attention to:
   - The color balance in neutrals.
   - The lightness of midtones.
   - The intensity of the most saturated colors.

Figure 14-4.
CIE xyY values for Eurostandard *(top)* and SWOP *(bottom)* printing inks as they appear in the Custom Printing Inks dialog box in Adobe Photoshop.

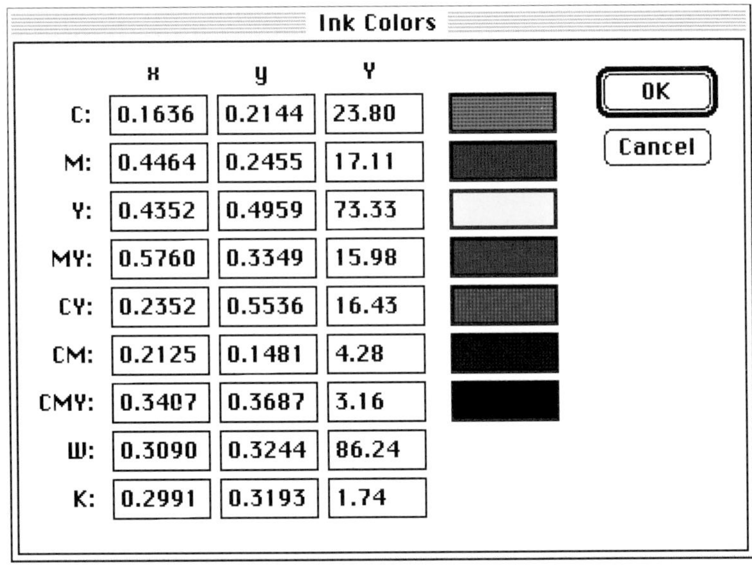

	x	y	Y
C:	0.1636	0.2144	23.80
M:	0.4464	0.2455	17.11
Y:	0.4352	0.4959	73.33
MY:	0.5760	0.3349	15.98
CY:	0.2352	0.5536	16.43
CM:	0.2125	0.1481	4.28
CMY:	0.3407	0.3687	3.16
W:	0.3090	0.3244	86.24
K:	0.2991	0.3193	1.74

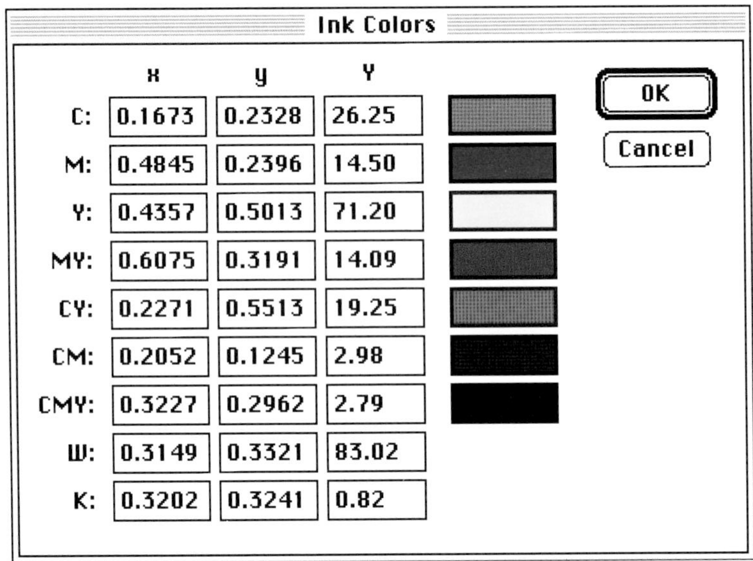

	x	y	Y
C:	0.1673	0.2328	26.25
M:	0.4845	0.2396	14.50
Y:	0.4357	0.5013	71.20
MY:	0.6075	0.3191	14.09
CY:	0.2271	0.5513	19.25
CM:	0.2052	0.1245	2.98
CMY:	0.3227	0.2962	2.79
W:	0.3149	0.3321	83.02
K:	0.3202	0.3241	0.82

The displayed image should be in the color mode in which you edit color (RGB, CMYK, or Lab), and the method used to convert the test image to CMYK should be same as the method used for color images. If you are converting to SWOP characteristics for printing you can use the IT8 image in this chapter as the printed reference.

Imagesetters. The imagesetter's beam intensity needs to be calibrated along with the film processing variables, such as development temperature and time. First, a test element containing small type elements and lines is output and the exposure intensity is adjusted until an emulsion density of around 4.0 (depending on the type of film) is achieved in solid areas with the type and lines remaining clean and sharp. Next, a gray scale with a range of tonal values between 0 and 100% is output and the dot values on the resulting film are measured with a transmission densitometer. The imagesetter is adjusted until it is successfully **linearized,** i.e., until the dot sizes recorded on film are the same as the dot values specified. Variation should be no more than 1–2% from the specified values.

Frequency-modulated screening requires an additional adjustment in the way in which the laser dots overlap in building up the image spot. The screening algorithm compensates for this.

Printers. The colorants used by any printing device (including digital printers and conventional printing presses) are defined in the device profile, so the main variables that must be calibrated are the colorant density and the amount of dot gain. The accepted tolerances for most conventional printing processes are ±0.1 density units and ±2% dot gain.

Note that SWOP and Eurostandard inks specify slightly different ink hues for cyan, magenta, and yellow. There is also some slight variation between the pigments produced by different ink manufacturers. Any changes to ink colors can be saved as a custom ink set in the color separation lookup table setup.

Proofing devices. Calibrating a proofing device involves printing a reference image, measuring the resulting output, and then either:

- Adjusting the device to make it conform to its characterization profile.
- Comparing the test image with one printed on the target printing press and adjusting the proofing device so that it behaves like the printing press to be used for the production run.

Proofing variables are colorant, hue, and density and the amount of dot gain produced. Proofing devices should ideally be set up more precisely than production presses, the tolerance levels being half that allowed on printing presses for these variables.

Printing presses. Printing press setup is controlled by the press operator. The mechanical conditions of the press and the characteristics of the ink used can induce fluctuations in the printing characteristics, but most printers work with, or close to, one of the industry-wide standards such as SWOP and Eurostandard. These standards classify papers as coated, uncoated, and newsprint. Most papers fall under these classifications, but certain types, such as recycled papers, may need further adjustments.

The press operator adjusts the ink flow on every job to regulate the ink densities that are transferred to the paper. Dot gain is controlled mainly by adjusting the ink viscosity, although other factors, such as printing pressures, can also be altered if necessary.

When a device cannot be calibrated (if, for example, it is incapable of achieving the appropriate adjustments or it is under the control of a third party), a transfer function can be created to compensate for the uncalibrated color values. Separate transfer functions can be applied to each color component with PostScript Level 2 devices. Transfer functions are of little use if the device does not behave consistently.

Color Conversion

Conversion into output device CMYK was extensively discussed in Chapter 7. A color management system controls this process in a manner that is transparent to the user. The device profiles generated by the characterization process are used to create a lookup table that will enable color values to be converted into the color space of the output device.

If it were necessary to produce a profile for every possible pair of devices, the number of profiles would become impossibly large as the number of possible source and destination profiles increases. Instead, color management systems use device-independent CIE-based color space as an intermediate color space in the transformation.

To make the conversion of color images more efficient, specific source and destination profiles are combined to generate a single lookup table. This table can be saved and applied every time an image is converted between the two specific devices. Color conversion is a highly repetitive operation performed for every single pixel in an image, and some CMS system vendors offer hardware acceleration through ASICs.

Figure 14-5.
Matrix Transformation.

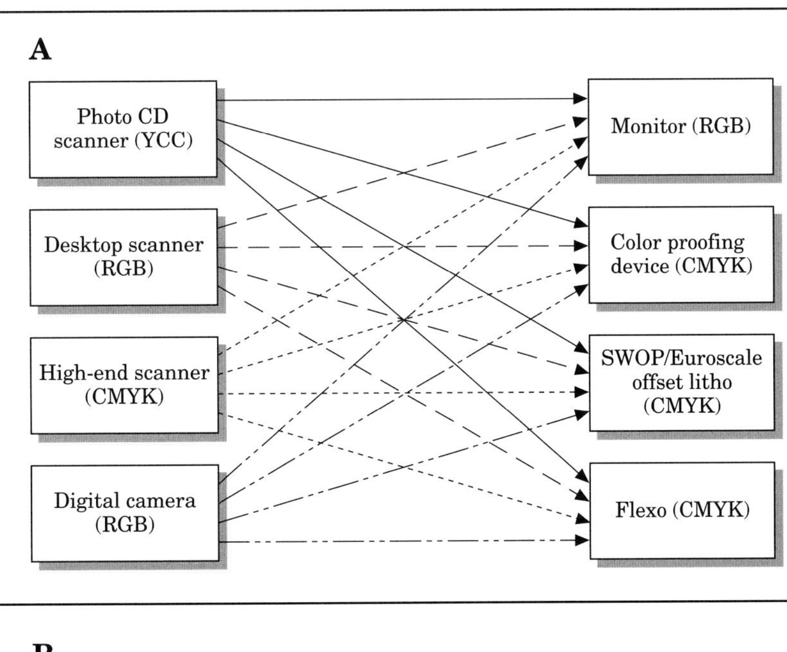

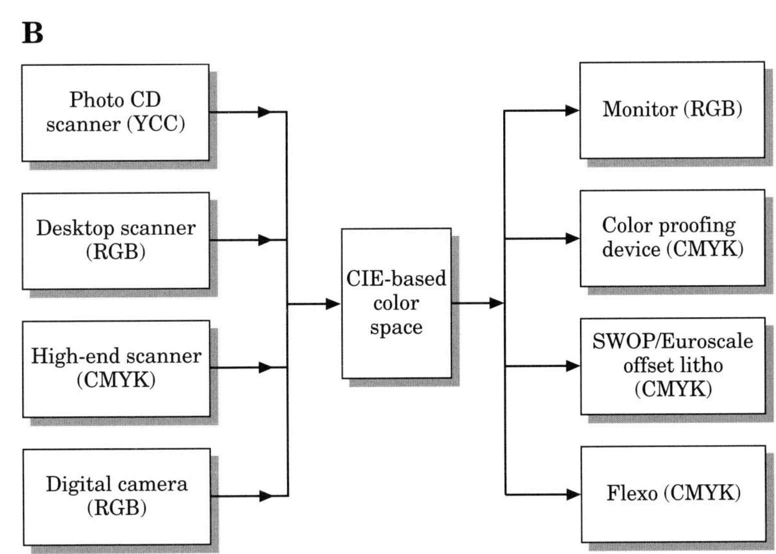

Generating profiles that define how color is to be converted directly from source and destination files is feasible if there are only a small number of color devices used to capture or output color. Each source and destination pair requires a separate profile. As the number of potential devices increases, the number of profiles becomes too large to handle (as shown in A).

The solution to this problem is to ensure that each device has a profile that defines the way it captures or outputs color in terms of a device-independent color space (as shown in B).

Figure 14-6.
Color lookup tables.

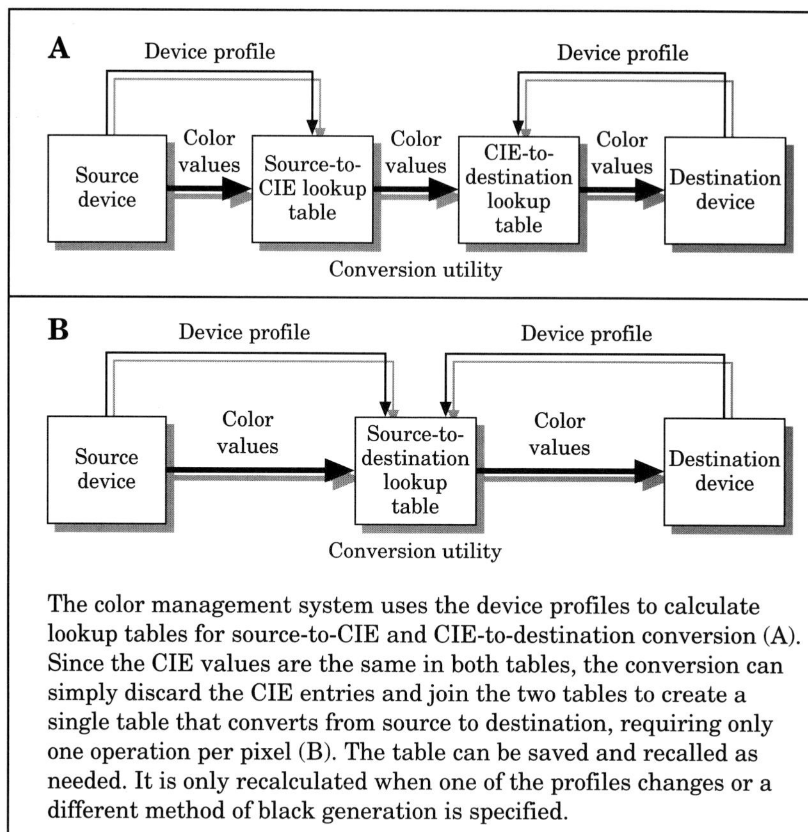

The color management system uses the device profiles to calculate lookup tables for source-to-CIE and CIE-to-destination conversion (A). Since the CIE values are the same in both tables, the conversion can simply discard the CIE entries and join the two tables to create a single table that converts from source to destination, requiring only one operation per pixel (B). The table can be saved and recalled as needed. It is only recalculated when one of the profiles changes or a different method of black generation is specified.

As described in Chapter 7, color conversion systems incorporate interpolation routines to calculate intermediate color values that do not have entries in the lookup table.

PostScript Color Management

The color management offered by Adobe in the PostScript language is slightly different from that of other color management systems. Like other elements of a page description such as resolution and screening, PostScript Level 2 treats conversion into device color values as a process that should take place in device space—in other words, in the output device itself. This is achieved by keeping color values in RGB or in device-independent color until actual output. The device-specific information is transferred to the output device interpreter that performs the conversions.

Device profiles are used by PostScript drivers to generate color space arrays and color rendering dictionaries (see Chapter 9). A color space array (CSA), which defines the way that the RGB values are captured by an input device, is used by the interpreter to convert the original RGB values into

Figure 14-7.
An RGB image *(top)* and the same image *(bottom)* after conversion in the EFICOLOR System program.

independent color space. The conversion between RGB and a CIE-based color space involves a straightforward linear conversion. Converting color values into RGB again so that they can be output on a monitor is simply a matter of applying the conversion in reverse.

For the reasons discussed in Chapter 7, the more complex nonlinear conversion to CMYK requires a multidimensional lookup table. Device profiles are used to create a color rendering dictionary (CRD), which is a lookup table that defines the way that actual CMYK printed colors are produced by an output device. A CRD converts from independent color space into device space.

Figure 14-8. PostScript color processing.

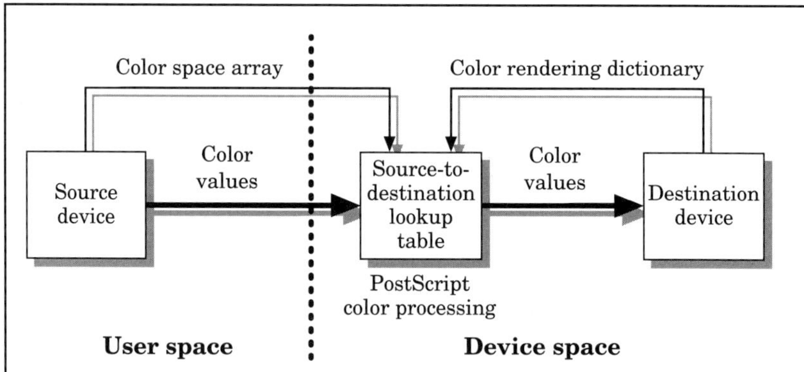

PostScript color processing is similar to color management, except that conversion can be carried out in the PostScript interpreter. Images can be kept in RGB except when they are actually being output. The advantages are greater device-independence and smaller file sizes.

Every Level 2 output device has a resident default CRD, but it is possible for user-defined CRDs to be used instead. A CSA can be included with a PostScript file, while a CRD can be downloaded by a PostScript interpreter just like a font is downloaded. If the CSA and CRD are available, and the ***setcolorspace*** operator has been used to turn on Level 2 color processing, conversions can be carried out entirely in device space, leaving the image in RGB or in device-independent color right up to the actual output. This approach allows the user to keep all image files in device-independent color and avoid converting the image until the output device is known. PostScript allows different objects within a page description to have a different CSA, according to the input device used.

Problems in Color Management

Critics of color management systems point out that there are a number of problems in using CIE-based color spaces to map color from one device space to another:

- CIE color spaces are not based on the actual visual appearance of color, but rather the way in which colors are recorded by measuring instruments.
- They are nonlinear in relation to human perception. (Equal changes in measurements in different parts of the color space do not correspond to equal changes in perception.)
- They are based on the CIE standard observer with a 2° angle of vision, and, as a result, do not account for the differences between surfaces, such as matte and gloss-coated papers.

It is important to be aware that CIE-based systems aim at achieving **colorimetric consistency,** and this is not the same as **appearance consistency.**

Different colorant systems have limitations on the range of colors they can reproduce. The gamut of colors that can be displayed on a color monitor differs from the printable gamut and also from the gamut that can be recorded on a transparency. Although all hues can be matched between any two systems, there will be differences in the range of saturation values, depending on the primary color components chosen, and the range of lightness values, depending on the smallest amount of colorant that can be transferred at the light end and the largest amount of colorant that can be transferred at the dark end. Thus the problem colors for reproduction are usually the highly saturated colors, the pale pastels, and the very deep or dark colors. This phenomenon is discussed further in Chapter 3.

Color management systems do not tend to handle the matching between one color gamut and another particularly well. Unless the input gamut is compressed to fit the gamut of the output system, the out-of-gamut colors will be **clipped,** resulting in a loss of detail in saturated colors. However, the input gamut should not be compressed in a linear way or color saturation will be reduced throughout the gamut. Since the sensitivity of the human visual response varies in different regions of the CIE-based color spaces, gamut compression should ideally depend on the actual color space region. For example, yellows can be compressed more than reds or blues.

Adaptive gamut compression is considered too complex to incorporate into a color management system, so gamut compression is handled instead by offering a range of rendering options that the user can choose from, depending on the subject being reproduced. These include:

- **Perceptual.** The gamut is compressed in a more or less linear way. Perceptual (also known as pictorial) rendering is suitable for color images, since it keeps the relative range of colors visually constant.
- **Colorimetric.** The gamut is clipped without compression so that all colors are matched as accurately as possible as long as they are within the gamut common to both systems. Colorimetric rendering is suitable for items that require

Figure 14-9.
Gamut mapping.

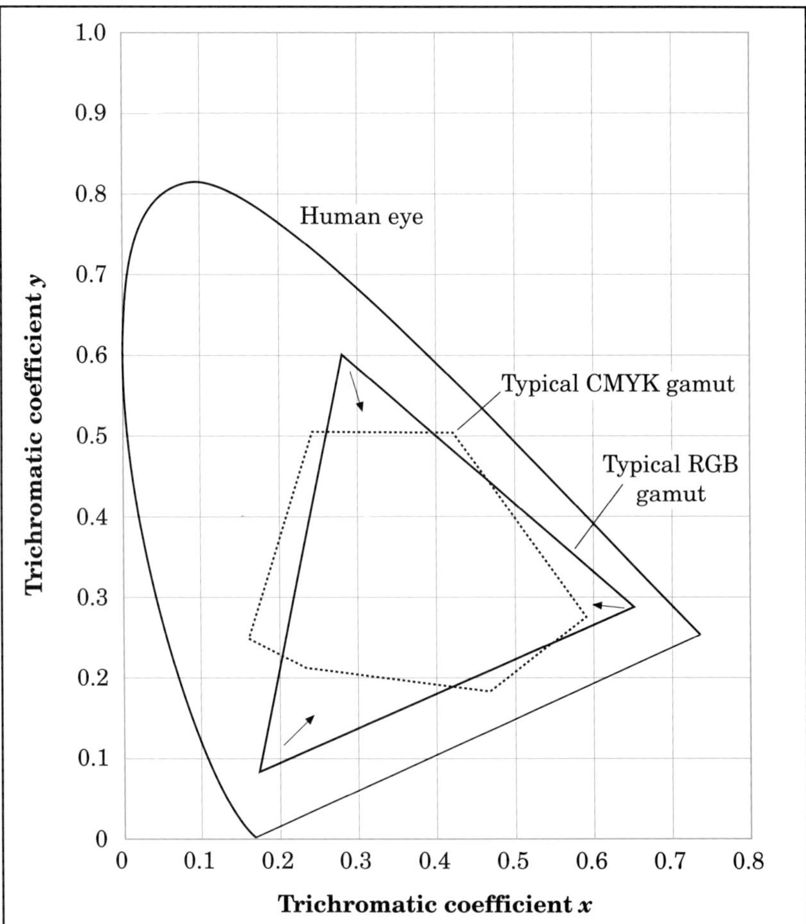

Different color devices are capable of recognizing or reproducing widely different color gamuts. If the source device gamut contains colors that cannot be reproduced by the chosen output device, the source gamut must be compressed in some way to avoid losing detail in the saturated colors. This is a similar problem to the need for tonal compression described in chapter four.

precise color matching such as logos and colors that identify specific brands, products, or companies.

- **Saturated.** Colors are pushed towards the gamut boundary, giving them the maximum saturation available in the output system. Saturated, or "graphical," rendering is useful for presentation graphics and other items that need bright and punchy colors.
- **PANTONE.** Special colors in the PANTONE system are matched as closely as possible in different colorant systems.

These relatively simple algorithms leave a great deal of room for improvement. One problem identified by Tony Johnson of Crosfield Electronics is that, in practice, hues appear to change when gamuts are compressed, and therefore need to be adjusted to maintain constant color appearance.

Johnson and others have developed an alternative approach to color conversion known as the Hunt-Alvey Color Appearance Model (ACAM). It places an emphasis on preserving color appearance and involves the following steps:

1. Convert to a CIE-based color space.
2. Compress the gamut in a nonlinear fashion.
3. Modify the appearance to suit the viewing conditions.
4. Convert to device color values.

Thus far ACAM is a theoretical solution that has yet to be implemented in actual products.

An occasional source of confusion for CMS users is whether the monitor should be treated as an output device (in which colors are displayed in device-dependent RGB), or as an input color space (in which colors are specified for reproduction). The job of the monitor is to display color values contained in digital files, and so it should be treated as an output device. The exception to this rule occurs with Photo CD images, which are more accurately displayed on screen if the monitor is selected as the source device. Yet whether PCD or Monitor RGB is specified as the source, the final CMYK image produced by the color management system is the same, as shown in Figure 14-10.

An issue that the vendors of color management systems have had to address is the possibility of conflict between the different methods of characterization and calibration. Monitors that are calibrated in an application often need to be recalibrated for a different application in order to maintain a consistent image appearance. Similarly, profiles and lookup

Figure 14-10. These two images were acquired from a Photo CD disc using Kodak's KEPS color management system. PCD was specified as the source for the top image while the RGB monitor was specified as the source for the bottom image. The screen appearance of the bottom picture was much closer to the final print. The color management system generated the same values when it converted to CMYK, regardless of which of the two source profiles was chosen.

tables created by different color management systems can generate widely divergent color reproductions unless they operate in the same way.

The majority of color management system vendors have agreed on a common framework for color management based on Apple's ColorSync 2.0, accompanied by a common profile format. This framework, which follows the outline shown in Figure 14-1, is supported by CMS vendors Kodak and Agfa, application developers Aldus, Adobe, and Microsoft, and hardware vendors Sun and Silicon Graphics. ColorSync functions at the operating system level and is incorporated in Adobe Acrobat (from version 2.0) and in Windows (from version 4.0), where it is known as MicroSync. It will also be available on workstations, and existing color management systems are being adapted to share its common profile format.

As a result of this cooperation, a standard way of handling the user interface, a standard test image (the IT8 reference image), and a common profile format that can used by any conforming CMS are being implemented.

None of the different color management systems address black generation in a standard way. There are a number of options for UCR and GCR (discussed in Chapter 7) that depend on the destination printing device and, to a lesser extent, on the requirements of the image. Color management systems enable different black generation options through separate profile versions, which is somewhat clumsy since the user must have multiple profile versions in order to specify black-generation options. Since the computational aspects of black generation are quite straightforward, it would be preferable for applications to embed user-defined values in tags in a TIFF file, or in OPI comments in the page description. These values could then be used by the RIP when building a lookup table for conversion into device color values. Because black generation is device-dependent, it should ideally be handled by the output device.

The traditional method of defining the conversion from one medium to another (such as original density to reproduction density) is by the use of gradation curves. Gradation curves can be combined to map the tone scale of a color original into CMYK dot values in a quadrant diagram (or Jones diagram) as shown in Figure 14-11. The quadrant diagram can be adapted for different purposes.

Quality Control

To monitor the performance of the printing press and to verify that the printing characteristics match the agreed-upon standard, the press operator inspects the control elements that are printed in waste areas on the sheet or web.

Digital control elements can be included in the file sent for output or, alternatively, films can be stripped in prior to platemaking. Use original test-image films not duplicates to ensure accurate dot-gain measurements. Digital control elements must be measured with a transmission densitometer to establish the actual dot size on film and to separate

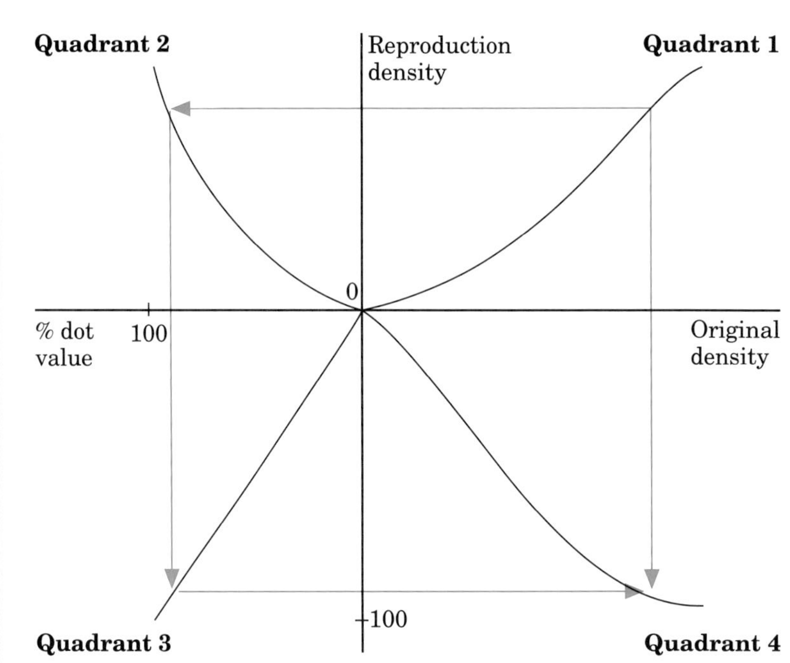

Figure 14-11. Quadrant diagram.

A quadrant diagram is a traditional way of mapping color values from the original to the reproduction. Quadrant 1 defines tonal compression into a density range of the output device. Quadrant 2 maps reproduction density to the dot percentage on the print with separate curves for cyan, magenta, and yellow included so that gray balance can be defined. Quadrant 3 is usually a linear transfer quadrant, but it can be used to define tonal changes during film or plate exposure. The original density is mapped to the required dot values on film by extending points from quadrant 1 clockwise and counterclockwise, then constructing a new curve where these lines meet in quadrant 4.

recorder gain (the difference between the specified dot sizes and the actual dot size on film) from dot gain.

The control strip can yield a mine of useful information, but the most important aspects of monitoring print quality are solid density, dot gain, color balance, and tonal value transfer to plate.

Density. The solid density for each color is measured on the solid patch that occurs at intervals along the strip. It is measured with a reflection densitometer, but it is also possible to make an approximate visual assessment by comparing it with printed strips with known densities. The solid density should not vary by more than 0.1 from the agreed-upon standard (variation in black can be a little higher, since it makes no difference to the color balance of an image unless high levels of GCR have been used).

Dot gain. Dot gain is evaluated by comparing the dot size on the print with the dot size in the corresponding patch on the film. It is essential to use the same dot size as a basis for measurement and communication. For example, the gain from a 50% film dot is used to adjust dot gain compensation in prepress, while the gain from a 75% or 80% film dot is normally used to standardize the press characteristics, and the amount of dot gain will be different at each tonal value.

Balance. Gray is chosen as a reference point for color balance because the eye's visual mechanism is more sensitive to color changes in neutral colors than in saturated colors. Color balance can then be visually assessed from the gray balance patch. This patch contains tints of CMY (the proportions are usually around C50, M40, Y40) that appear as a neutral gray when printed correctly. A noticeable color cast in this patch provides an early warning that the ink weights or dot gain are out of balance and the image's color balance is drifting. If the densities and gains of the process inks are in balance, then the color balance of the print should also be correct. If the density or dot gain of the three process colors rises or falls together, but remains in balance, the print will look slightly lighter or darker, but the color balance will remain the same.

It is not essential that the patch appears as a precise neutral gray, but it should remain consistent and reasonably close to a neutral, midtone gray throughout the run. The patch also offers a useful point of comparison with the proof. If there is a color cast in the reproduction, but the gray balance patch prints correctly as a neutral gray, then the cast was generated during prepress rather than printing, and the calibration of the different devices should be checked.

Tonal value transfer. If plates are exposed incorrectly, the dot values can become distorted. A set of highlight dots in the 0.5–6% range (exact sizes depend on the make of control strip) and microlines (4 to 30 microns) are included on the control strip to monitor any changes between the dot size on film and the dot size on plate. When correctly exposed, the plate should hold a 2% dot and a 10–11 micron line. (If frequency-modulated screens are being used, the recommendation is 6–8 microns and a bare 1% dot.) Badly distorted tonal value transfer elements are usually a sign that a duplicate strip has been used, in which case any readings for plate exposure, gray balance, or dot gain will not be reliable.

Recommended values for these and other variables are contained in graphic arts standards, such as SWOP and Eurostandard. Standards are useful because they provide an industry-wide guideline, saving each plant the unnecessary trouble of establishing its own aimpoints for all the different aspects of the reproduction process. They also provide a focus for negotiation between client and supplier on what the printer should be able to produce and what the client should expect to pay for a certain level of quality.

Bibliography

Adobe Systems. *Document Structuring Conventions Specification v. 3.0.* Adobe (1990).

———. *Encapsulated PostScript File Format v. 3.0.* Adobe (1990).

———. *PostScript Language Reference Manual, Second Edition.* Addison Wesley (1990).

Agfa. *An Introduction to Digital Color Prepress.* Agfa Compugraphic (1990).

Aldus Corporation. *Open Prepress Interface Specification v. 1.3.* Aldus (1993).

———. *TIFF Revision v. 6.0.* Aldus (1992).

Amato, L. *PostScript in Prepress.* Scitex Europe (1993).

Ames, P. and Warnock, J. *Beyond Paper.* Adobe Press (1994).

Bann, B. and Gargan, J. *Colour Proof Correction—Question and Answer Book.* Phaidon (1990).

Brehm, P. V. *Introduction to Densitometry.* Graphic Communications Association (1990).

Bruce, V. and Green, P. R. *Visual Perception.* Lawrence Earlbaum Associates (1990).

Cost, F. *Using Photo CD for Desktop Prepress.* RIT Research (1993).

Eastman Kodak Company. *Kodak Photo CD: A Planning Guide for Developers.* Eastman Kodak (1992).

Field, G. *Color and Its Reproduction, Second Edition.* Graphic Arts Technical Foundation (1993).

———. *Color Scanning and Imaging Systems.* Graphic Arts Technical Foundation (1990).

———. *Tone and Color Correction.* Graphic Arts Technical Foundation (1991).

Fink, P. *PostScript Screening.* Adobe Press (1992).

Flexographic Technical Association. *Flexography—Principles and Practice.* Flexographic Technical Association (1988).

Graphic Arts Technical Foundation. *Lithographers Manual.* Graphic Arts Technical Foundation (1994).

Gonzales, R. and Woods, R. *Digital Image Processing.* Addison Wesley (1992).

Gravure Education Foundation/Gravure Association of America. *Gravure: Process and Technology.* Gravure Association of America (1991).

Green, P. *Quality Control for Print Buyers.* Blueprint (1992).

Hunt, R. W. G. *The Reproduction of Colour, Fourth Edition.* Fountain Press (1987).

———. *Measuring Colour, Second Edition.* Ellis Horwood (1991).

Kieran, M. *Desktop Publishing in Color.* Bantam (1991).

———. *Understanding Desktop Color.* Bantam (1994).

Molla, R. K. *Electronic Color Separation.* RK Printing and Publishing (1988).

Mortimer, A. *Colour Reproduction in the Printing Industry.* Pira International (1991).

Nothmann, G. *Nonimpact Printing.* Graphic Arts Technical Foundation (1989).

Nyman, M. *4 Colors and One Image.* Peachpit Press (1993).

Reid, G. C. *PostScript Language Program Design.* Addison Wesley (1988).

Rimmer, S. *Bit-mapped Graphics, Second Edition.* McGraw Hill (1993).

Scitex Graphic Arts Users Association. *Computer-ready Electronic File (CREF) Guidelines.* Scitex Graphic Arts Users Association (1993).

Southworth, M. and Southworth, D. *Quality and Productivity in the Graphic Arts.* Graphic Arts Publishing (1990).

———. *Color Separation on the Desktop.* Graphic Arts Publishing (1993).

Stevenson, D. *Handbook of Printing Processes.* Graphic Arts Technical Foundation (1994).

Tritton, K. *Pira Guide to Colour Control for Lithography.* Pira International (1994).

Yeo, P. (ed.) *The DTP Manual.* Blueprint (1994).

Zaucha, R. *The Scanner Book: How to Make Sellable Color Separations on Any Scanner.* Blue Monday (1991).

Index

About the Author

Phil Green is a lecturer in printing technology at the London College of Printing and Distributive Trades (part of the London Institute), where he teaches a range of subjects including information systems, electronic imaging, research methods, print production, and process control to both undergraduates and apprentices.

Beginning as a trainee printer in 1972, Green has had a diverse career in the graphic arts, including positions dealing with camera operating, stripping, multicolor press operating, and production management. In 1979, he founded the worker-owned Blackrose Press, a small lithographic printer in London.

He has recently developed course modules on electronic imaging and digital color for a new degree in printing and publishing and for a European Community technical college program in computers in the graphic arts. Green has an M.S. degree from the University of Surrey.

A regular contributor to books, journals, conferences, and seminars on print and paper topics, he is the author of *Quality Control for Print Buyers.* Green also conducts a series of seminars for professional print buyers and desktop publishers.

The author is interested in discussing the topics covered in this book or receiving your feedback and suggestions. He can be reached at 100277.3163.compuserve.com.